Selected Problems to Accompany
Mathematics in Action

Custom Edition for Math 033 Mercer County Community College

Taken from:
Basic Mathematics, Tenth Edition
by Marvin L. Bittinger

Printed in the United States of America

10 9 8 7 6 5 4 3 2 1

ISBN 0-536-32226-0

2006360891

JK/HA

Please visit our web site at *www.pearsoncustom.com*

PEARSON CUSTOM PUBLISHING
75 Arlington Street, Suite 300, Boston, MA 02116
A Pearson Education Company

Contents

1 WHOLE NUMBERS

1.1   Addition   2
1.2   Subtraction   4
1.3   Rounding and Estimating; Order   6
1.4   Multiplication   8
1.5   Division   11
1.6   Applications and Problem Solving   15
    Translating for Success   **24**
1.7   Exponential Notation and Order of Operations   32

2 RATIO AND PROPORTION

2.1   Introduction to Ratios   36
2.2   Proportions   43
2.3   Applications of Proportions   51
    Translating for Success   **56**

3 REAL NUMBERS

3.1   Addition of Real Numbers   64
3.2   Subtraction of Real Numbers   65
3.3   Multiplication of Real Numbers   68
3.4   Division of Real Numbers and Order of Operations   69

4 FRACTION NOTATION AND MIXED NUMERALS

4.1 Addition and Applications   72
4.2 Subtraction, Order, and Applications   73
4.3 Addition and Subtraction Using Mixed Numerals; Applications   74

5 FRACTION NOTATION: MULTIPLICATION AND DIVISION

5.1 Multiplication and Applications   78
5.2 Division and Applications   79

6 DECIMAL NOTATION

6.1 Addition and Subtraction   82
6.2 Multiplication   85
6.3 Division   87

7 PERCENT NOTATION

7.1 Percent and Fraction Notation   92
7.2 Solving Percent Problems Using Percent Equations   95
7.3 Applications of Percent   96
7.4 Sales Tax, Commission, and Discount   101

8 ALGEBRA: SOLVING EQUATIONS AND PROBLEMS

8.1 Solving Equations: The Addition Principle   106

8.2 Solving Equations: The Multiplication Principle   107

8.3 Using the Principles Together   108

ANSWERS (Student's Edition only)   **A-1**

APPENDIX   **A-7**

Whole Numbers

1

1.1   Addition

1.2   Subtraction

1.3   Rounding and Estimating; Order

1.4   Multiplication

1.5   Division

1.6   Applications and Problem Solving

1.7   Exponential Notation and Order of Operations

Addition

EXERCISE SET

a Add.

1.
$$\begin{array}{r} 3\ 6\ 4 \\ +\ \ \ 2\ 3 \\ \hline \end{array}$$

2.
$$\begin{array}{r} 1\ 5\ 2\ 1 \\ +\ \ \ \ 3\ 4\ 8 \\ \hline \end{array}$$

3.
$$\begin{array}{r} 1\ 7\ 1\ 6 \\ +\ 3\ 4\ 8\ 2 \\ \hline \end{array}$$

4.
$$\begin{array}{r} 7\ 5\ 0\ 3 \\ +\ 2\ 6\ 8\ 3 \\ \hline \end{array}$$

5.
$$\begin{array}{r} 8\ 6 \\ +\ 7\ 8 \\ \hline \end{array}$$

6.
$$\begin{array}{r} 7\ 3 \\ +\ 6\ 9 \\ \hline \end{array}$$

7.
$$\begin{array}{r} 9\ 9 \\ +\ \ \ 1 \\ \hline \end{array}$$

8.
$$\begin{array}{r} 9\ 9\ 9 \\ +\ \ \ 1\ 1 \\ \hline \end{array}$$

9. 8113 + 390

10. 271 + 3338

11. 356 + 4910

12. 280 + 34,702

13. 3870 + 92 + 7 + 497

14. 10,120 + 12,989 + 5738

15.
$$\begin{array}{r} 4\ 8\ 2\ 5 \\ +\ 1\ 7\ 8\ 3 \\ \hline \end{array}$$

16.
$$\begin{array}{r} 3\ 6\ 5\ 4 \\ +\ 2\ 7\ 0\ 0 \\ \hline \end{array}$$

17.
$$\begin{array}{r} 2\ 3,4\ 4\ 3 \\ +\ 1\ 0,9\ 8\ 9 \\ \hline \end{array}$$

18.
$$\begin{array}{r} 4\ 5,8\ 7\ 9 \\ +\ 2\ 1,7\ 8\ 6 \\ \hline \end{array}$$

19.
$$\begin{array}{r} 7\ 7,5\ 4\ 3 \\ +\ 2\ 3,7\ 6\ 7 \\ \hline \end{array}$$

20.
$$\begin{array}{r} 9\ 9,9\ 9\ 9 \\ +\ \ \ \ \ \ 1\ 1\ 2 \\ \hline \end{array}$$

21.
$$\begin{array}{r} 4\ 5 \\ 2\ 5 \\ 3\ 6 \\ 4\ 4 \\ +\ 8\ 0 \\ \hline \end{array}$$

22.
$$\begin{array}{r} 3\ 8 \\ 2\ 7 \\ 3\ 2 \\ 1\ 4 \\ +\ 7\ 6 \\ \hline \end{array}$$

23.
$$\begin{array}{r} 1\ 2,0\ 7\ 0 \\ 2,9\ 5\ 4 \\ +\ \ \ 3,4\ 0\ 0 \\ \hline \end{array}$$

24.
$$\begin{array}{r} 4\ 2,4\ 8\ 7 \\ 8\ 3,1\ 4\ 1 \\ +\ 3\ 6,7\ 1\ 2 \\ \hline \end{array}$$

25.
$$\begin{array}{r} 4\ 8\ 3\ 5 \\ 7\ 2\ 9 \\ 9\ 2\ 0\ 4 \\ 8\ 9\ 8\ 6 \\ +\ 7\ 9\ 3\ 1 \\ \hline \end{array}$$

26.
$$\begin{array}{r} 9\ 8\ 9 \\ 5\ 6\ 6 \\ 8\ 3\ 4 \\ 9\ 2\ 0 \\ +\ 7\ 0\ 3 \\ \hline \end{array}$$

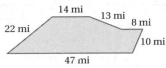 Find the perimeter of each figure.

27.

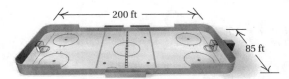
14 mi
13 mi
8 mi
22 mi
10 mi
47 mi

28.

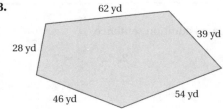
62 yd
39 yd
28 yd
46 yd
54 yd

29. Find the perimeter of a standard hockey rink.

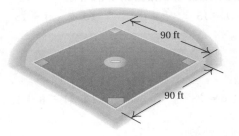
200 ft
85 ft

30. In Major League Baseball, how far does a batter travel in circling the bases when a home run has been hit?

90 ft
90 ft

31. **D**W Explain in your own words what the associative law of addition means.

32. **D**W Describe a situation that corresponds to this mathematical expression:

80 mi + 245 mi + 336 mi.

SKILL MAINTENANCE

The exercises that follow begin an important feature called *Skill Maintenance exercises*. These exercises provide an ongoing review of topics previously covered in the book. You will see them in virtually every exercise set. It has been found that this kind of continuing review can significantly improve your performance on a final examination.

33. What does the digit 8 mean in 486,205?

34. Write a word name for the number in the following sentence:

In fiscal year 2004, Starbucks Corporation had total net revenues of $5,294,247,000.

Source: Starbucks Corporation

SYNTHESIS

35. A fast way to add all the numbers from 1 to 10 inclusive is to pair 1 with 9, 2 with 8, and so on. Use a similar approach to add all numbers from 1 to 100 inclusive.

a   Write a related addition sentence.

1. $7 - 4 = 3$ **2.** $12 - 5 = 7$ **3.** $13 - 8 = 5$ **4.** $9 - 9 = 0$

5. $23 - 9 = 14$ **6.** $20 - 8 = 12$ **7.** $43 - 16 = 27$ **8.** $51 - 18 = 33$

Write two related subtraction sentences.

9. $6 + 9 = 15$ **10.** $7 + 9 = 16$ **11.** $8 + 7 = 15$ **12.** $8 + 0 = 8$

13. $17 + 6 = 23$ **14.** $11 + 8 = 19$ **15.** $23 + 9 = 32$ **16.** $42 + 10 = 52$

b   Subtract.

17.
$$\begin{array}{r} 6\ 5 \\ -\ 2\ 1 \\ \hline \end{array}$$

18.
$$\begin{array}{r} 8\ 7 \\ -\ 3\ 4 \\ \hline \end{array}$$

19.
$$\begin{array}{r} 8\ 6\ 6 \\ -\ 3\ 3\ 3 \\ \hline \end{array}$$

20.
$$\begin{array}{r} 5\ 2\ 6 \\ -\ 3\ 2\ 3 \\ \hline \end{array}$$

21. $86 - 47$ **22.** $73 - 28$ **23.** $981 - 747$ **24.** $887 - 698$

25.
$$\begin{array}{r} 7\ 7\ 6\ 9 \\ -\ 2\ 3\ 8\ 7 \\ \hline \end{array}$$

26.
$$\begin{array}{r} 6\ 4\ 3\ 1 \\ -\ 2\ 8\ 9\ 6 \\ \hline \end{array}$$

27.
$$\begin{array}{r} 7\ 6\ 4\ 0 \\ -\ 3\ 8\ 0\ 9 \\ \hline \end{array}$$

28.
$$\begin{array}{r} 8\ 0\ 0\ 3 \\ -\ \ \ 5\ 9\ 9 \\ \hline \end{array}$$

29.
$$\begin{array}{r} 1\ 2,6\ 4\ 7 \\ -\ \ \ 4,8\ 9\ 9 \\ \hline \end{array}$$

30.
$$\begin{array}{r} 1\ 6,2\ 2\ 2 \\ -\ \ \ 5,8\ 8\ 8 \\ \hline \end{array}$$

31. $90{,}237 - 47{,}209$ **32.** $84{,}703 - 298$

33.
   8 0
− 2 4

34.
   9 0
− 7 8

35.
  6 9 0
− 2 3 6

36.
  8 0 3
− 4 1 8

37.
  6 8 0 8
− 3 0 5 9

38.
  6 4 0 8
−   2 5 8

39.
  2 3 0 0
−   1 0 9

40.
  6 0 0 7
− 1 5 8 9

41. 101,734 − 5760

42. 15,017 − 7809

43. 10,008 − 19

44. 21,043 − 8909

45.
  7 0 0 0
− 2 7 9 4

46.
  8 0 0 1
− 6 5 4 3

47.
  4 8,0 0 0
− 3 7,6 9 5

48.
  1 7,0 4 3
− 1 1,5 9 8

49. D**W** Describe two situations that correspond to the subtraction $20 − $17, one "take away" and one "how many more."

50. D**W** Is subtraction commutative (is there a commutative law of subtraction)? Why or why not?

Add.

51.
  9 4 6
+   7 8

52.
  9 0 7 8
+ 3 6 5 4

53.
  5 7,8 7 7
+ 3 2,4 0 6

54.
  8 0 0 4
  6 7 8 9
  7 7 2 0
+ 6 8 5 1

55. 567 + 778

56. 901 + 23

57. 12,885 + 9807

58. 9909 + 1011

59. Write a word name for 6,375,602.

60. What does the digit 7 mean in 6,375,602?

61. Fill in the missing digits to make the subtraction true:
9,☐48,621 − 2,097,☐81 = 7,251,140.

62. ▦ Subtract: 3,928,124 − 1,098,947.

EXERCISE SET

a Round to the nearest ten.

1. 48   **2.** 532   **3.** 467   **4.** 8945

5. 731   **6.** 17   **7.** 895   **8.** 798

Round to the nearest hundred.

9. 146   **10.** 874   **11.** 957   **12.** 650

13. 9079   **14.** 4645   **15.** 32,850   **16.** 198,402

Round to the nearest thousand.

17. 5876   **18.** 4500   **19.** 7500   **20.** 2001

21. 45,340   **22.** 735,562   **23.** 373,405   **24.** 6,713,855

b Estimate the sum or difference by first rounding to the nearest ten. Show your work.

25.
```
    7 8
  + 9 7
```

26.
```
    6 2
    9 7
    4 6
  + 8 8
```

27.
```
  8 0 7 4
- 2 3 4 7
```

28.
```
    6 7 3
  -    2 8
```

Estimate the sum by first rounding to the nearest ten. Do any of the given sums seem to be incorrect when compared to the estimate? Which ones?

29.
```
    4 5
    7 7
    2 5
  + 5 6
  ─────
    3 4 3
```

30.
```
    4 1
    2 1
    5 5
  + 6 0
  ─────
    1 7 7
```

31.
```
    6 2 2
      7 8
      8 1
  + 1 1 1
  ─────
    9 3 2
```

32.
```
    8 3 6
    3 7 4
    7 9 4
  + 9 3 8
  ─────
    3 9 4 7
```

Estimate the sum or difference by first rounding to the nearest hundred. Show your work.

33.
```
    7 3 4 8
  + 9 2 4 7
```

34.
```
    5 6 8
    4 7 2
    9 3 8
  + 4 0 2
```

35.
```
  6 8 5 2
- 1 7 4 8
```

36.
```
  9 4 3 8
- 2 7 8 7
```

Planning a Kitchen.   Perfect Kitchens offers custom kitchen packages with three choices for each of four items: cabinets, countertops, appliances, and flooring. The chart below lists the price for each choice.

Perfect Kitchens lets you customize your kitchen with one choice from each of the following four features:

CABINETS	TYPE	PRICE
(a)	Oak	$7450
(b)	Cherry	8820
(c)	Painted	9630

COUNTERTOPS	TYPE	PRICE
(d)	Laminate	$1595
(e)	Solid surface	2870
(f)	Granite	3528

APPLIANCES	PRICE RANGE	PRICE
(g)	Low	$1540
(h)	Medium	3575
(i)	High	6245

FLOORING	TYPE	PRICE
(j)	Vinyl	$ 625
(k)	Ceramic tile	985
(l)	Hardwood	1160

37. Estimate the cost of remodeling a kitchen with choices (a), (d), (g), and (j) by rounding to the nearest hundred dollars.

38. Estimate the cost of a kitchen with choices (c), (f), (i), and (l) by rounding to the nearest hundred dollars.

39. Sara and Ben are planning to remodel their kitchen and have a budget of $17,700. Estimate by rounding to the nearest hundred dollars the cost of their kitchen remodeling project if they choose options (b), (e), (i), and (k). Can they afford their choices?

40. The Davidsons must make a final decision on the kitchen choices for their new home. The allotted kitchen budget is $16,000. Estimate by rounding to the nearest hundred dollars the kitchen cost if they choose options (a), (f), (h), and (l). Does their budget allotment cover the cost?

41. Suppose you are planning a new kitchen and must stay within a budget of $14,500. Decide on the options you would like and estimate the cost by rounding to the nearest hundred dollars. Does your budget support your choices?

42. Suppose you are planning a new kitchen and must stay within a budget of $18,500. Decide on the options you would like and estimate the cost by rounding to the nearest hundred dollars. Does your budget support your choices?

Multiplication
EXERCISE SET

a   Multiply.

1. $\begin{array}{r} 8\,7 \\ \times\ 1\,0 \\ \hline \end{array}$

2. $\begin{array}{r} 1\,0\,0 \\ \times\ \ 9\,6 \\ \hline \end{array}$

3. $\begin{array}{r} 2\,3\,4\,0 \\ \times\ 1\,0\,0\,0 \\ \hline \end{array}$

4. $\begin{array}{r} 8\,0\,0 \\ \times\ \ \ 7\,0 \\ \hline \end{array}$

5. $\begin{array}{r} 6\,5 \\ \times\ \ 8 \\ \hline \end{array}$

6. $\begin{array}{r} 8\,7 \\ \times\ \ 4 \\ \hline \end{array}$

7. $\begin{array}{r} 9\,4 \\ \times\ \ 6 \\ \hline \end{array}$

8. $\begin{array}{r} 7\,6 \\ \times\ \ 9 \\ \hline \end{array}$

9. $3 \cdot 509$

10. $7 \cdot 806$

11. $7(9229)$

12. $4(7867)$

13. $90(53)$

14. $60(78)$

15. $(47)(85)$

16. $(34)(87)$

17. $\begin{array}{r} 6\,4\,0 \\ \times\ \ 7\,2 \\ \hline \end{array}$

18. $\begin{array}{r} 7\,7\,7 \\ \times\ \ 7\,7 \\ \hline \end{array}$

19. $\begin{array}{r} 4\,4\,4 \\ \times\ \ 3\,3 \\ \hline \end{array}$

20. $\begin{array}{r} 5\,0\,9 \\ \times\ \ 8\,8 \\ \hline \end{array}$

21. $\begin{array}{r} 5\,0\,9 \\ \times\ 4\,0\,8 \\ \hline \end{array}$

22. $\begin{array}{r} 4\,3\,2 \\ \times\ 3\,7\,5 \\ \hline \end{array}$

23. $\begin{array}{r} 8\,5\,3 \\ \times\ 9\,3\,6 \\ \hline \end{array}$

24. $\begin{array}{r} 3\,4\,6 \\ \times\ 6\,5\,0 \\ \hline \end{array}$

25. $\begin{array}{r} 6\,4\,2\,8 \\ \times\ 3\,2\,2\,4 \\ \hline \end{array}$

26. $\begin{array}{r} 8\,9\,2\,8 \\ \times\ 3\,1\,7\,2 \\ \hline \end{array}$

27. $\begin{array}{r} 3\,4\,8\,2 \\ \times\ \ \ 1\,0\,4 \\ \hline \end{array}$

28. $\begin{array}{r} 6\,4\,0\,8 \\ \times\ 6\,0\,6\,4 \\ \hline \end{array}$

29. $\begin{array}{r} 5\ 0\ 0\ 6 \\ \times\ 4\ 0\ 0\ 8 \\ \hline \end{array}$	30. $\begin{array}{r} 6\ 7\ 8\ 9 \\ \times\ 2\ 3\ 3\ 0 \\ \hline \end{array}$	31. $\begin{array}{r} 5\ 6\ 0\ 8 \\ \times\ 4\ 5\ 0\ 0 \\ \hline \end{array}$	32. $\begin{array}{r} 4\ 5\ 6\ 0 \\ \times\ 7\ 8\ 9\ 0 \\ \hline \end{array}$
33. $\begin{array}{r} 8\ 7\ 6 \\ \times\ 3\ 4\ 5 \\ \hline \end{array}$	34. $\begin{array}{r} 3\ 5\ 5 \\ \times\ 2\ 9\ 9 \\ \hline \end{array}$	35. $\begin{array}{r} 7\ 8\ 8\ 9 \\ \times\ 6\ 2\ 2\ 4 \\ \hline \end{array}$	36. $\begin{array}{r} 6\ 5\ 0\ 1 \\ \times\ 3\ 4\ 4\ 9 \\ \hline \end{array}$

b Estimate the product by first rounding to the nearest ten. Show your work.

37. $\begin{array}{r} 4\ 5 \\ \times\ 6\ 7 \\ \hline \end{array}$	38. $\begin{array}{r} 5\ 1 \\ \times\ 7\ 8 \\ \hline \end{array}$	39. $\begin{array}{r} 3\ 4 \\ \times\ 2\ 9 \\ \hline \end{array}$	40. $\begin{array}{r} 6\ 3 \\ \times\ 5\ 4 \\ \hline \end{array}$

Estimate the product by first rounding to the nearest hundred. Show your work.

41. $\begin{array}{r} 8\ 7\ 6 \\ \times\ 3\ 4\ 5 \\ \hline \end{array}$	42. $\begin{array}{r} 3\ 5\ 5 \\ \times\ 2\ 9\ 9 \\ \hline \end{array}$	43. $\begin{array}{r} 4\ 3\ 2 \\ \times\ 1\ 9\ 9 \\ \hline \end{array}$	44. $\begin{array}{r} 7\ 8\ 9 \\ \times\ 4\ 3\ 4 \\ \hline \end{array}$

45. *Toyota Sienna.* A pharmaceutical company buys a Toyota Sienna for each of its 112 sales representatives. Each car costs $27,896 plus an additional $540 per car in destination charges.

a) Estimate the total cost of the purchase by rounding the cost of each car, the destination charge, and the number of sales representatives to the nearest hundred.
b) Estimate the total cost of the purchase by rounding the cost of each car to the nearest thousand and the destination charge and the number of reps to the nearest hundred.

Source: Toyota

46. A travel club of 176 people decides to fly from Los Angeles to Tokyo. The cost of a round-trip ticket is $643.

a) Estimate the total cost of the trip by rounding the cost of the airfare and the number of travelers to the nearest ten.
b) Estimate the total cost of the trip by rounding the cost of the airfare and the number of travelers to the nearest hundred.

C Find the area of the region.

47.

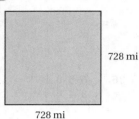

728 mi

728 mi

48.

129 yd

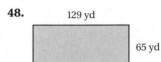

65 yd

49. Find the area of the region formed by the base lines on a Major League Baseball diamond.

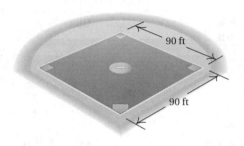

90 ft

90 ft

50. Find the area of a standard-sized hockey rink.

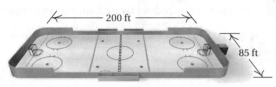

200 ft

85 ft

51. D_W Describe a situation that corresponds to each multiplication: $4 \cdot \$150$; $\$4 \cdot 150$.

52. D_W Explain the multiplication illustrated in the diagram below.

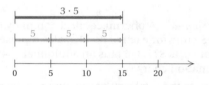

$3 \cdot 5$

5   5   5

0   5   10   15   20

SKILL MAINTENANCE

Add.

53.
    4 9 0 8
    5 6 6 7
  + 2 1 1 0

54.
    9 8 7 6
      8 7 6
        7 6
  +   6

55.
    3 4 0,7 9 8
  +   8 6,6 7 9

56.
    8 8,7 7 7
  + 2 2,3 3 3

Subtract.

57.
    4 9 0 8
  − 3 6 6 7

58.
    9 8 7 6
  −   9 8 7

59.
    3 4 0,7 9 8
  −   8 6,6 7 9

60.
    8 8,7 7 7
  − 2 2,3 3 3

61. Round 6,375,602 to the nearest thousand.

62. Round 6,375,602 to the nearest ten.

SYNTHESIS

63. ▦ An 18-story office building is box-shaped. Each floor measures 172 ft by 84 ft with a 20-ft by 35-ft rectangular area lost to an elevator and a stairwell. How much area is available as office space?

a   Write a related multiplication sentence.

1. $18 \div 3 = 6$ **2.** $72 \div 9 = 8$ **3.** $22 \div 22 = 1$ **4.** $32 \div 1 = 32$

5. $54 \div 6 = 9$ **6.** $90 \div 10 = 9$ **7.** $37 \div 1 = 37$ **8.** $28 \div 28 = 1$

Write two related division sentences.

9. $9 \times 5 = 45$ **10.** $2 \cdot 7 = 14$ **11.** $37 \cdot 1 = 37$ **12.** $4 \cdot 12 = 48$

13. $8 \times 8 = 64$ **14.** $9 \cdot 7 = 63$ **15.** $11 \cdot 6 = 66$ **16.** $1 \cdot 43 = 43$

b   Divide, if possible. If not possible, write "not defined."

17. $72 \div 6$ **18.** $54 \div 9$ **19.** $\dfrac{23}{23}$ **20.** $\dfrac{37}{37}$

21. $22 \div 1$ **22.** $\dfrac{56}{1}$ **23.** $\dfrac{16}{0}$ **24.** $74 \div 0$

Divide.

25. $277 \div 5$ **26.** $699 \div 3$ **27.** $864 \div 8$ **28.** $869 \div 8$

29. $4 \overline{)\ 1\ 2\ 2\ 8}$ **30.** $3 \overline{)\ 2\ 1\ 2\ 4}$ **31.** $6 \overline{)\ 4\ 5\ 2\ 1}$ **32.** $9 \overline{)\ 9\ 1\ 1\ 0}$

33. $297 \div 4$ **34.** $389 \div 2$ **35.** $738 \div 8$ **36.** $881 \div 6$

37. $5 \overline{)8515}$ **38.** $3 \overline{)6027}$ **39.** $9 \overline{)8888}$ **40.** $8 \overline{)4139}$

41. $127{,}000 \div 10$ **42.** $127{,}000 \div 100$ **43.** $127{,}000 \div 1000$ **44.** $4260 \div 10$

45. $70 \overline{)3692}$ **46.** $20 \overline{)5798}$ **47.** $30 \overline{)875}$ **48.** $40 \overline{)987}$

49. $852 \div 21$ **50.** $942 \div 23$ **51.** $85 \overline{)7672}$ **52.** $54 \overline{)2729}$

53. $111 \overline{)3219}$ **54.** $102 \overline{)5612}$ **55.** $8 \overline{)843}$ **56.** $7 \overline{)749}$

57. $5 \overline{)8047}$ **58.** $9 \overline{)7273}$ **59.** $5 \overline{)5036}$ **60.** $7 \overline{)7074}$

61. $1058 \div 46$ **62.** $7242 \div 24$ **63.** $3425 \div 32$ **64.** $48 \overline{)4899}$

65. $24 \overline{)8880}$ **66.** $36 \overline{)7563}$ **67.** $28 \overline{)17,067}$ **68.** $36 \overline{)28,929}$

69. $80 \overline{)24,320}$ **70.** $90 \overline{)88,560}$ **71.** $285 \overline{)999,999}$

72. $306 \overline{)888,888}$ **73.** $456 \overline{)3,679,920}$ **74.** $803 \overline{)5,622,606}$

75. D_W Is division associative? Why or why not? Give an example.

76. D_W Suppose a student asserts that "$0 \div 0 = 0$ because nothing divided by nothing is nothing." Devise an explanation to persuade the student that the assertion is false.

 VOCABULARY REINFORCEMENT

In each of Exercises 77–84, fill in the blank with the correct term from the given list. Some of the choices may not be used and some may be used more than once.

77. The distance around an object is its _____ .

78. A sentence like $10 - 3 = 7$ is called a(n) _____ ; a sentence like $31 < 33$ is called a(n) _____ .

79. For large numbers, _____ are separated by commas into groups of three, called _____ .

80. The number 0 is called the _____ identity.

81. In the sentence $28 \div 7 = 4$, the _____ is 28.

82. In the sentence $10 \times 1000 = 10,000$, 10 and 1000 are called _____ and 10,000 is called the _____ .

83. The _____ is the number from which another number is being subtracted.

84. The sentence $3 \times (6 \times 2) = (3 \times 6) \times 2$ illustrates the _____ law of multiplication.

associative	minuend
commutative	subtrahend
addends	digits
factors	periods
perimeter	additive
dividend	multiplicative
quotient	equation
product	inequality

85. Complete the following table.

a	b	$a \cdot b$	$a + b$
	68	3672	
84			117
		32	12

86. Find a pair of factors whose product is 36 and:

a) whose sum is 13.
b) whose difference is 0.
c) whose sum is 20.
d) whose difference is 9.

87. A group of 1231 college students is going to take buses for a field trip. Each bus can hold only 42 students. How many buses are needed?

88. ▦ Fill in the missing digits to make the equation true:
$$34,584,132 \div 76\square = 4\square,386.$$

1.6 APPLICATIONS AND PROBLEM SOLVING

Objective

a Solve applied problems involving addition, subtraction, multiplication, or division of whole numbers.

a A Problem-Solving Strategy

Applications and problem solving are the most important uses of mathematics. To solve a problem using the operations on the whole numbers, we first look at the situation. We try to translate the problem to an equation. Then we solve the equation. We check to see if the solution of the equation is a solution of the original problem. We are using the following five-step strategy.

FIVE STEPS FOR PROBLEM SOLVING

1. *Familiarize* yourself with the situation.

   a) Carefully read and reread until you understand *what* you are being asked to find.
   b) Draw a diagram or see if there is a formula that applies to the situation.
   c) Assign a letter, or *variable*, to the unknown.

2. *Translate* the problem to an equation using the letter or variable.
3. *Solve* the equation.
4. *Check* the answer in the original wording of the problem.
5. *State* the answer to the problem clearly with appropriate units.

EXAMPLE 1 *International Adoptions.* The top ten countries of origin for United States international adoptions in 2003 and 2002 are listed in the table below. Find the total number of adoptions from China, South Korea, India, and Vietnam in 2003.

INTERNATIONAL ADOPTIONS

RANK	2003 COUNTRY OF ORIGIN	NUMBER	2002 COUNTRY OF ORIGIN	NUMBER
1	China (mainland)	6859	China (mainland)	5053
2	Russia	5209	Russia	4939
3	Guatemala	2328	Guatemala	2219
4	South Korea	1790	South Korea	1779
5	Kazakhstan	825	Ukraine	1106
6	Ukraine	702	Kazakhstan	819
7	India	472	Vietnam	766
8	Vietnam	382	India	466
9	Colombia	272	Colombia	334
10	Haiti	250	Bulgaria	260

Source: U.S. Department of State

Refer to the table on the preceding page to answer Margin Exercises 1–3.

1. Find the total number of adoptions from China, Russia, Kazakhstan, and India in 2002.

2. Find the total number of adoptions from Russia, Guatemala, Vietnam, Colombia, and Haiti in 2003.

3. Find the total number of adoptions from the top ten countries in 2003.

1. Familiarize. We can make a drawing or at least visualize the situation.

$$
\underset{\substack{\text{from} \\ \text{China}}}{6859} \;+\; \underset{\substack{\text{from} \\ \text{South Korea}}}{1790} \;+\; \underset{\substack{\text{from} \\ \text{India}}}{472} \;+\; \underset{\substack{\text{from} \\ \text{Vietnam}}}{382}
$$

Since we are combining numbers of adoptions, addition can be used. First, we define the unknown. We let $n =$ the total number of adoptions from China, South Korea, India, and Vietnam.

2. Translate. We translate to an equation:

$$6859 + 1790 + 472 + 382 = n.$$

3. Solve. We solve the equation by carrying out the addition.

$$
\begin{array}{r}
\overset{2\ \ 3\ \ 1}{6\ 8\ 5\ 9} \\
1\ 7\ 9\ 0 \\
4\ 7\ 2 \\
+\quad 3\ 8\ 2 \\
\hline
9\ 5\ 0\ 3
\end{array}
\qquad
\begin{array}{r}
6859 + 1790 + 472 + 382 = n \\
9503 = n
\end{array}
$$

4. Check. We check 9503 in the original problem. There are many ways in which this can be done. For example, we can repeat the calculation. (We leave this to the student.) Another way is to check whether the answer is reasonable. In this case, we would expect the total to be greater than the number of adoptions from any of the individual countries, which it is. We can also estimate by rounding. Here we round to the nearest hundred.

$$6859 + 1790 + 472 + 382 \approx 6900 + 1800 + 500 + 400$$
$$= 9600$$

Since $9600 \approx 9503$, we have a partial check. If we had an estimate like 4800 or 7500, we might be suspicious that our calculated answer is incorrect. Since our estimated answer is close to our calculation, we are further convinced that our answer checks.

5. State. The total number of adoptions from China, South Korea, India, and Vietnam in 2003 is 9503.

Do Exercises 1–3.

Answers on page A-1

EXAMPLE 2 *Checking Account Balance.* The balance in Tyler's checking account is $528. He uses his debit card to buy the Roto Zip Spiral Saw Combo shown in this ad. Find the new balance in his checking account.

4. Checking Account Balance.
The balance in Heidi's checking account is $2003. She uses her debit card to buy the same Roto Zip Spiral Saw Combo, featured in Example 2, that Tyler did. Find the new balance in her checking account.

NOW
$**129**⁰⁰

Source: Reproduced with permission from the copyright owner (©2004 by Robert Bosch Tool Corporation). Further reproductions strictly prohibited.

1. **Familiarize.** We first make a drawing or at least visualize the situation. We let M = the new balance in his account. This gives us the following:

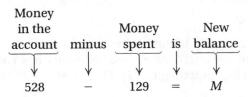

Take away
$129

$528   New balance

2. **Translate.** We can think of this as a "take-away" situation. We translate to an equation.

Money in the account	minus	Money spent	is	New balance
↓	↓	↓	↓	↓
528	−	129	=	M

3. **Solve.** This sentence tells us what to do. We subtract.

$$\begin{array}{r} \overset{\overset{11}{}}{\overset{4\ \not{1}\ 18}{\not{5}\ \not{2}\ \not{8}}} \\ -\ 1\ 2\ 9 \\ \hline 3\ 9\ 9 \end{array}$$

$528 - 129 = M$
$399 = M$

4. **Check.** To check our answer of $399, we can repeat the calculation. We note that the answer should be less than the original amount, $528, which it is. We can add the difference, 399, to the subtrahend, 129: $129 + 399 = 528$. We can also estimate:

$528 - 129 \approx 530 - 130 = 400 \approx 399.$

5. **State.** Tyler has a new balance of $399 in his checking account.

Answer on page A-1

5. Home Vacuum. William has $228. He wants to purchase the home vacuum shown in the ad below. How much more does he need?

In the real world, problems may not be stated in written words. You must still become familiar with the situation before you can solve the problem.

EXAMPLE 3 *Travel Distance.* Abigail is driving from Indianapolis to Salt Lake City to interview for a news anchor position. The distance from Indianapolis to Salt Lake City is 1634 mi. She travels 1154 mi to Denver. How much farther must she travel?

1. **Familiarize.** We first make a drawing or at least visualize the situation. We let $x =$ the remaining distance to Salt Lake City.

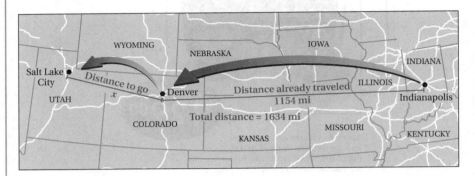

2. **Translate.** We see that this is a "how much more" situation. We translate to an equation.

Distance already traveled	plus	Distance to go	is	Total distance of trip
↓	↓	↓	↓	↓
1154	+	x	=	1634

3. **Solve.** To solve the equation, we subtract 1154 on both sides:

$$1154 + x = 1634$$
$$1154 + x - 1154 = 1634 - 1154$$
$$x = 480.$$

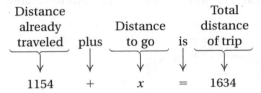

4. **Check.** We check our answer of 480 mi in the original problem. This number should be less than the total distance, 1634 mi, which it is. We can add the difference, 480, to the subtrahend, 1154: $1154 + 480 = 1634$. We can also estimate:

$$1634 - 1154 \approx 1600 - 1200$$
$$= 400 \approx 480.$$

The answer, 480 mi, checks.

5. **State.** Abigail must travel 480 mi farther to Salt Lake City.

Do Exercise 5.

Answer on page A-1

EXAMPLE 4 *Total Cost of Chairs.* What is the total cost of 6 Logan side chairs from Restoration Hardware if each one costs $210?

1. **Familiarize.** We first make a drawing or at least visualize the situation. We let $T =$ the cost of 6 chairs. Repeated addition works well in this case.

$ 210 $ 210 $ 210 $ 210 $ 210 $ 210

2. **Translate.** We translate to an equation.

Number of chairs   times   Cost of each chair   is   Total cost

$$6 \times \$210 = T$$

3. **Solve.** This sentence tells us what to do. We multiply.

$$\begin{array}{r} 2\ 1\ 0 \\ \times\qquad 6 \\ \hline 1\ 2\ 6\ 0 \end{array}$$

$$6 \times 210 = T$$
$$1260 = T$$

4. **Check.** We have an answer, 1260, that is much greater than the cost of any individual chair, which is reasonable. We can repeat our calculation. We can also check by estimating:

$$6 \times 210 \approx 6 \times 200 = 1200 \approx 1260.$$

The answer checks.

5. **State.** The total cost of 6 chairs is $1260.

Do Exercise 6.

EXAMPLE 5 *Truck Bed Cover.* The dimensions of a fiberglass truck bed cover for a pickup truck are 79 in. by 68 in. What is the area of the cover?

79 in.

68 in.

6. Total Cost of Gas Grills. What is the total cost of 14 gas grills, each with 520 sq in. of total cooking surface and porcelain cast-iron cooking grates, if each one costs $398?

Answer on page A-1

7. Bed Sheets. The dimensions of a flat sheet for a queen-size bed are 90 in. by 102 in. What is the area of the sheet?

1. **Familiarize.** The truck bed cover is a rectangle that measures 79 in. by 68 in. We let A = the area and use the area formula $A = l \cdot w$.

2. **Translate.** Using this formula, we have

$$A = \text{length} \cdot \text{width} = l \cdot w = 79 \cdot 68.$$

3. **Solve.** We carry out the multiplication.

$$
\begin{array}{r}
7\ 9 \\
\times\ 6\ 8 \\
\hline
6\ 3\ 2 \\
4\ 7\ 4\ 0 \\
\hline
5\ 3\ 7\ 2
\end{array}
\qquad
\begin{aligned}
A &= 79 \cdot 68 \\
A &= 5372
\end{aligned}
$$

4. **Check.** We repeat our calculation. We also note that the answer is greater than either the length or the width, which it should be. (This might not be the case if we were using fractions or decimals.) The answer checks.

5. **State.** The area of the truck bed cover is 5372 sq in.

Do Exercise 7.

EXAMPLE 6 *Cartons of Soda.* A bottling company produces 3304 cans of soda. How many 12-can cartons can be filled? How many cans will be left over?

1. **Familiarize.** We first make a drawing. We let n = the number of 12-can cartons that can be filled. The problem can be considered as repeated subtraction, taking successive sets of 12 cans and putting them into n cartons.

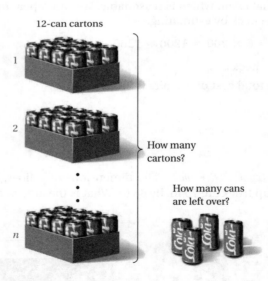

2. **Translate.** We translate to an equation.

Number of cans	divided by	Number in each carton	is	Number of cartons
↓	↓	↓	↓	↓
3304	÷	12	=	n

Answer on page A-1

3. Solve. We solve the equation by carrying out the division.

$$
\begin{array}{r}
2\ 7\ 5 \\
1\ 2\ )\overline{\ 3\ 3\ 0\ 4\ } \\
2\ 4\ 0\ 0 \\
\hline
9\ 0\ 4 \\
8\ 4\ 0 \\
\hline
6\ 4 \\
6\ 0 \\
\hline
4
\end{array}
$$

$$3304 \div 12 = n$$
$$275 \text{ R } 4 = n$$

4. Check. We can check by multiplying the number of cartons by 12 and adding the remainder, 4:

$12 \cdot 275 = 3300,$

$3300 + 4 = 3304.$

5. State. Thus, 275 twelve-can cartons can be filled. There will be 4 cans left over.

Do Exercise 8.

EXAMPLE 7 *Automobile Mileage.* The Pontiac G6 GT gets 21 miles to the gallon (mpg) in city driving. How many gallons will it use in 3843 mi of city driving?

Source: General Motors

1. Familiarize. We first make a drawing. It is often helpful to be descriptive about how we define a variable. In this case, we let $g =$ the number of gallons ("g" comes from "gallons").

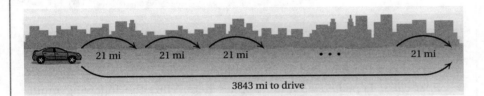

21 mi   21 mi   21 mi   • • •   21 mi

3843 mi to drive

2. Translate. Repeated addition applies here. Thus the following multiplication applies to the situation.

Number of miles per gallon	times	Number of gallons needed	is	Number of miles to drive
21	·	g	=	3843

3. Solve. To solve the equation, we divide by 21 on both sides.

$21 \cdot g = 3843$

$\dfrac{21 \cdot g}{21} = \dfrac{3843}{21}$

$g = 183$

$$
\begin{array}{r}
1\ 8\ 3 \\
2\ 1\ )\overline{\ 3\ 8\ 4\ 3\ } \\
2\ 1\ 0\ 0 \\
\hline
1\ 7\ 4\ 3 \\
1\ 6\ 8\ 0 \\
\hline
6\ 3 \\
6\ 3 \\
\hline
0
\end{array}
$$

8. Cartons of Soda. The bottling company in Example 6 also uses 6-can cartons. How many 6-can cartons can be filled with 2269 cans of cola? How many will be left over?

Answer on page A-1

9. Automobile Mileage. The Pontiac G6 GT gets 29 miles to the gallon (mpg) in highway driving. How many gallons will it take to drive 2291 mi of highway driving?

Source: General Motors

4. Check. To check, we multiply 183 by 21: $21 \times 183 = 3843$.

5. State. The Pontiac G6 GT will use 183 gal.

Do Exercise 9.

Multistep Problems

Sometimes we must use more than one operation to solve a problem, as in the following example.

EXAMPLE 8 *Aircraft Seating.* Boeing Corporation builds commercial aircraft. A Boeing 767 has a seating configuration with 4 rows of 6 seats across in first class and 35 rows of 7 seats across in economy class. Find the total seating capacity of the plane.

Sources: The Boeing Company; Delta Airlines

1. **Familiarize.** We first make a drawing.

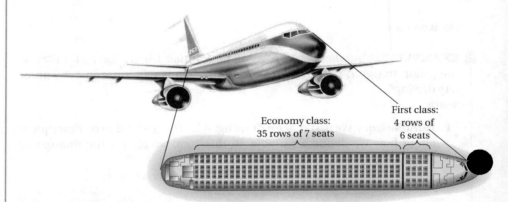

Economy class: 35 rows of 7 seats

First class: 4 rows of 6 seats

2. **Translate.** There are three parts to the problem. We first find the number of seats in each class. Then we add.

First-class: Repeated addition applies here. Thus the following multiplication corresponds to the situation. We let F = the number of seats in first class.

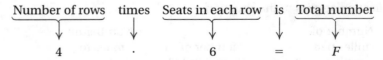

Number of rows	times	Seats in each row	is	Total number
4	·	6	=	F

Economy class: Repeated addition applies here. Thus the following multiplication corresponds to the situation. We let E = the number of seats in economy class.

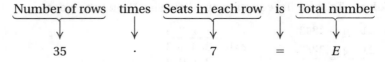

Number of rows	times	Seats in each row	is	Total number
35	·	7	=	E

We let T = the total number of seats in both classes.

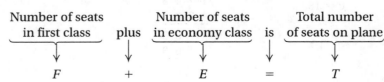

Number of seats in first class	plus	Number of seats in economy class	is	Total number of seats on plane
F	+	E	=	T

3. Solve. We solve each equation and add the solutions.

$$4 \cdot 6 = F \qquad 35 \cdot 7 = E \qquad F + E = T$$
$$24 = F \qquad 245 = E \qquad 24 + 245 = T$$
$$269 = T$$

4. Check. To check, we repeat our calculations. (We leave this to the student.) We could also check by rounding, multiplying, and adding.

5. State. There are 269 seats in a Boeing 767.

Do Exercise 10.

As you consider the following exercises, here are some words and phrases that may be helpful to look for when you are translating problems to equations.

KEY WORDS, PHRASES, AND CONCEPTS

ADDITION (+)	SUBTRACTION (−)
add	subtract
added to	subtracted from
sum	difference
total	minus
plus	less than
more than	decreased by
increased by	take away
	how much more
	missing addend

MULTIPLICATION (·)	DIVISION (÷)
multiply	divide
multiplied by	divided by
product	quotient
times	repeated subtraction
of	missing factor
repeated addition	finding equal quantities
rectangular arrays	

10. Aircraft Seating. A Boeing 767 used for foreign travel has three classes of seats. First class has 3 rows of 5 seats across; business class has 6 rows with 6 seats across and 1 row with 2 seats on each of the outside aisles. Economy class has 18 rows with 7 seats across. Find the total seating capacity of the plane.

Sources: The Boeing Company; Delta Airlines

Economy class: 18 rows of 7 seats

First class: 3 rows of 5 seats

Business class: 6 rows of 6 seats…

…with 2 seats on each outside aisle

Answer on page A-1

Translating for Success

1. **Brick-mason Expense.** A commercial contractor is building 30 two-unit condominiums in a retirement community. The brick-mason expense for each building is $10,860. What is the total cost of bricking the buildings?

2. **Heights.** Dean's sons are on the high school basketball team. Their heights are 73 in., 69 in., and 76 in. How much taller is the tallest son than the shortest son?

3. **Account Balance.** You have $423 in your checking account. Then you deposit $73 and use your debit card for purchases of $76 and $69. How much is left in your account?

4. **Purchasing Camcorder.** A camcorder is on sale for $423. Jenny has only $69. How much more does she need to buy the camcorder?

5. **Purchasing Coffee Makers.** Sara purchases 8 coffee makers for the newly remodeled bed-and-breakfast hotel that she manages. If she pays $52 for each coffee maker, what is the total cost of her purchase?

The goal of these matching questions is to practice step (2), *Translate*, of the five-step problem-solving process. Translate each word problem to an equation and select a correct translation from equations A–O.

A. $8 \cdot 52 = n$

B. $69 \cdot n = 76$

C. $73 - 76 - 69 = n$

D. $423 + 73 - 76 - 69 = n$

E. $30 \cdot 10{,}860 = n$

F. $15 \cdot n = 195$

G. $69 + n = 423$

H. $n = 10{,}860 - 300$

I. $n = 423 \div 69$

J. $30 \cdot n = 10{,}860$

K. $15 \cdot 195 = n$

L. $n = 52 - 8$

M. $69 + n = 76$

N. $15 \div 195 = n$

O. $52 + n = 60$

Answers on page A-1

6. **Hourly Rate.** Miller Auto Repair charges $52 an hour for labor. Jackson Auto Care charges $60 per hour. How much more does Jackson charge than Miller?

7. **College Band.** A college band with 195 members marches in a 15-row formation in the homecoming halftime performance. How many members are in each row?

8. **Shoe Purchase.** A professional football team purchases 15 pairs of shoes at $195 a pair. What is the total cost of this purchase?

9. **Loan Payment.** Kendra borrows $10,860 for a new boat. The loan is to be paid off in 30 payments. How much is each payment?

10. **College Enrollment.** At the beginning of the fall term, the total enrollment in Lakeview Community College was 10,860. By the end of the first two weeks, 300 students withdrew. How many students were then enrolled?

1.6 EXERCISE SET

a Solve.

Longest Broadway Run.   The bar graph below lists the five broadway shows with the greatest number of performances as of May 3, 2004.

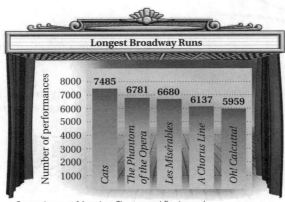

Source: League of American Theatres and Producers, Inc.

1. What was the total number of performances of all five shows?

2. What was the total number of performances of the top three shows?

3. How many more performances of *Cats* were there than performances of *The Phantom of the Opera*?

4. How many more performances of *Les Misérables* were there than performances of *Oh! Calcutta!*?

5. *Boundaries Between Countries.*   The boundary between mainland United States and Canada including the Great Lakes is 3987 miles long. The length of the boundary between the United States and Mexico is 1933 miles. How much longer is the Canadian border?
Source: U.S. Geological Survey

6. *Caffeine.*   Hershey's 6-oz milk chocolate almond bar contains 25 milligrams of caffeine. A 20-oz bottle of Coca-Cola has 32 more milligrams of caffeine than the Hershey bar. How many milligrams of caffeine does the 20-oz bottle of Coca-Cola have?
Source: *National Geographic,* "Caffeine," by T. R. Reid, January 2005

7. A carpenter drills 216 holes in a rectangular array in a pegboard. There are 12 holes in each row. How many rows are there?

8. Lou works as a CPA. He arranges 504 entries on a spreadsheet in a rectangular array that has 36 rows. How many entries are in each row?

Bachelor's Degree. The line graph below illustrates data about bachelor's degrees awarded to men and women from 1970 to 2002. Use this graph when answering Exercises 9–12.

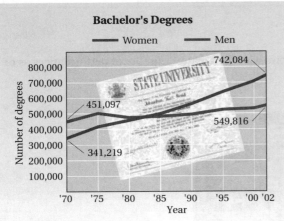

Bachelor's Degrees

—— Women   —— Men

Number of degrees (y-axis): 100,000 to 800,000

742,084
451,097
549,816
341,219

Year (x-axis): '70 '75 '80 '85 '90 '95 '00 '02

Source: U.S. Department of Education

9. Find the total number of bachelor's degrees awarded in 1970 and the total number awarded in 2002.

10. Determine how many more bachelor's degrees were awarded in 2002 than in 1970.

11. How many more bachelor's degrees were awarded to women than to men in 2002?

12. How many more bachelor's degrees were awarded to men than to women in 1970?

13. *Median Mortgage Debt.* The median mortgage debt in 2001 was $29,475 more than the median mortgage debt in 1989. The debt in 1989 was $39,802. What was the median mortgage debt in 2001?
Source: Federal Reserve Board Survey of Consumer Finances; Consumer Bank Association 2003 Home Equity Study; Freddie Mac

14. *Olympics in Athens.* In the first modern Olympics in Athens, Greece, in 1896, there were 43 events. In 2004, there were 258 more events in the Summer Olympics in Athens. How many events were there in 2004?
Source: *USA Today* research; The Olympic Games: Athens 1896–Athens 2004

15. *Longest Rivers.* The longest river in the world is the Nile in Egypt at 4100 mi. The longest river in the United States is the Missouri–Mississippi at 3860 mi. How much longer is the Nile?

16. *Speeds on Interstates.* Recently, speed limits on interstate highways in many Western states were raised from 65 mph to 75 mph. By how many miles per hour were they raised?

17. There are 24 hours (hr) in a day and 7 days in a week. How many hours are there in a week?

18. There are 60 min in an hour and 24 hr in a day. How many minutes are there in a day?

19. *Crossword.*   The *USA Today* crossword puzzle is a rectangle containing 15 rows with 15 squares in each row. How many squares does the puzzle have altogether?

20. *Pixels.*   A computer screen consists of small rectangular dots called *pixels*. How many pixels are there on a screen that has 600 rows with 800 pixels in each row?

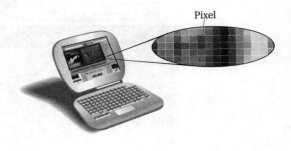

Pixel

21. *Refrigerator Purchase.*   Gourmet Deli has a chain of 24 restaurants. It buys a commercial refrigerator for each store at a cost of $1019 each. Find the total cost of the purchase.

22. *Microwave Purchase.*   Bridgeway College is constructing new dorms, in which each room has a small kitchen. It buys 96 microwave ovens at $88 each. Find the total cost of the purchase.

23. *"Seinfeld" Episodes.*   "Seinfeld" was a long-running television comedy with 177 episodes. A local station picks up the syndicated reruns. If the station runs 5 episodes per week, how many full weeks will pass before it must start over with past episodes? How many episodes will be left for the last week?

24. A lab technician separates a vial containing 70 cubic centimeters (cc) of blood into test tubes, each of which contains 3 cc of blood. How many test tubes can be filled? How much blood is left over?

25. *Automobile Mileage.*   The 2005 Hyundai Tucson GLS gets 26 miles to the gallon (mpg) in highway driving. How many gallons will it use in 6136 mi of highway driving?
Source: Hyundai

26. *Automobile Mileage.*   The 2005 Volkswagen Jetta (5 cylinder) gets 24 miles to the gallon (mpg) in city driving. How many gallons will it use in 3960 mi of city driving?
Source: Volkswagen of America, Inc.

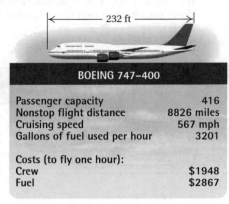

BOEING 747–400	
Passenger capacity	416
Nonstop flight distance	8826 miles
Cruising speed	567 mph
Gallons of fuel used per hour	3201
Costs (to fly one hour):	
Crew	$1948
Fuel	$2867

BOEING 777–200	
Passenger capacity	368
Nonstop flight distance	5210 miles
Cruising speed	615 mph
Gallons of fuel used per hour	2021
Costs (to fly one hour):	
Crew	$1131
Fuel	$1816

Source: Éclat Consulting; Boeing

27. The nonstop flight distance of the Boeing 747 jet is how much greater than the nonstop flight distance of the Boeing 777 jet?

28. How much larger is the passenger capacity of the Boeing 747 jet than the passenger capacity of the Boeing 777 jet?

29. How many gallons of fuel are needed for a 4-hour flight of the Boeing 747?

30. How much longer is the Boeing 747 than the Boeing 777?

31. What is the total cost for the crew and fuel for a 3-hour flight of the Boeing 747 jet?

32. What is the total cost for the crew and fuel for a 2-hour flight of the Boeing 777 jet?

33. Dana borrows $5928 for a used car. The loan is to be paid off in 24 equal monthly payments. How much is each payment (excluding interest)?

34. A family borrows $7824 to build a sunroom on the back of their home. The loan is to be paid off in equal monthly payments of $163 (excluding interest). How many months will it take to pay off the loan?

35. *High School Court.* The standard basketball court used by high school players has dimensions of 50 ft by 84 ft.
   a) What is its area?
   b) What is its perimeter?

36. *NBA Court.* The standard basketball court used by college and NBA players has dimensions of 50 ft by 94 ft.
   a) What is its area?
   b) What is its perimeter?
   c) How much greater is the area of an NBA court than a high school court? (See Exercise 35.)

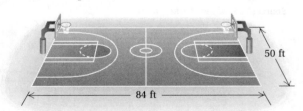

37. *Clothing Imports and Exports.* In the United States, the exports of clothing in 2003 totaled $2,596,000,000 while the imports totaled $31,701,000,000. How much more were the imports than the exports?

Source: U.S. Census Bureau, Foreign Trade Division

38. *Corn Imports and Exports.* In the United States, the exports of corn in 2003 totaled $2,264,000,000 while the imports totaled $130,000,000. How much more were the exports than the imports?

Source: U.S. Census Bureau, Foreign Trade Division

39. *Colonial Population.* Before the establishment of the U.S. Census in 1790, it was estimated that the Colonial population in 1780 was 2,780,400. This was an increase of 2,628,900 from the population in 1680. What was the Colonial population in 1680?

Source: *Time Almanac,* 2005

40. *Deaths by Firearms.* Deaths by firearms totaled 29,573 in 2001. This was a decrease of 10,022 from the deaths by firearms in 1993. How many deaths by firearms were there in 1993?

Source: Center for Disease Control and Prevention, *National Vital Statistics Reports,* vol 52, no. 3, September 18, 2003

41. *Hershey Bars.* Hershey Chocolate USA makes small, fun-size chocolate bars. How many 20-bar packages can be filled with 11,267 bars? How many bars will be left over?

42. *Reese's Peanut Butter Cups.* H. B. Reese Candy Co. makes small, fun-size peanut butter cups. The company manufactures 23,579 cups and fills 1025 packages. How many cups are in a package? How many cups will be left over?

43. *Map Drawing.* A map has a scale of 64 mi to the inch. How far apart *in reality* are two cities that are 6 in. apart on the map? How far apart *on the map* are two cities that, in reality, are 1728 mi apart?

44. *Map Drawing.* A map has a scale of 150 mi to the inch. How far apart *on the map* are two cities that, in reality, are 2400 mi apart? How far apart *in reality* are two cities that are 13 in. apart on the map?

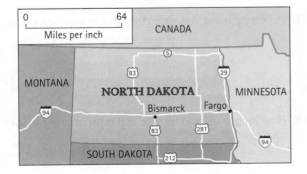

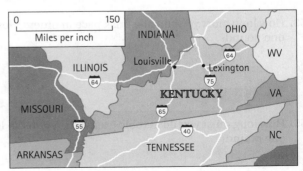

45. *Crossword.* The *Los Angeles Times* crossword puzzle is a rectangle containing 441 squares arranged in 21 rows. How many columns does the puzzle have?

46. *Sheet of Stamps.* A sheet of 100 stamps typically has 10 rows of stamps. How many stamps are in each row?

47. Copies of this book are generally shipped from the warehouse in cartons containing 24 books each. How many cartons are needed to ship 1355 books?

48. According to the H. J. Heinz Company, 16-oz bottles of catsup are generally shipped in cartons containing 12 bottles each. How many cartons are needed to ship 528 bottles of catsup?

49. Elena buys 5 video games at $64 each and pays for them with $10 bills. How many $10 bills does it take?

50. Pedro buys 5 video games at $64 each and pays for them with $20 bills. How many $20 bills does it take?

51. You have $568 in your bank account. You use your debit card for $46, $87, and $129. Then you deposit $94 back in the account after the return of some books. How much is left in your account?

52. The balance in your bank account is $749. You use your debit card for $34 and $65. Then you make a deposit of $123 from your paycheck. What is your new balance?

Weight Loss. Many Americans exercise for weight control. It is known that one must burn off about 3500 calories in order to lose one pound. The chart shown here details how much of certain types of exercise is required to burn 100 calories. Use this chart for Exercises 53–56.

To burn off 100 calories, you must:

- Run for 8 minutes at a brisk pace, or
- Swim for 2 minutes at a brisk pace, or
- Bicycle for 15 minutes at 9 mph, or
- Do aerobic exercises for 15 minutes.

53. How long must you run at a brisk pace in order to lose one pound?

54. How long must you swim in order to lose one pound?

55. How long must you do aerobic exercises in order to lose one pound?

56. How long must you bicycle at 9 mph in order to lose one pound?

57. *Bones in the Hands and Feet.* There are 27 bones in each human hand and 26 bones in each human foot. How many bones are there in all in the hands and feet?

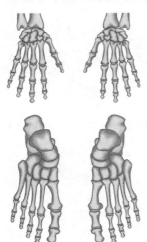

58. *Subway Travel.* The distance to Mars is about 303,000,000 miles. The number of miles that people in the United States traveled on subways in 2003 approximately equaled 22 round trips to Mars. What was the total distance traveled on subways?

Source: American Public Transportation Association, NASA

59. *Index Cards.* Index cards of dimension 3 in. by 5 in. are normally shipped in packages containing 100 cards each. How much writing area is available if one uses the front and back sides of a package of these cards?

60. An office for adjunct instructors at a community college has 6 bookshelves, each of which is 3 ft wide. The office is moved to a new location that has dimensions of 16 ft by 21 ft. Is it possible for the bookshelves to be put side by side on the 16-ft wall?

61. **Dw** In the newspaper article "When Girls Play, Knees Fail," the author discusses the fact that female athletes have six times the number of knee injuries that male athletes have. What information would be needed if you were to write a math problem based on the article? What might the problem be?

Source: *The Arizona Republic,* 2/9/00, p. C1

62. **Dw** Write a problem for a classmate to solve. Design the problem so that the solution is "The driver still has 329 mi to travel."

SKILL MAINTENANCE

Round 234,562 to the nearest:

63. Hundred.

64. Ten.

65. Thousand.

Estimate the computation by rounding to the nearest thousand.

66. 2783 + 4602 + 5797 + 8111

67. 28,430 − 11,977

68. 2100 + 5800

69. 5800 − 2100

Estimate the product by rounding to the nearest hundred.

70. 787 · 363

71. 887 · 799

72. 10,362 · 4531

SYNTHESIS

73. 🖩 *Speed of Light.* Light travels about 186,000 miles per second (mi/sec) in a vacuum as in outer space. In ice it travels about 142,000 mi/sec, and in glass it travels about 109,000 mi/sec. In 18 sec, how many more miles will light travel in a vacuum than in ice? than in glass?

74. Carney Community College has 1200 students. Each professor teaches 4 classes and each student takes 5 classes. There are 30 students and 1 teacher in each classroom. How many professors are there at Carney Community College?

EXERCISE SET

a Write exponential notation.

1. $3 \cdot 3 \cdot 3 \cdot 3$

2. $2 \cdot 2 \cdot 2 \cdot 2 \cdot 2$

3. $5 \cdot 5$

4. $13 \cdot 13 \cdot 13$

5. $7 \cdot 7 \cdot 7 \cdot 7 \cdot 7$

6. $10 \cdot 10$

7. $10 \cdot 10 \cdot 10$

8. $1 \cdot 1 \cdot 1 \cdot 1$

b Evaluate.

9. 7^2

10. 5^3

11. 9^3

12. 10^2

13. 12^4

14. 10^5

15. 11^2

16. 6^3

c Simplify.

17. $12 + (6 + 4)$

18. $(12 + 6) + 18$

19. $52 - (40 - 8)$

20. $(52 - 40) - 8$

21. $1000 \div (100 \div 10)$

22. $(1000 \div 100) \div 10$

23. $(256 \div 64) \div 4$

24. $256 \div (64 \div 4)$

25. $(2 + 5)^2$

26. $2^2 + 5^2$

27. $(11 - 8)^2 - (18 - 16)^2$

28. $(32 - 27)^3 + (19 + 1)^3$

29. $16 \cdot 24 + 50$

30. $23 + 18 \cdot 20$

31. $83 - 7 \cdot 6$

32. $10 \cdot 7 - 4$

33. $10 \cdot 10 - 3 \cdot 4$

34. $90 - 5 \cdot 5 \cdot 2$

35. $4^3 \div 8 - 4$

36. $8^2 - 8 \cdot 2$

37. $17 \cdot 20 - (17 + 20)$

38. $1000 \div 25 - (15 + 5)$

39. $6 \cdot 10 - 4 \cdot 10$

40. $3 \cdot 8 + 5 \cdot 8$

41. $300 \div 5 + 10$

42. $144 \div 4 - 2$

43. $3 \cdot (2 + 8)^2 - 5 \cdot (4 - 3)^2$

44. $7 \cdot (10 - 3)^2 - 2 \cdot (3 + 1)^2$

45. $4^2 + 8^2 \div 2^2$

46. $6^2 - 3^4 \div 3^3$

47. $10^3 - 10 \cdot 6 - (4 + 5 \cdot 6)$

48. $7^2 + 20 \cdot 4 - (28 + 9 \cdot 2)$

49. $6 \cdot 11 - (7 + 3) \div 5 - (6 - 4)$

50. $8 \times 9 - (12 - 8) \div 4 - (10 - 7)$

51. $120 - 3^3 \cdot 4 \div (5 \cdot 6 - 6 \cdot 4)$

52. $80 - 2^4 \cdot 15 \div (7 \cdot 5 - 45 \div 3)$

53. $2^3 \cdot 2^8 \div 2^6$

54. $2^7 \div 2^5 \cdot 2^4 \div 2^2$

55. Find the average of $64, $97, and $121.

56. Find the average of four test grades of 86, 92, 80, and 78.

57. Find the average of 320, 128, 276, and 880.

58. Find the average of $1025, $775, $2062, $942, and $3721.

d Simplify.

59. $8 \times 13 + \{42 \div [18 - (6 + 5)]\}$

60. $72 \div 6 - \{2 \times [9 - (4 \times 2)]\}$

61. $[14 - (3 + 5) \div 2] - [18 \div (8 - 2)]$

62. $[92 \times (6 - 4) \div 8] + [7 \times (8 - 3)]$

33

63. $(82 - 14) \times [(10 + 45 \div 5) - (6 \cdot 6 - 5 \cdot 5)]$

64. $(18 \div 2) \cdot \{[(9 \cdot 9 - 1) \div 2] - [5 \cdot 20 - (7 \cdot 9 - 2)]\}$

65. $4 \times \{(200 - 50 \div 5) - [(35 \div 7) \cdot (35 \div 7) - 4 \times 3]\}$

66. $15(23 - 4 \cdot 2)^3 \div (3 \cdot 25)$

67. $\{[18 - 2 \cdot 6] - [40 \div (17 - 9)]\} + \{48 - 13 \times 3 + [(50 - 7 \cdot 5) + 2]\}$

68. $(19 - 2^4)^5 - (141 \div 47)^2$

69. $\mathbf{D_W}$ Consider the problem in Example 8 of Section 1.8. How can you translate the problem to a single equation involving what you have learned about order of operations? How does the single equation relate to how we solved the problem?

70. $\mathbf{D_W}$ Consider the expressions $9 - (4 \cdot 2)$ and $(3 \cdot 4)^2$. Are the parentheses necessary in each case? Explain.

SKILL MAINTENANCE

Solve.

71. $x + 341 = 793$

72. $4197 + x = 5032$

73. $7 \cdot x = 91$

74. $1554 = 42 \cdot y$

75. $3240 = y + 898$

76. $6000 = 1102 + t$

77. $25 \cdot t = 625$

78. $10,000 = 100 \cdot t$

Solve.

79. *Colorado.* The state of Colorado is roughly the shape of a rectangle that is 273 mi by 382 mi. What is its area?

80. On a long four-day trip, a family bought the following amounts of gasoline for their motor home:

23 gallons,   24 gallons,
26 gallons,   25 gallons.

How much gasoline did they buy in all?

SYNTHESIS

Each of the answers in Exercises 81–83 is incorrect. First find the correct answer. Then place as many parentheses as needed in the expression in order to make the incorrect answer correct.

81. $1 + 5 \cdot 4 + 3 = 36$

82. $12 \div 4 + 2 \cdot 3 - 2 = 2$

83. $12 \div 4 + 2 \cdot 3 - 2 = 4$

84. Use one occurrence each of 1, 2, 3, 4, 5, 6, 7, 8, and 9 and any of the symbols $+$, $-$, $\times$, $\div$, and ( ) to represent 100.

Ratio and Proportion

Real-World Application

The number of women attending Purdue University's veterinary school of medicine has grown to surpass the number of men in the past three decades. In 1971, 53 men and 12 women were enrolled. In 1979, 36 men and 36 women were enrolled, and in 2004, there were 58 women and 12 men. What was the ratio of women to men in 1971, in 1979, and in 2004? What was the ratio of men to total enrollment in 2004?

Source: Purdue University School of Veterinary Medicine, *Indianapolis Star*

This problem appears as Example 7 in Section 2.1.

2.1   Introduction to Ratios
2.2   Proportions
2.3   Applications of Proportions

Objectives

a Find fraction notation for ratios.

b Simplify ratios.

1. Find the ratio of 5 to 11.

2. Find the ratio of 57.3 to 86.1.

3. Find the ratio of $6\frac{3}{4}$ to $7\frac{2}{5}$.

4. **Rainfall.** The greatest amount of rainfall ever recorded for a 12-month period was 739 in. in Kukui, Maui, Hawaii, from December 1981 to December 1982. Find the ratio of rainfall to time in months.
Source: *The Handy Science Answer Book*

Answers on page A-2

a Ratios

RATIO
A **ratio** is the quotient of two quantities.

In the 2004–2005 season, the Detroit Pistons basketball team averaged 93.3 points per game and allowed their opponents an average of 89.5 points per game. The *ratio* of points earned to points allowed is given by the fraction notation

Points earned $\longrightarrow \dfrac{93.3}{89.5}$ or by the colon notation $93.3:89.5.$
Points allowed $\longrightarrow$

We read both forms of notation as "the ratio of 93.3 to 89.5," listing the numerator first and the denominator second.

RATIO NOTATION
The **ratio** of a to b is given by the fraction notation $\dfrac{a}{b}$, where a is the numerator and b is the denominator, or by the colon notation $a:b$.

EXAMPLE 1 Find the ratio of 7 to 8.

The ratio is $\dfrac{7}{8}$,   or $7:8.$

EXAMPLE 2 Find the ratio of 31.4 to 100.

The ratio is $\dfrac{31.4}{100}$,   or $31.4:100.$

EXAMPLE 3 Find the ratio of $4\frac{2}{3}$ to $5\frac{7}{8}$. You need not simplify.

The ratio is $\dfrac{4\frac{2}{3}}{5\frac{7}{8}}$,   or $4\frac{2}{3}:5\frac{7}{8}.$

Do Exercises 1–3.

In most of our work, we will use fraction notation for ratios.

EXAMPLE 4 *Wind Speeds.* The average wind speed in Chicago is 10.4 mph. The average wind speed in Boston is 12.5 mph. Find the ratio of the wind speed in Chicago to the wind speed in Boston.
Source: *The Handy Geography Answer Book*

The ratio is $\dfrac{10.4}{12.5}.$

EXAMPLE 5 *Batting.* In the 2004 season, Vladimir Guerrero of the Anaheim Angels got 206 hits in 612 at-bats. What was the ratio of hits to at-bats? of at-bats to hits?

Source: Major League Baseball

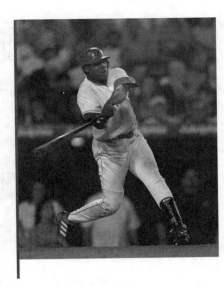

The ratio of hits to at-bats is

$$\frac{206}{612}.$$

The ratio of at-bats to hits is

$$\frac{612}{206}.$$

Do Exercises 4–6. (Exercise 4 is on the preceding page.)

EXAMPLE 6 Refer to the triangle below.

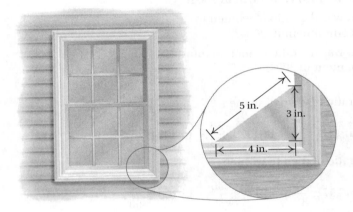

5 in. 3 in. 4 in.

a) What is the ratio of the length of the longest side to the length of the shortest side?

$$\frac{5}{3}$$

b) What is the ratio of the length of the shortest side to the length of the longest side?

$$\frac{3}{5}$$

Do Exercise 7.

5. Fat Grams. In one serving ($\frac{1}{2}$-cup) of fried scallops, there are 12 g of fat. In one serving ($\frac{1}{2}$-cup) of fried oysters, there are 14 g of fat. What is the ratio of grams of fat in one serving of scallops to grams of fat in one serving of oysters?

Source: *Better Homes and Gardens: A New Cook Book*

6. Earned Runs. In the 2004 season, Roger Clemens of the Houston Astros gave up 71 earned runs in 214.1 innings pitched. What was the ratio of earned runs to innings pitched? of innings pitched to earned runs?

Source: Major League Baseball

7. In the triangle below, what is the ratio of the length of the shortest side to the length of the longest side?

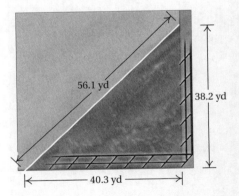

56.1 yd 38.2 yd 40.3 yd

Answers on page A-2

8. Soap Box Derby. Participation in the All-American Soap Box Derby World Championship has increased by more than 300 competitors since 1985. In 2004, there were 483 participants, 278 boys and 205 girls. What was the ratio of girls to boys? of boys to girls? of boys to total number of participants?

Source: All-American Soap Box Derby

EXAMPLE 7 *Veterinary Medicine.* The number of women attending Purdue University's veterinary school of medicine has grown to surpass the number of men in the past three decades.

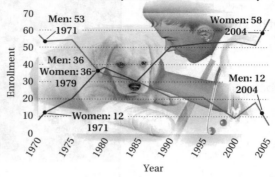

Enrollment in Veterinary Medicine: Purdue University

Men: 53 1971
Women: 58 2004
Men: 36 Women: 36 1979
Men: 12 2004
Women: 12 1971

Sources: Purdue University School of Veterinary Medicine; *Indianapolis Star*

a) What was the ratio of women to men in 1971? in 1979? in 2004?

b) What was the ratio of men to women in 1971? in 1979? in 2004?

c) What was the ratio of women to total enrollment in 2004?

d) What was the ratio of men to total enrollment in 2004?

a) The ratio of women to men

in 1971: $\dfrac{12}{53}$; in 1979: $\dfrac{36}{36}$; in 2004: $\dfrac{58}{12}$.

b) The ratio of men to women

in 1971: $\dfrac{53}{12}$; in 1979: $\dfrac{36}{36}$; in 2004: $\dfrac{12}{58}$.

c) The ratio of women to total enrollment

in 2004: $\dfrac{58}{70}$.

d) The ratio of men to total enrollment

in 2004: $\dfrac{12}{70}$.

Do Exercise 8.

b   Simplifying Notation for Ratios

Sometimes a ratio can be simplified. This provides a means of finding other numbers with the same ratio.

EXAMPLE 8 Find the ratio of 6 to 8. Then simplify and find two other numbers in the same ratio.

Answer on page A-2

We write the ratio in fraction notation and then simplify:

$$\frac{6}{8} = \frac{2 \cdot 3}{2 \cdot 4} = \frac{2}{2} \cdot \frac{3}{4} = 1 \cdot \frac{3}{4} = \frac{3}{4}.$$

Thus, 3 and 4 have the same ratio as 6 and 8. We can express this by saying "6 is to 8" as "3 is to 4."

Do Exercise 9.

EXAMPLE 9 Find the ratio of 2.4 to 10. Then simplify and find two other numbers in the same ratio.

We first write the ratio in fraction notation. Next, we multiply by 1 to clear the decimal from the numerator. Then we simplify.

$$\frac{2.4}{10} = \frac{2.4}{10} \cdot \frac{10}{10} = \frac{24}{100} = \frac{4 \cdot 6}{4 \cdot 25} = \frac{4}{4} \cdot \frac{6}{25} = \frac{6}{25}$$

Thus, 2.4 is to 10 as 6 is to 25.

Do Exercises 10 and 11.

EXAMPLE 10 A standard HDTV screen with a width of 40 in. has a height of $22\frac{1}{2}$ in. Find the ratio of width to height and simplify.

The ratio is $\dfrac{40}{22\frac{1}{2}} = \dfrac{40}{22.5} = \dfrac{400}{225}$

$$= \frac{25 \cdot 16}{25 \cdot 9} = \frac{25}{25} \cdot \frac{16}{9}$$

$$= \frac{16}{9}.$$

Thus we can say the ratio of width to height is 16 to 9, which can also be expressed as $16 : 9$.

Do Exercise 12.

9. Find the ratio of 18 to 27. Then simplify and find two other numbers in the same ratio.

10. Find the ratio of 3.6 to 12. Then simplify and find two other numbers in the same ratio.

11. Find the ratio of 1.2 to 1.5. Then simplify and find two other numbers in the same ratio.

12. In Example 10, find the ratio of the height of the HDTV screen to the width and simplify.

Answers on page A-2

Study Tips   TIME MANAGEMENT (PART 2)

Here are some additional tips to help you with time management.

- **Avoid "time killers."** We live in a media age, and the Internet, e-mail, television, and movies all are time killers. Allow yourself a break to enjoy some college and outside activities. But keep track of the time you spend on such activities and compare it to the time you spend studying.

- **Prioritize your tasks.** Be careful about taking on too many college activities that fall outside of academics. Examples of such activities are decorating a homecoming float, joining a fraternity or sorority, and participating on a student council committee. Any of these is important but keep your involvement to a minimum to be sure that you have enough time for your studies.

- **Be aggressive about your study tasks.** Instead of worrying over your math homework or test preparation, do something to get yourself started. Work a problem here and a problem there, and before long you will accomplish the task at hand. If the task is large, break it down into smaller parts, and do one at a time. You will be surprised at how quickly the large task can then be completed.

a   Find fraction notation for the ratio. You need not simplify.

1. 4 to 5 $\frac{4}{5}$ 4:5   5)4

2. 3 to 2 $\frac{3}{2}$ 3 ÷ 2

3. 178 to 572 $\frac{178}{572}$

4. 329 to 967

5. 0.4 to 12 $\frac{0.4}{12}$

6. 2.3 to 22 $\frac{2.3}{22}$ 23 ÷ 22

7. 3.8 to 7.4

8. 0.6 to 0.7

9. 56.78 to 98.35

10. 456.2 to 333.1

11. $8\frac{3}{4}$ to $9\frac{5}{6}$

12. $10\frac{1}{2}$ to $43\frac{1}{4}$ $\frac{10\frac{1}{2}}{43\frac{1}{4}}$

13. *Corvette Accidents.*   Of every 5 fatal accidents involving a Corvette, 4 do not involve another vehicle. Find the ratio of fatal accidents involving just a Corvette to those involving a Corvette and at least one other vehicle.
Source: *Harper's Magazine*

14. *Price of a Book.*   The recent paperback book *A Short History of Nearly Everything* by Bill Bryson had a list price of $15.95 but was sold by Amazon.com for $10.85. What was the ratio of the sale price to the list price? of the list price to the sale price?
Source: www.amazon.com

15. *Physicians.*   In 2001, there were 356 physicians in Connecticut per 100,000 residents. In Wyoming, there were 173 physicians per 100,000 residents. Find the ratio of the number of physicians to residents in Connecticut and in Wyoming.
Source: U.S. Census Bureau, American Medical Association

16. *Silicon in the Earth's Crust.*   Of every 100 tons of the earth's crust, there will be about 28 tons of silicon in its content. What is the ratio of silicon to the weight of crust? of the weight of crust to the weight of silicon?
Source: *The Handy Science Answer Book*

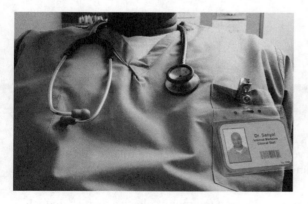

17. *Heart Disease.*   In the state of Minnesota, of every 1000 people, 93.2 will die of heart disease. Find the ratio of those who die of heart disease to all people.
Source: "Reforming the Health Care System; State Profiles 1999," AARP

18. *Cancer Deaths.*   In the state of Texas, of every 1000 people, 122.8 will die of cancer. Find the ratio of those who die of cancer to all people.
Source: "Reforming the Health Care System; State Profiles 1999," AARP

19. *Batting.* In the 2004 season, Todd Helton of the Colorado Rockies got 190 hits in 547 at-bats. What was the ratio of hits to at-bats? of at-bats to hits?

Source: Major League Baseball

20. *Batting.* In the 2004 season, Manny Ramirez of the Boston Red Sox got 175 hits in 568 at-bats. What was the ratio of hits to at-bats? of at-bats to hits?

Source: Major League Baseball

21. *Field Hockey.* A diagram of the playing area for field hockey is shown below. What is the ratio of width to length? of length to width?

Source: *Sports: The Complete Visual Reference*

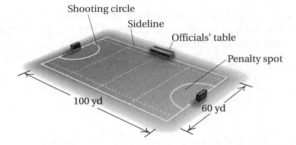

Shooting circle

Sideline

Officials' table

Penalty spot

100 yd   60 yd

22. *The Leaning Tower of Pisa.* At the time of this writing, the Leaning Tower of Pisa is still standing. It is 184.5 ft tall but leans about 17 ft out from its base. What is the ratio of the distance it leans to its height? its height to the distance it leans?

Source: *The Handy Science Answer Book*

184.5 ft

17 ft

reduce

solve? (reduce to its smallest ten

b   Find the ratio of the first number to the second and simplify.

23. 4 to 6 $\frac{4}{6}$ $\boxed{\frac{2}{3}}$

24. 6 to 10 $\frac{6}{10}$ $\boxed{\frac{3}{5}}$

25. 18 to 24

26. 28 to 36

27. 4.8 to 10

28. 5.6 to 10

29. 2.8 to 3.6

30. 4.8 to 6.4

31. 20 to 30

32. 40 to 60

33. 56 to 100

34. 42 to 100

35. 128 to 256

36. 232 to 116

37. 0.48 to 0.64

38. 0.32 to 0.96

39. In this rectangle, find the ratios of length to width and of width to length.

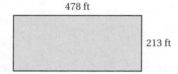

478 ft

213 ft

40. In this right triangle, find the ratios of shortest length to longest length and of longest length to shortest length.

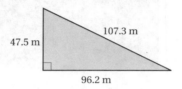

47.5 m

107.3 m

96.2 m

41. D_W Can every ratio be written as the ratio of some number to 1? Why or why not?

42. D_W What can be concluded about a rectangle's width if the ratio of length to perimeter is 1 to 3? Make some sketches and explain your reasoning.

SKILL MAINTENANCE

Use = or ≠ for □ to write a true sentence.

43. $\frac{12}{8}$ □ $\frac{6}{4}$

44. $\frac{4}{7}$ □ $\frac{5}{9}$

45. $\frac{7}{2}$ □ $\frac{31}{9}$

46. $\frac{17}{25}$ □ $\frac{68}{100}$

Divide. Write decimal notation for the answer.

47. 200 ÷ 4

48. 95 ÷ 10

49. 232 ÷ 16

50. 342 ÷ 2.25

Solve.

51. Rocky is $187\frac{1}{10}$ cm tall and his daughter is $180\frac{3}{4}$ cm tall. How much taller is Rocky?

52. Aunt Louise is $168\frac{1}{4}$ cm tall and her son is $150\frac{7}{10}$ cm tall. How much taller is Aunt Louise?

SYNTHESIS

53. Find the ratio of $3\frac{3}{4}$ to $5\frac{7}{8}$ and simplify.

Fertilizer. Exercises 54 and 55 refer to a common lawn fertilizer known as "5, 10, 15." This mixture contains 5 parts of potassium for every 10 parts of phosphorus and 15 parts of nitrogen (this is often denoted 5:10:15).

54. Find the ratio of potassium to nitrogen and of nitrogen to phosphorus.

55. Simplify the ratio 5:10:15.

During the 2004 season, Peyton Manning of the Indianapolis Colts completed 336 passes out of 497 attempts. His pass-completion rate was

$$\text{Completion rate} = \frac{336 \text{ completions}}{497 \text{ attempts}} = \frac{336}{497} \frac{\text{completion}}{\text{attempt}}$$

$$\approx 0.676 \frac{\text{completion}}{\text{attempt}}.$$

The rate was 0.676 completion per attempt.

Ben Roethlisberger of the Pittsburgh Steelers completed 196 passes out of 295 attempts. His pass-completion rate was

$$\text{Completion rate} = \frac{196 \text{ completions}}{295 \text{ attempts}} = \frac{196}{295} \frac{\text{completion}}{\text{attempt}}$$

$$\approx 0.664 \frac{\text{completion}}{\text{attempt}}.$$

The rate was 0.664 completion per attempt. We can see that the rates are not equal.

Source: National Football League

Instead of comparing the rates in decimal notation, we can compare the ratios

$$\frac{336}{497} \quad \text{and} \quad \frac{196}{295}$$

using cross products.

$$= \frac{336 \cdot 295}{99,120} \quad \frac{336}{497} \overset{?}{=} \frac{196}{295} \quad = \frac{497 \cdot 196}{97,412}$$

Since

$$99,120 \neq 97,412, \text{ we know that}$$

$$\frac{336}{497} \neq \frac{196}{295}.$$

Thus the ratios are not equal. If the ratios had been equal, we would say they are proportional.

a Proportions

When two pairs of numbers (such as 3, 2 and 6, 4) have the same ratio, we say that they are **proportional.** The equation

$$\frac{3}{2} = \frac{6}{4}$$

states that the pairs 3, 2 and 6, 4 are proportional. Such an equation is called a **proportion.** We sometimes read $\frac{3}{2} = \frac{6}{4}$ as "3 is to 2 as 6 is to 4."

Determine whether the two pairs of numbers are proportional.

1. 3, 4 and 6, 8

2. 1, 4 and 10, 39

3. 1, 2 and 20, 39

Determine whether the two pairs of numbers are proportional.

4. 6.4, 12.8 and 5.3, 10.6

5. 6.8, 7.4 and 3.4, 4.2

6. Determine whether $4\frac{2}{3}$, $5\frac{1}{2}$ and 14, $16\frac{1}{2}$ are proportional.

Answers on page A-2

EXAMPLE 1   Determine whether 1, 2, and 3, 6 are proportional.

We can use cross products:

$$1 \cdot 6 = 6 \qquad \overset{?}{\underset{}{\frac{1}{2} = \frac{3}{6}}} \qquad 2 \cdot 3 = 6.$$

Since the cross products are the same, $6 = 6$, we know that $\frac{1}{2} = \frac{3}{6}$, so the numbers are proportional.

EXAMPLE 2   Determine whether 2, 5 and 4, 7 are proportional.

We can use cross products:

$$2 \cdot 7 = 14 \qquad \overset{?}{\underset{}{\frac{2}{5} = \frac{4}{7}}} \qquad 5 \cdot 4 = 20.$$

Since the cross products are not the same, $14 \neq 20$, we know that $\frac{2}{5} \neq \frac{4}{7}$, so the numbers are not proportional.

Do Exercises 1–3.

EXAMPLE 3   Determine whether 3.2, 4.8 and 0.16, 0.24 are proportional.

We can use cross products:

$$3.2 \times 0.24 = 0.768 \qquad \overset{?}{\underset{}{\frac{3.2}{4.8} = \frac{0.16}{0.24}}} \qquad 4.8 \times 0.16 = 0.768.$$

Since the cross products are the same, $0.768 = 0.768$, we know that $\frac{3.2}{4.8} = \frac{0.16}{0.24}$, so the numbers are proportional.

Do Exercises 4 and 5.

EXAMPLE 4   Determine whether $4\frac{2}{3}$, $5\frac{1}{2}$ and $8\frac{7}{8}$, $16\frac{1}{3}$ are proportional.

We can use cross products:

$$4\frac{2}{3} \cdot 16\frac{1}{3} = \frac{14}{3} \cdot \frac{49}{3} \qquad \overset{?}{\underset{}{\frac{4\frac{2}{3}}{5\frac{1}{2}} = \frac{8\frac{7}{8}}{16\frac{1}{3}}}} \qquad 5\frac{1}{2} \cdot 8\frac{7}{8} = \frac{11}{2} \cdot \frac{71}{8}$$

$$= \frac{686}{9} \qquad\qquad\qquad\qquad = \frac{781}{16}$$

$$= 76\frac{2}{9} \qquad\qquad\qquad\qquad = 48\frac{13}{16}.$$

Since the cross products are not the same, $76\frac{2}{9} \neq 48\frac{13}{16}$, we know that the numbers are not proportional.

Do Exercise 6.

b   Solving Proportions

Let's now look at solving proportions. Consider the proportion

$$\frac{x}{3} = \frac{4}{6}.$$

One way to solve a proportion is to use cross products. Then we can divide on both sides to get the variable alone:

$$x \cdot 6 = 3 \cdot 4$$ Equating cross products (finding cross products and setting them equal)

$$\frac{x \cdot 6}{6} = \frac{3 \cdot 4}{6}$$ Dividing by 6 on both sides

$$x = \frac{3 \cdot 4}{6} = \frac{12}{6} = 2.$$

We can check that 2 is the solution by replacing x with 2 and using cross products:

$$2 \cdot 6 = 12 \qquad \frac{2}{3} \overset{?}{=} \frac{4}{6} \qquad 3 \cdot 4 = 12.$$

Since the cross products are the same, it follows that $\frac{2}{3} = \frac{4}{6}$; so the numbers 2, 3 and 4, 6 are proportional, and 2 is the solution of the equation.

SOLVING PROPORTIONS

To solve $\dfrac{x}{a} = \dfrac{c}{d}$, equate *cross products* and divide on both sides to get x alone.

Do Exercise 7.

EXAMPLE 5   Solve: $\dfrac{x}{7} = \dfrac{5}{3}$. Write a mixed numeral for the answer.

We have

$$\frac{x}{7} = \frac{5}{3}$$

$$x \cdot 3 = 7 \cdot 5$$ Equating cross products

$$\frac{x \cdot 3}{3} = \frac{7 \cdot 5}{3}$$ Dividing by 3

$$x = \frac{7 \cdot 5}{3}$$

$$x = \frac{35}{3}, \text{ or } 11\frac{2}{3}.$$

The solution is $11\frac{2}{3}$.

Do Exercise 8.

EXAMPLE 6   Solve: $\dfrac{7.7}{15.4} = \dfrac{y}{2.2}$.

We have

$$\frac{7.7}{15.4} = \frac{y}{2.2}$$

$$7.7 \times 2.2 = 15.4 \times y$$ Equating cross products

$$\frac{7.7 \times 2.2}{15.4} = \frac{15.4 \times y}{15.4}.$$ Dividing by 15.4

7. Solve: $\dfrac{x}{63} = \dfrac{2}{9}$.

8. Solve: $\dfrac{x}{9} = \dfrac{5}{4}$.

Answers on page A-2

Study Tips

WRITING ALL THE STEPS

Take the time to include all the steps when working your homework problems. Doing so will help you organize your thinking and avoid computational errors. If you find a wrong answer, having all the steps allows easier checking of your work. It will also give you complete, step-by-step solutions of the exercises that can be used to study for an exam.

Writing down all the steps and keeping your work organized may also give you a better chance of getting partial credit.

"Success comes before work only in the dictionary."

9. Solve: $\dfrac{21}{5} = \dfrac{n}{2.5}$.

Then

$$\dfrac{7.7 \times 2.2}{15.4} = y$$

$$\dfrac{16.94}{15.4} = y \qquad \text{Multiplying}$$

$$1.1 = y. \qquad \text{Dividing:} \quad 15.4\overline{)16.9_\wedge 4}$$

$$\begin{array}{r} 1.1 \\ 15.4\,)\overline{16.9_\wedge 4} \\ \underline{15\ 4\ 0} \\ 1\ 5\ 4 \\ \underline{1\ 5\ 4} \\ 0 \end{array}$$

The solution is 1.1.

Do Exercise 9.

10. Solve: $\dfrac{6}{x} = \dfrac{25}{11}$.

EXAMPLE 7 Solve: $\dfrac{8}{x} = \dfrac{5}{3}$. Write decimal notation for the answer.

We have

$$\dfrac{8}{x} = \dfrac{5}{3}$$

$$8 \cdot 3 = x \cdot 5 \qquad \text{Equating cross products}$$

$$\dfrac{8 \cdot 3}{5} = \dfrac{x \cdot 5}{5} \qquad \text{Dividing by 5}$$

$$\dfrac{8 \cdot 3}{5} = x$$

$$\dfrac{24}{5} = x \qquad \text{Multiplying}$$

$$4.8 = x. \qquad \text{Simplifying}$$

The solution is 4.8.

Do Exercise 10.

11. Solve: $\dfrac{0.4}{0.9} = \dfrac{4.8}{t}$.

EXAMPLE 8 Solve: $\dfrac{3.4}{4.93} = \dfrac{10}{n}$.

We have

$$\dfrac{3.4}{4.93} = \dfrac{10}{n}$$

$$3.4 \times n = 4.93 \times 10 \qquad \text{Equating cross products}$$

$$\dfrac{3.4 \times n}{3.4} = \dfrac{4.93 \times 10}{3.4} \qquad \text{Dividing by 3.4}$$

$$n = \dfrac{4.93 \times 10}{3.4}$$

$$n = \dfrac{49.3}{3.4} \qquad \text{Multiplying}$$

$$n = 14.5. \qquad \text{Dividing}$$

The solution is 14.5.

Do Exercise 11.

wers on page A-2

2.3

APPLICATIONS OF PROPORTIONS

a Applications and Problem Solving

Proportions have applications in such diverse fields as business, chemistry, health sciences, and home economics, as well as to many areas of daily life. Proportions are useful in making predictions.

EXAMPLE 1 *Predicting Total Distance.* Donna drives her delivery van 800 mi in 3 days. At this rate, how far will she drive in 15 days?

1. **Familiarize.** We let d = the distance traveled in 15 days.

2. **Translate.** We translate to a proportion. We make each side the ratio of distance to time, with distance in the numerator and time in the denominator.

$$\text{Distance in 15 days} \to \frac{d}{15} = \frac{800}{3} \gets \text{Distance in 3 days}$$
$$\text{Time} \to \qquad\qquad\qquad \gets \text{Time}$$

It may help to verbalize the proportion above as "the unknown distance d is to 15 days as the known distance 800 miles is to 3 days."

3. **Solve.** Next, we solve the proportion:

$$3 \cdot d = 15 \cdot 800 \qquad \text{Equating cross products}$$

$$\frac{3 \cdot d}{3} = \frac{15 \cdot 800}{3} \qquad \text{Dividing by 3 on both sides}$$

$$d = \frac{15 \cdot 800}{3}$$

$$d = 4000. \qquad \text{Multiplying and dividing}$$

4. **Check.** We substitute into the proportion and check cross products:

$$\frac{4000}{15} = \frac{800}{3};$$

$$4000 \cdot 3 = 12,000; \qquad 15 \cdot 800 = 12,000.$$

The cross products are the same.

5. **State.** Donna will drive 4000 mi in 15 days.

Do Exercise 1.

Problems involving proportion can be translated in more than one way. In Example 1, any one of the following is a correct translation:

$$\frac{800}{3} = \frac{d}{15}, \qquad \frac{15}{d} = \frac{3}{800}, \qquad \frac{15}{3} = \frac{d}{800}, \qquad \frac{800}{d} = \frac{3}{15}.$$

Equating the cross products in each equation gives us the equation $3 \cdot d = 15 \cdot 800$.

1. Calories Burned. Your author generally exercises for 2 hr each day. The readout on an exercise machine tells him that if he exercises for 24 min, he will burn 356 calories. How many calories will he burn if he exercises for 30 min?

Source: Star Trac Treadmill

2. Determining Paint Needs.
Lowell and Chris run a summer painting company to support their college expenses. They can paint 1600 ft^2 of clapboard with 4 gal of paint. How much paint would be needed for a building with 6000 ft^2 of clapboard?

EXAMPLE 2 *Recommended Dosage.* To control a fever, a doctor suggests that a child who weighs 28 kg be given 320 mg of Tylenol. If the dosage is proportional to the child's weight, how much Tylenol is recommended for a child who weighs 35 kg?

1. **Familiarize.** We let t = the number of milligrams of Tylenol.
2. **Translate.** We translate to a proportion, keeping the amount of Tylenol in the numerators.

$$\text{Tylenol suggested} \rightarrow \frac{320}{28} = \frac{t}{35} \leftarrow \text{Tylenol suggested}$$
$$\text{Child's weight} \rightarrow \qquad\qquad \leftarrow \text{Child's weight}$$

3. **Solve.** Next, we solve the proportion:

$$320 \cdot 35 = 28 \cdot t \qquad \text{Equating cross products}$$

$$\frac{320 \cdot 35}{28} = \frac{28 \cdot t}{28} \qquad \text{Dividing by 28 on both sides}$$

$$\frac{320 \cdot 35}{28} = t$$

$$400 = t. \qquad \text{Multiplying and dividing}$$

4. **Check.** We substitute into the proportion and check cross products:

$$\frac{320}{28} = \frac{400}{35};$$

$$320 \cdot 35 = 11{,}200; \qquad 28 \cdot 400 = 11{,}200.$$

The cross products are the same.

5. **State.** The dosage for a child who weighs 35 kg is 400 mg.

Do Exercise 2.

EXAMPLE 3 *Purchasing Tickets.* Carey bought 8 tickets to an international food festival for $52. How many tickets could she purchase with $90?

1. **Familiarize.** We let n = the number of tickets that can be purchased with $90.
2. **Translate.** We translate to a proportion, keeping the number of tickets in the numerators.

$$\text{Tickets} \rightarrow \frac{8}{52} = \frac{n}{90} \leftarrow \text{Tickets}$$
$$\text{Cost} \rightarrow \qquad\qquad \leftarrow \text{Cost}$$

Answer on page A-2

3. Solve. Next, we solve the proportion:

$$52 \cdot n = 8 \cdot 90 \qquad \text{Equating cross products}$$

$$\frac{52 \cdot n}{52} = \frac{8 \cdot 90}{52} \qquad \text{Dividing by 52 on both sides}$$

$$n = \frac{8 \cdot 90}{52}$$

$$n \approx 13.8. \qquad \text{Multiplying and dividing}$$

Because it is impossible to buy a fractional part of a ticket, we must round our answer *down* to 13.

4. Check. As a check, we use a different approach: We find the cost per ticket and then divide $90 by that price. Since $52 \div 8 = 6.50$ and $90 \div 6.50 \approx 13.8$, we have a check.

5. State. Carey could purchase 13 tickets with $90.

Do Exercise 3.

EXAMPLE 4 *Women's Hip Measurements.* For improved health, it is recommended that a woman's waist-to-hip ratio be 0.85 (or lower). Marta's hip measurement is 40 in. To meet the recommendation, what should Marta's waist measurement be?

Source: David Schmidt, "Lifting Weight Myths," *Nutrition Action Newsletter* 20, no. 4, October 1993

Waist measurement is the smallest measurement below the ribs but above the navel.

Hip measurement is the largest measurement around the widest part of the buttocks.

1. Familiarize. Note that $0.85 = \frac{85}{100}$. We let $w =$ Marta's waist measurement.

2. Translate. We translate to a proportion as follows:

$$\begin{array}{c} \text{Waist measurement} \rightarrow \\ \text{Hip measurement} \rightarrow \end{array} \frac{w}{40} = \frac{85}{100}. \begin{array}{c} \text{Recommended} \\ \text{waist-to-hip ratio} \end{array}$$

3. Solve. Next, we solve the proportion:

$$100 \cdot w = 40 \cdot 85 \qquad \text{Equating cross products}$$

$$\frac{100 \cdot w}{100} = \frac{40 \cdot 85}{100} \qquad \text{Dividing by 100 on both sides}$$

$$w = \frac{40 \cdot 85}{100}$$

$$w = 34. \qquad \text{Multiplying and dividing}$$

3. Purchasing Shirts. If 2 shirts can be bought for $47, how many shirts can be bought with $200?

4. Men's Hip Measurements. It is recommended that a man's waist-to-hip ratio be 0.95 (or lower). Malcolm's hip measurement is 40 in. To meet the recommendation, what should Malcolm's waist measurement be?

Source: David Schmidt, "Lifting Weight Myths," *Nutrition Action Newsletter* 20, no. 4, October 1993

Answers on page A-2

5. Construction Plans. In Example 5, the length of the actual deck is 28.5 ft. What is the length of the deck on the blueprints?

4. Check. As a check, we divide 34 by 40: $34 \div 40 = 0.85$. This is the desired ratio.

5. State. Marta's recommended waist measurement is 34 in. (or less).

Do Exercise 4 on the preceding page.

EXAMPLE 5 *Construction Plans.* Architects make blueprints of projects being constructed. These are scale drawings in which lengths are in proportion to actual sizes. The Hennesseys are constructing a rectangular deck just outside their house. The architectural blueprints are rendered such that $\frac{3}{4}$ in. on the drawing is actually 2.25 ft on the deck. The width of the deck on the drawing is 4.3 in. How wide is the deck in reality?

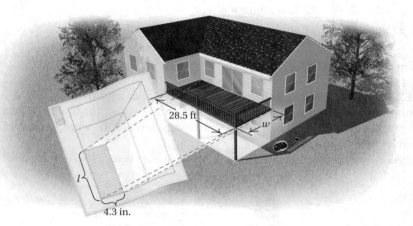

1. Familiarize. We let $w =$ the width of the deck.

2. Translate. Then we translate to a proportion, using 0.75 for $\frac{3}{4}$ in.

$$\text{Measure on drawing} \rightarrow \frac{0.75}{2.25} = \frac{4.3}{w} \leftarrow \text{Width of drawing}$$
$$\text{Measure on deck} \rightarrow \qquad\qquad \leftarrow \text{Width of deck}$$

3. Solve. Next, we solve the proportion:

$$0.75 \times w = 2.25 \times 4.3 \qquad \text{Equating cross products}$$

$$\frac{0.75 \times w}{0.75} = \frac{2.25 \times 4.3}{0.75} \qquad \text{Dividing by 0.75 on both sides}$$

$$w = \frac{2.25 \times 4.3}{0.75}$$

$$w = 12.9.$$

4. Check. We substitute into the proportion and check cross products:

$$\frac{0.75}{2.25} = \frac{4.3}{12.9};$$

$$0.75 \times 12.9 = 9.675; \qquad 2.25 \times 4.3 = 9.675.$$

The cross products are the same.

5. State. The width of the deck is 12.9 ft.

Do Exercise 5.

Answer on page A-2

EXAMPLE 6 *Estimating a Wildlife Population.* To determine the number of fish in a lake, a conservationist catches 225 fish, tags them, and throws them back into the lake. Later, 108 fish are caught, and it is found that 15 of them are tagged. Estimate how many fish are in the lake.

1. **Familiarize.** We let F = the number of fish in the lake.

2. **Translate.** We translate to a proportion as follows:

Fish tagged originally $\rightarrow$ $\dfrac{225}{F} = \dfrac{15}{108}$ $\leftarrow$ Tagged fish caught later
Fish in lake $\rightarrow$ $\phantom{\dfrac{225}{F}}$ $\leftarrow$ Fish caught later

3. **Solve.** Next, we solve the proportion:

$225 \cdot 108 = F \cdot 15$ Equating cross products

$\dfrac{225 \cdot 108}{15} = \dfrac{F \cdot 15}{15}$ Dividing by 15 on both sides

$\dfrac{225 \cdot 108}{15} = F$

$1620 = F.$ Multiplying and dividing

4. **Check.** We substitute into the proportion and check cross products:

$\dfrac{225}{1620} = \dfrac{15}{108};$

$225 \cdot 108 = 24{,}300;$ $1620 \cdot 15 = 24{,}300.$

The cross products are the same.

5. **State.** We estimate that there are 1620 fish in the lake.

Do Exercise 6.

6. Estimating a Deer Population. To determine the number of deer in a forest, a conservationist catches 612 deer, tags them, and releases them. Later, 244 deer are caught, and it is found that 72 of them are tagged. Estimate how many deer are in the forest.

Answer on page A-2

Translating for Success

Answers on page A-2

The goal of these matching questions is to practice step (2), *Translate*, of the five-step problem-solving process. Translate each word problem to an equation and select a correct translation from equations A–O.

A. $\dfrac{310}{15.5} = \dfrac{465}{x}$

B. $180 = 1\frac{1}{2} \cdot x$

C. $x = 71\frac{1}{8} - 76\frac{1}{2}$

D. $71\frac{1}{8} \cdot x = 74$

E. $74 \cdot 71\frac{1}{8} = x$

F. $x = 83.7 + 62.4$

G. $71\frac{1}{8} + x = 76\frac{1}{2}$

H. $x = 1\frac{2}{3} \cdot 180$

I. $\dfrac{140}{6} = \dfrac{x}{1\frac{1}{2}}$

J. $x = 2(83.7 + 62.4)$

K. $\dfrac{465}{15.5} = \dfrac{310}{x}$

L. $x = 83.7 \cdot 62.4$

M. $x = 180 \div 1\frac{2}{3}$

N. $\dfrac{140}{1\frac{1}{2}} = \dfrac{x}{6}$

O. $x = 1\frac{2}{3} \div 180$

1. *Calories in Cereal.* There are 140 calories in a $1\frac{1}{2}$-cup serving of Brand A cereal. How many calories are there in 6 cups of the cereal?

2. *Calories in Cereal.* There are 140 calories in 6 cups of Brand B cereal. How many calories are there in a $1\frac{1}{2}$-cup serving of the cereal?

3. *Gallons of Gasoline.* Jared's SUV traveled 310 miles on 15.5 gallons of gasoline. At this rate, how many gallons would be needed to travel 465 miles?

4. *Gallons of Gasoline.* Elizabeth's new fuel-efficient car traveled 465 miles on 15.5 gallons of gasoline. At this rate, how many gallons will be needed to travel 310 miles?

5. *Perimeter.* Find the perimeter of a rectangular field that measures 83.7 m by 62.4 m.

6. *Electric Bill.* Last month Todd's electric bills for his two rentals were $83.70 and $62.40. What was the total electric bill for the two properties?

7. *Package Tape.* A postal service center uses rolls of package tape that each contain 180 feet of tape. If it takes an average of $1\frac{2}{3}$ ft per package, how many packages can be taped with one roll?

8. *Online Price.* Jane spent $180 for an area rug in a department store. Later she saw the same rug for sale online and realized she had paid $1\frac{1}{2}$ times the online price. What was the online price?

9. *Heights of Sons.* Henry's three sons play basket-ball on three different college teams. Jeff, Jason, and Jared's heights are 74 in., $71\frac{1}{8}$ in., and $76\frac{1}{2}$ in., respectively. How much taller is Jared than Jason?

10. *Total Investment.* An investor bought 74 shares of stock at $71\frac{1}{8}$ per share. What was the total investment?

Quaeenkqua Woods   21

a   Solve.

1. *Study Time and Test Grades.* An English instructor asserted that students' test grades are directly proportional to the amount of time spent studying. Lisa studies 9 hr for a particular test and gets a score of 75. At this rate, how many hours would she have had to study to get a score of 92?

2. *Study Time and Test Grades.* A mathematics instructor asserted that students' test grades are directly proportional to the amount of time spent studying. Brent studies 15 hr for a particular test and gets a score of 85. At this rate, what score would he have received if he had studied 16 hr?

3. *Cap'n Crunch's Peanut Butter Crunch® Cereal.* The nutritional chart on the side of a box of Quaker Cap'n Crunch's Peanut Butter Crunch® Cereal states that there are 110 calories in a $\frac{3}{4}$-cup serving. How many calories are there in 6 cups of the cereal?

4. *Rice Krispies® Cereal.* The nutritional chart on the side of a box of Kellogg's Rice Krispies® Cereal states that there are 120 calories in a $1\frac{1}{4}$-cup serving. How many calories are there in 5 cups of the cereal?

Nutrition Facts

Serving Size 3/4 Cup (27g)
Servings Per Container about 15

Amount Per Serving	Cereal Alone	with 1/2 Cup Vitamin A&D Fortified Skim Milk
Calories	110	150
Calories from Fat	25	25
	% Daily Value	
Total Fat 2.5g	4%	4%
Saturated Fat 0.5g	3%	3%
Polyunsaturated Fat 0.5g		
Monounsaturated Fat 1g		
Cholesterol 0mg	0%	0%
Sodium 200mg	8%	11%
Potassium 65mg	2%	8%
Total Carbohydrate 21g	7%	9%
Dietary Fiber 1g	3%	3%
Sugars 9g		
Other Carbohydrate 12g		
Protein 2g		

Nutrition Facts

Serving Size 1¼ Cups (33g/1.2oz)
Servings Per Container about 12

Amount Per Serving	Cereal	Cereal with 1/2 Cup Vitamins A&D Fat Free Milk
Calories	120	160
Calories from Fat	0	0
	% Daily Value	
Total Fat 0g	0%	0%
Saturated Fat 0g	0%	0%
Trans Fat 0g		
Cholesterol 0mg	0%	0%
Sodium 320mg	13%	16%
Potassium 40mg	1%	7%
Total Carbohydrate 29g	10%	11%
Dietary Fiber 0g	0%	0%
Sugars 3g		
Other Carbohydrate 26g		
Protein 2g		

5. *Overweight Americans.* A study recently confirmed that of every 100 Americans, 60 are considered overweight. There were 295 million Americans in 2005. How many would be considered overweight?
   Source: U.S. Centers for Disease Control

6. *Cancer Death Rate in Illinois.* It is predicted that for every 1000 people in the state of Illinois, 130.9 will die of cancer. The population of Chicago is about 2,721,547. How many of these people will die of cancer?
   Source: *2001 New York Times Almanac*

7. *Gasoline Mileage.* Nancy's van traveled 84 mi on 6.5 gal of gasoline. At this rate, how many gallons would be needed to travel 126 mi?

8. *Bicycling.* Roy bicycled 234 mi in 14 days. At this rate, how far would Roy travel in 42 days?

9. *Quality Control.* A quality-control inspector examined 100 lightbulbs and found 7 of them to be defective. At this rate, how many defective bulbs will there be in a lot of 2500?

10. *Grading.* A professor must grade 32 essays in a literature class. She can grade 5 essays in 40 min. At this rate, how long will it take her to grade all 32 essays?

11. *Painting.* Fred uses 3 gal of paint to cover 1275 ft^2 of siding. How much siding can Fred paint with 7 gal of paint?

12. *Waterproofing.* Bonnie can waterproof 450 ft^2 of decking with 2 gal of sealant. How many gallons should Bonnie buy for a 1200-ft^2 deck?

13. *Publishing.* Every 6 pages of an author's manuscript corresponds to 5 published pages. How many published pages will a 540-page manuscript become?

14. *Turkey Servings.* An 8-lb turkey breast contains 36 servings of meat. How many pounds of turkey breast would be needed for 54 servings?

15. *Exchanging Money.* On 26 April 2005, 1 U.S. dollar was worth about 0.52521 British pound.
  a) How much would 45 U.S. dollars be worth in British pounds?
  b) How much would a car cost in U.S. dollars that costs 8640 British pounds?

16. *Exchanging Money.* On 26 April 2005, 1 U.S. dollar was worth about 1.1894 Swiss francs.
  a) How much would 360 U.S. dollars be worth in Swiss francs?
  b) How much would a pair of jeans cost in U.S. dollars that costs 80 Swiss francs?

17. *Exchanging Money.* On 26 April 2005, 1 U.S. dollar was worth about 106.03 Japanese yen.
  a) How much would 200 U.S. dollars be worth in Japanese yen?
  b) Dan was traveling in Japan and bought a skateboard that cost 3180 Japanese yen. How much would it cost in U.S. dollars?

18. *Exchanging Money.* On 26 April 2005, 1 U.S. dollar was worth about 11.059 Mexican pesos.
  a) How much would 120 U.S. dollars be worth in Mexican pesos?
  b) Jackie was traveling in Mexico and bought a watch that cost 3600 Mexican pesos. How much would it cost in U.S. dollars?

19. *Gas Mileage.* A 2005 Ford Mustang GT Convertible will go 372 mi on 15.5 gal of gasoline in highway driving.
   a) How many gallons of gasoline will it take to drive 2690 mi from Boston to Phoenix?
   b) How far can the car be driven on 140 gal of gasoline?
   Source: Ford

20. *Gas Mileage.* A 2005 Volkswagen Passat will go 462 mi on 16.5 gal of gasoline in highway driving.
   a) How many gallons of gasoline will it take to drive 1650 mi from Pittsburgh to Albuquerque?
   b) How far can the car be driven on 130 gal of gasoline?
   Source: Volkswagen of America, Inc.

21. *Lefties.* In a class of 40 students, on average, 6 will be left-handed. If a class includes 9 "lefties," how many students would you estimate are in the class?

22. *Sugaring.* When 38 gal of maple sap are boiled down, the result is 2 gal of maple syrup. How much sap is needed to produce 9 gal of syrup?

23. *Mileage.* Jean bought a new car. In the first 8 months, it was driven 9000 mi. At this rate, how many miles will the car be driven in 1 yr?

24. *Coffee Production.* Coffee beans from 14 trees are required to produce the 17 lb of coffee that the average person in the United States drinks each year. How many trees are required to produce 375 lb of coffee?

25. *Metallurgy.* In a metal alloy, the ratio of zinc to copper is 3 to 13. If there are 520 lb of copper, how many pounds of zinc are there?

26. *Class Size.* A college advertises that its student-to-faculty ratio is 14 to 1. If 56 students register for Introductory Spanish, how many sections of the course would you expect to see offered?

27. *Painting.* Helen can paint 950 ft^2 with 2 gal of paint. How many 1-gal cans does she need in order to paint a 30,000-ft^2 wall?

28. *Snow to Water.* Under typical conditions, $1\frac{1}{2}$ ft of snow will melt to 2 in. of water. To how many inches of water will $5\frac{1}{2}$ ft of snow melt?

29. *Grass-Seed Coverage.* It takes 60 oz of grass seed to seed 3000 ft² of lawn. At this rate, how much would be needed for 5000 ft² of lawn?

30. *Grass-Seed Coverage.* In Exercise 29, how much seed would be needed for 7000 ft² of lawn?

31. *Estimating a Deer Population.* To determine the number of deer in a game preserve, a forest ranger catches 318 deer, tags them, and releases them. Later, 168 deer are caught, and it is found that 56 of them are tagged. Estimate how many deer are in the game preserve.

32. *Estimating a Trout Population.* To determine the number of trout in a lake, a conservationist catches 112 trout, tags them, and throws them back into the lake. Later, 82 trout are caught, and it is found that 32 of them are tagged. Estimate how many trout there are in the lake.

33. *Map Scaling.* On a road atlas map, 1 in. represents 16.6 mi. If two cities are 3.5-in. apart on the map, how far apart are they in reality?

34. *Map Scaling.* On a map, $\frac{1}{4}$ in. represents 50 mi. If two cities are $3\frac{1}{4}$-in. apart on the map, how far apart are they in reality?

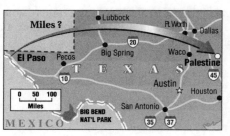

35. *Points per Game.* At one point in the 2000–2001 NBA season, Allen Iverson of the Philadelphia 76ers had scored 884 points in 33 games.

    a) At this rate, how many games would it take him to score 1500 points?

    b) There are 82 games in an entire NBA season. At this rate, how many points would Iverson score in the entire season?

    Source: National Basketball Association

36. *Points per Game.* At one point in the 2000–2001 NBA season, Shaquille O'Neal, then of the Los Angeles Lakers, had scored 826 points in 32 games.

    a) At this rate, how many games would it take him to score 2000 points?

    b) There are 82 games in an entire NBA season. At this rate, how many points would O'Neal score in the entire season?

37. $\mathbf{D_W}$ Can unit prices be used to solve proportions that involve money? Explain why or why not.

38. $\mathbf{D_W}$ *Earned Run Average.* In baseball, the average number of runs given up by a pitcher in nine innings is his *earned run average*, or *ERA*. Set up a formula for determining a player's ERA. Then verify it using the fact that in the 2000 season, Daryl Kile of the St. Louis Cardinals gave up 101 earned runs in $232\frac{1}{3}$ innings to compile an ERA of 3.91. Then use your formula to determine the ERA of Randy Johnson of the Arizona Diamondbacks, who gave up 73 earned runs in $248\frac{2}{3}$ innings. Is a low ERA considered good or bad?

    Source: Major League Baseball

SKILL MAINTENANCE

Determine whether each number is prime, composite, or neither.

39. 1   **40.** 28   **41.** 83   **42.** 93   **43.** 47

Find the prime factorization of each number.

44. 808   **45.** 28   **46.** 866   **47.** 93   **48.** 2020

SYNTHESIS

49. ▦ Carney College is expanding from 850 to 1050 students. To avoid any rise in the student-to-faculty ratio, the faculty of 69 professors must also increase. How many new faculty positions should be created?

50. ▦ In recognition of her outstanding work, Sheri's salary has been increased from $26,000 to $29,380. Tim is earning $23,000 and is requesting a proportional raise. How much more should he ask for?

51. *Baseball Statistics.* Cy Young, one of the greatest baseball pitchers of all time, gave up an average of 2.63 earned runs every 9 innings. Young pitched 7356 innings, more than anyone in the history of baseball. How many earned runs did he give up?

52. ▦ *Real-Estate Values.* According to Coldwell Banker Real Estate Corporation, a home selling for $189,000 in Austin, Texas, would sell for $665,795 in San Francisco. How much would a $450,000 home in San Francisco sell for in Austin? Round to the nearest $1000.

    Source: Coldwell Banker Real Estate Corporation

53. ▦ The ratio 1:3:2 is used to estimate the relative costs of a CD player, receiver, and speakers when shopping for a stereo. That is, the receiver should cost three times the amount spent on the CD player and the speakers should cost twice as much as the amount spent on the CD player. If you had $900 to spend, how would you allocate the money, using this ratio?

3.4 EXERCISE SET

a Simplify.

1. $8 - 2 \cdot 3 - 9$

2. $8 - (2 \cdot 3 - 9)$

3. $(8 - 2 \cdot 3) - 9$

4. $(8 - 2)(3 - 9)$

5. $16 \cdot (-24) + 50$

6. $10 \cdot 20 - 15 \cdot 24$

7. $2^4 + 2^3 - 10$

8. $40 - 3^2 - 2^3$

9. $5^3 + 26 \cdot 71 - (16 + 25 \cdot 3)$

10. $4^3 + 10 \cdot 20 + 8^2 - 23$

11. $4 \cdot 5 - 2 \cdot 6 + 4$

12. $4 \cdot (6 + 8)/(4 + 3)$

13. $4^3/8$

14. $5^3 - 7^2$

15. $8(-7) + 6(-5)$

16. $10(-5) + 1(-1)$

17. $19 - 5(-3) + 3$

18. $14 - 2(-6) + 7$

19. $9 \div (-3) + 16 \div 8$

20. $-32 - 8 \div 4 - (-2)$

21. $-4^2 + 6$

22. $-5^2 + 7$

23. $-8^2 - 3$

24. $-9^2 - 11$

25. $12 - 20^3$

26. $20 + 4^3 \div (-8)$

27. $2 \times 10^3 - 5000$

28. $-7(3^4) + 18$

29. $6[9 - (3 - 4)]$

30. $8[(6 - 13) - 11]$

31. $-1000 \div (-100) \div 10$

32. $256 \div (-32) \div (-4)$

33. $8 - (7 - 9)$

34. $(8 - 7) - 9$

35. $\dfrac{10 - 6^2}{9^2 + 3^2}$

36. $\dfrac{5^2 - 4^3 - 3}{9^2 - 2^2 - 1^5}$

37. $\dfrac{20(8 - 3) - 4(10 - 3)}{10(2 - 6) - 2(5 + 2)}$

38. $\dfrac{(3 - 5)^2 - (7 - 13)}{(12 - 9)^2 + (11 - 14)^2}$

39. 🖩 **D**W Jake keys 18/2 · 3 into his calculator and expects the result to be 3. What mistake is he making?

40. **D**W Explain how multiplication can be used to justify why the quotient of two negative integers is positive.

Fraction Notation and Mixed Numerals

4.1 Addition and Applications

4.2 Subtraction, Order, and Applications

4.3 Addition and Subtraction Using Mixed Numerals; Applications

a   Add and simplify.

1. $\dfrac{7}{8} + \dfrac{1}{8}$

2. $\dfrac{2}{5} + \dfrac{3}{5}$

3. $\dfrac{1}{8} + \dfrac{5}{8}$

4. $\dfrac{3}{10} + \dfrac{3}{10}$

5. $\dfrac{2}{3} + \dfrac{5}{6}$

6. $\dfrac{5}{6} + \dfrac{1}{9}$

7. $\dfrac{1}{8} + \dfrac{1}{6}$

8. $\dfrac{1}{6} + \dfrac{3}{4}$

9. $\dfrac{4}{5} + \dfrac{7}{10}$

10. $\dfrac{3}{4} + \dfrac{1}{12}$

11. $\dfrac{5}{12} + \dfrac{3}{8}$

12. $\dfrac{7}{8} + \dfrac{1}{16}$

13. $\dfrac{3}{20} + \dfrac{3}{4}$

14. $\dfrac{2}{15} + \dfrac{2}{5}$

15. $\dfrac{5}{6} + \dfrac{7}{9}$

16. $\dfrac{5}{8} + \dfrac{5}{6}$

17. $\dfrac{3}{10} + \dfrac{1}{100}$

18. $\dfrac{9}{10} + \dfrac{3}{100}$

19. $\dfrac{5}{12} + \dfrac{4}{15}$

20. $\dfrac{3}{16} + \dfrac{1}{12}$

21. $\dfrac{9}{10} + \dfrac{99}{100}$

22. $\dfrac{3}{10} + \dfrac{27}{100}$

23. $\dfrac{7}{8} + \dfrac{0}{1}$

24. $\dfrac{0}{1} + \dfrac{5}{6}$

25. $\dfrac{3}{8} + \dfrac{1}{6}$

26. $\dfrac{5}{8} + \dfrac{1}{6}$

27. $\dfrac{5}{12} + \dfrac{7}{24}$

28. $\dfrac{1}{18} + \dfrac{7}{12}$

29. $\dfrac{3}{16} + \dfrac{5}{16} + \dfrac{4}{16}$

30. $\dfrac{3}{8} + \dfrac{1}{8} + \dfrac{2}{8}$

31. $\dfrac{8}{10} + \dfrac{7}{100} + \dfrac{4}{1000}$

32. $\dfrac{1}{10} + \dfrac{2}{100} + \dfrac{3}{1000}$

33. $\dfrac{3}{8} + \dfrac{5}{12} + \dfrac{8}{15}$

34. $\dfrac{1}{2} + \dfrac{3}{8} + \dfrac{1}{4}$

35. $\dfrac{15}{24} + \dfrac{7}{36} + \dfrac{91}{48}$

36. $\dfrac{5}{7} + \dfrac{25}{52} + \dfrac{7}{4}$

29.
$$34$$
$$-\ 18\tfrac{5}{8}$$

30.
$$23$$
$$-\ 19\tfrac{3}{4}$$

31.
$$21\tfrac{1}{6}$$
$$-\ 13\tfrac{3}{4}$$

32.
$$42\tfrac{1}{10}$$
$$-\ 23\tfrac{7}{12}$$

33.
$$14\tfrac{1}{8}$$
$$-\ \ \ \tfrac{3}{4}$$

34.
$$28\tfrac{1}{6}$$
$$-\ \ \ 5$$

35.
$$25\tfrac{1}{9}$$
$$-\ 13\tfrac{5}{6}$$

36.
$$23\tfrac{5}{16}$$
$$-\ 14\tfrac{7}{12}$$

C Solve.

37. *Sewing from a Pattern.* Suppose you want to make an outfit in size 8. Using 45-in. fabric, you need $1\tfrac{3}{8}$ yd for the dress, $\tfrac{5}{8}$ yd of contrasting fabric for the band at the bottom, and $3\tfrac{3}{8}$ yd for the jacket. How many yards of 45-in. fabric are needed to make the outfit?

$1\tfrac{3}{8}$ yd + $\tfrac{5}{8}$ yd + $3\tfrac{3}{8}$ yd = $5\tfrac{3}{8}$ yd of 45 in fabric.

38. *Sewing from a Pattern.* Suppose you want to make an outfit in size 12. Using 45-in. fabric, you need $2\tfrac{3}{4}$ yd for the dress and $3\tfrac{1}{2}$ yd for the jacket. How many yards of 45-in. fabric are needed to make the outfit?

$2\tfrac{3}{4}$ yd $3\tfrac{1}{2}$ yd = $6\tfrac{1}{4}$ (H5-in fabric.

39. For a family barbecue, Cayla bought packages of hamburger weighing $1\tfrac{2}{3}$ lb and $5\tfrac{3}{4}$ lb. What was the total weight of the meat? $1\tfrac{2}{3} + 5\tfrac{3}{4} = 7\tfrac{5}{12}$

40. Marsha's Butcher Shop sold packages of sliced turkey breast weighing $1\tfrac{1}{3}$ lb and $4\tfrac{3}{5}$ lb. What was the total weight of the meat? $= 3\tfrac{4}{15}$

41. Tara is 66 in. tall and her son, Tom, is $59\tfrac{7}{12}$ in. tall. How much taller is Tara?

42. Nicholas is $73\tfrac{2}{3}$ in. tall and his daughter, Kendra, is $71\tfrac{5}{16}$ in. tall. How much shorter is Kendra?

Fraction Notation: Multiplication and Division

5

5.1   Multiplication and Applications

5.2   Division and Applications

a Multiply.

1. $3 \cdot \dfrac{1}{5}$

2. $2 \cdot \dfrac{1}{3}$

3. $5 \times \dfrac{1}{8}$

4. $4 \times \dfrac{1}{5}$

5. $\dfrac{2}{11} \cdot 4$

6. $\dfrac{2}{5} \cdot 3$

7. $10 \cdot \dfrac{7}{9}$

8. $9 \cdot \dfrac{5}{8}$

9. $\dfrac{2}{5} \cdot 1$

10. $\dfrac{3}{8} \cdot 1$

11. $\dfrac{2}{5} \cdot 3$

12. $\dfrac{3}{5} \cdot 4$

13. $7 \cdot \dfrac{3}{4}$

14. $7 \cdot \dfrac{2}{5}$

15. $17 \times \dfrac{5}{6}$

16. $\dfrac{3}{7} \cdot 40$

b Multiply.

17. $\dfrac{1}{2} \cdot \dfrac{1}{3}$

18. $\dfrac{1}{6} \cdot \dfrac{1}{4}$

19. $\dfrac{1}{4} \times \dfrac{1}{10}$

20. $\dfrac{1}{3} \times \dfrac{1}{10}$

21. $\dfrac{2}{3} \times \dfrac{1}{5}$

22. $\dfrac{3}{5} \times \dfrac{1}{5}$

23. $\dfrac{2}{5} \cdot \dfrac{2}{3}$

24. $\dfrac{3}{4} \cdot \dfrac{3}{5}$

25. $\dfrac{3}{4} \cdot \dfrac{3}{4}$

26. $\dfrac{3}{7} \cdot \dfrac{4}{5}$

27. $\dfrac{2}{3} \cdot \dfrac{7}{13}$

28. $\dfrac{3}{11} \cdot \dfrac{4}{5}$

29. $\dfrac{1}{10} \cdot \dfrac{7}{10}$

30. $\dfrac{3}{10} \cdot \dfrac{3}{10}$

31. $\dfrac{7}{8} \cdot \dfrac{7}{8}$

32. $\dfrac{4}{5} \cdot \dfrac{4}{5}$

33. $\dfrac{1}{10} \cdot \dfrac{1}{100}$

34. $\dfrac{3}{10} \cdot \dfrac{7}{100}$

35. $\dfrac{14}{15} \cdot \dfrac{13}{19}$

36. $\dfrac{12}{13} \cdot \dfrac{12}{13}$

c Solve.

37. *Tossed Salad.* The recipe for Cherry Brie Tossed Salad calls for $\dfrac{3}{4}$ cup of sliced almonds. How much is needed to make $\dfrac{1}{2}$ of the recipe?

Source: Reprinted with permission from *Taste of Home* magazine, www.tasteofhome.com

38. It takes $\dfrac{2}{3}$ yd of ribbon to make a bow. How much ribbon is needed to make 5 bows?

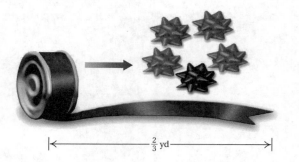

$\dfrac{2}{3}$ yd

a Find the reciprocal.

1. $\dfrac{5}{6}$

2. $\dfrac{7}{8}$

3. 6

4. 4

5. $\dfrac{1}{6}$

6. $\dfrac{1}{4}$

7. $\dfrac{10}{3}$

8. $\dfrac{17}{4}$

b Divide and simplify. | Don't forget to simplify! |

9. $\dfrac{3}{5} \div \dfrac{3}{4}$

10. $\dfrac{2}{3} \div \dfrac{3}{4}$

11. $\dfrac{3}{5} \div \dfrac{9}{4}$

12. $\dfrac{6}{7} \div \dfrac{3}{5}$

13. $\dfrac{4}{3} \div \dfrac{1}{3}$

14. $\dfrac{10}{9} \div \dfrac{1}{3}$

15. $\dfrac{1}{3} \div \dfrac{1}{6}$

16. $\dfrac{1}{4} \div \dfrac{1}{5}$

17. $\dfrac{3}{8} \div 3$

18. $\dfrac{5}{6} \div 5$

19. $\dfrac{12}{7} \div 4$

20. $\dfrac{18}{5} \div 2$

21. $12 \div \dfrac{3}{2}$

22. $24 \div \dfrac{3}{8}$

23. $28 \div \dfrac{4}{5}$

24. $40 \div \dfrac{2}{3}$

25. $\dfrac{5}{8} \div \dfrac{5}{8}$

26. $\dfrac{2}{5} \div \dfrac{2}{5}$

27. $\dfrac{8}{15} \div \dfrac{4}{5}$

28. $\dfrac{6}{13} \div \dfrac{3}{26}$

29. $\dfrac{9}{5} \div \dfrac{4}{5}$

30. $\dfrac{5}{12} \div \dfrac{25}{36}$

31. $120 \div \dfrac{5}{6}$

32. $360 \div \dfrac{8}{7}$

Decimal Notation

6

6.1 Addition and Subtraction
6.2 Multiplication
6.3 Division

EXERCISE SET

a   Add.

1.   3 1 6.2 5
      +   1 8.1 2

2.   6 4 1.8 0 3
      +   1 4.9 3 5

3.   6 5 9.4 0 3
      + 9 1 6.8 1 2

4.   4 2 0 3.2 8
      +   3.3 9

5.   9.1 0 4
      + 1 2 3.4 5 6

6.   8 1.0 0 8
      +   3.4 0 9

7. 20.0124 + 30.0124

8. 0.687 + 0.9

9. 39 + 1.007

10. 2.3 + 0.729 + 23

11.   4 7.8
         2 1 9.8 5 2
          4 3.5 9
       + 6 6 6.7 1 3

12.   1 3.7 2
             9.1 1 2
         6 5 4 2.7 9 0 8
       +   2 3.9 0 1

13. 0.34 + 3.5 + 0.127 + 768

14. 17 + 3.24 + 0.256 + 0.3689

15. 99.6001 + 7285.18 + 500.042 + 870

16. 65.987 + 9.4703 + 6744.02 + 1.0003 + 200.895

b   Subtract.

17.   5 1.3 1
       −   2.2 9

18.   4 4.3 4 5
       −   3.1 0 5

19.   9 2.3 4 1
       −   6.4 2

20.   9 7.0 1
       −   3.1 5

21.   2.5
       − 0.0 0 2 5

22.   3 9.0
       −   0.2 8

23.   3.4
       − 0.0 0 3

24.   2.8
       − 2.0 8

25. 28.2 − 19.35

26. 100.16 − 0.118

27. 34.07 − 30.7

28. 36.2 − 16.28

29. $8.45 - 7.405$

30. $3.801 - 2.81$

31. $6.003 - 2.3$

32. $9.087 - 8.807$

33. $1 - 0.0098$

34. $2 - 1.0908$

35. $100 - 0.34$

36. $624 - 18.79$

37. $7.48 - 2.6$

38. $18.4 - 5.92$

39. $3 - 2.006$

40. $263.7 - 102.08$

41. $19 - 1.198$

42. $2548.98 - 2.007$

43. $65 - 13.87$

44. $45 - 0.999$

45.
$$\begin{array}{r} 3\ 2.7\ 9\ 7\ 8 \\ -\ \ \ 0.0\ 5\ 9\ 2 \end{array}$$

46.
$$\begin{array}{r} 0.4\ 9\ 6\ 3\ 4 \\ -\ 0.1\ 2\ 6\ 7\ 8 \end{array}$$

47.
$$\begin{array}{r} 6.0\ 7 \\ -\ 2.0\ 0\ 7\ 8 \end{array}$$

48.
$$\begin{array}{r} 1.0 \\ -\ 0.9\ 9\ 9\ 9 \end{array}$$

C   Solve.

49. $x + 17.5 = 29.15$

50. $t + 50.7 = 54.07$

51. $17.95 + p = 402.63$

52. $w + 1.3004 = 47.8$

53. $13,083.3 = x + 12,500.33$

54. $100.23 = 67.8 + z$

55. $x + 2349 = 17,684.3$

56. $1830.4 + t = 23,067$

Find the errors, if any, in each checkbook.

57.

DATE	CHECK NUMBER	TRANSACTION DESCRIPTION	√ T	(−) PAYMENT/ DEBIT	(+ OR −) OTHER	(+) DEPOSIT/ CREDIT	BALANCE FORWARD 9704 56
8/8	342	Bill Rydman		27 44			9677 12
8/9		Deposit <Beauty Contest>				1000 00	10,677 12
8/12	343	Chuck Taylor		123 95			10,553 17
8/14	344	Jennifer Crum		124 02			10,677 19
8/22	345	Neon Johnny's Pizza		12 43			10,664 76
8/24		Deposit <Bowling Tournament>				2500 00	13,164 76
8/29	346	Border's Bookstore		137 78			13,302 54
9/2		Deposit <Bodybuilder Contest>				18 88	13,283 66
9/3	347	Fireman's Fund		2800 00			10,483 66

58.

DATE	CHECK NUMBER	TRANSACTION DESCRIPTION	√ T	(−) PAYMENT/ DEBIT	(+ OR −) OTHER	(+) DEPOSIT/ CREDIT	BALANCE FORWARD 1876 43
4/1	500	Bart Kaufman		500 12			1376 31
4/3	501	Jim Lawler		28 56			1347 75
4/3		Deposit <State Lottery>				10,000 00	11,347 75
4/3	502	Victoria Montoya		464 00			10,883 75
4/3		Deposit <Jewelry Sale>				2500 00	8383 75
4/4	503	Baskin & Robbins		1600 00			6783 75
4/8	504	Golf Galaxy		1349 98			5433 77
4/12	505	Don Mitchell Pro Shops		658 97			4774 80
4/13		Deposit <Publisher's Clearing House>				100000 00	104,774 80
4/15	506	American Airlines		6885 58			98,889 22

59. D_W Explain the error in the following:
Add.

$$13.07 + 9.205 = 10.512$$

$$
\begin{array}{r}
\overset{1}{1}3.07 \\
+\ 9.205 \\
\hline
22.075
\end{array}
$$

60. D_W Explain the error in the following:
Subtract.

$$73.089 - 5.0061 = 2.3028$$

$$
\begin{array}{r}
73.089 \\
-\ 5.0061 \\
\hline
68.0829
\end{array}
$$

CHAPTER 6: Decimal Notation

a   Translate to an equation. Do not solve.

1. What is 32% of 78?

2. 98% of 57 is what?

3. 89 is what percent of 99?

4. What percent of 25 is 8?

5. 13 is 25% of what?

6. 21.4% of what is 20?

b   Translate to an equation and solve.

7. What is 85% of 276?

8. What is 74% of 53?

9. 150% of 30 is what?

10. 100% of 13 is what?

11. What is 6% of $300?

12. What is 4% of $45?

13. 3.8% of 50 is what?

14. $33\frac{1}{3}$% of 480 is what?
$\left(Hint:\ 33\frac{1}{3}\% = \frac{1}{3}.\right)$

15. $39 is what percent of $50?

16. $16 is what percent of $90?

17. 20 is what percent of 10?

18. 60 is what percent of 20?

19. What percent of $300 is $150?

20. What percent of $50 is $40?

21. What percent of 80 is 100?

22. What percent of 60 is 15?

23. 20 is 50% of what?

24. 57 is 20% of what?

EXERCISE SET

a Solve.

1. *Wild Horses.* There are 27,369 wild horses on land managed by the Federal Bureau of Land Management. It is estimated that 48.4% of this total is in Nevada. How many wild horses are in Nevada?

Source: Bureau of Land Management, 2005

2. *U.S. Armed Forces* There are 1,168,195 people in the United States in active military service. The numbers in the four armed services are listed in the table below. What percent of the total does each branch represent? Round the answers to the nearest tenth of a percent.

U.S. ARMED FORCES WORLDWIDE, 2004	
Total	1,168,195
Air Force	314,477
Army	391,126
Marine Corps	135,324
Navy	327,268

Source: U.S. Department of Defense

3. *Car Value.* The base price of a Nissan 350Z is $34,000. This vehicle is expected to retain 62% of its value at the end of three years and 52% at the end of five years. What is the value of a Nissan 350Z after three years? after five years?

Source: November/December *Kelley Blue Book Residual Values Guide*

4. *Panda Survival.* Breeding the much-loved panda bear in captivity has been quite difficult for zookeepers.

a) From 1964 to 1997, of 133 panda cubs born in captivity, only 90 lived to be one month old. What percent lived to be one month old?

b) In 1999, Mark Edwards of the San Diego Zoo developed a nutritional formula on which 18 of 20 newborns lived to be one month old. What percent lived to be one month old?

5. *Overweight and Obese.* Of the 294 million people in the United States, 60% are considered overweight and 25% are considered obese. How many are overweight? How many are obese?

Source: U.S. Centers for Disease Control

6. *Smoking and Diabetes.* Of the 294 million people in the United States, 26% are smokers. How many are smokers?

Source: SAMHSA, Office of Applied Studies, National Survey on Drug Use and Health

7. A lab technician has 680 mL of a solution of water and acid; 3% is acid. How many milliliters are acid? water?

8. A lab technician has 540 mL of a solution of alcohol and water; 8% is alcohol. How many milliliters are alcohol? water?

9. *Mississippi River.* The Mississippi River, which extends from Minneapolis, Minnesota, to the Gulf of Mexico, is 2348 miles long. Approximately 77% of the river is navigable. How many miles of the river are navigable?

Source: National Oceanic and Atmospheric Administration

Mississippi River

10. *Immigrants.* In 2003, 705,827 immigrants entered the United States. Of this total, 16.4% were from Mexico and 7.1% were from India. How many immigrants came from Mexico? from India?

Source: U.S. Department of Justice, *2003 Yearbook of Immigration Statistics*

11. *Hispanic Population.* The Hispanic population is growing rapidly in the United States. In 2003, the population of the United States was about 291,000,000 and 13.7% of this total was Hispanic. How many Hispanic people lived in the United States in 2003?

Source: U.S. Bureau of the Census

12. *Age 65 and Over.* By 2010, it is predicted that 13.2% of the U.S. population will be 65 and over. If the population of the United States in 2010 is 307,000,000, how many people will be 65 and over?

Source: U.S. Bureau of the Census

13. *Test Results.* On a test of 40 items, Christina got 91% correct. (There was partial credit on some items.) How many items did she get correct? incorrect?

14. *Test Results.* On a test of 80 items, Pedro got 93% correct. (There was partial credit on some items.) How many items did he get correct? incorrect?

15. *Test Results.* On a test, Maj Ling got 86%, or 81.7, of the items correct. (There was partial credit on some items.) How many items were on the test?

16. *Test Results.* On a test, Juan got 85%, or 119, of the items correct. How many items were on the test?

17. *TV Usage.* Of the 8760 hr in a year, most television sets are on for 2190 hr. What percent is this?

18. *Colds from Kissing.* In a medical study, it was determined that if 800 people kiss someone who has a cold, only 56 will actually catch a cold. What percent is this?

Source: U.S. Centers for Disease Control

19. *Maximum Heart Rate.* Treadmill tests are often administered to diagnose heart ailments. A guideline in such a test is to try to get you to reach your *maximum heart rate,* in beats per minute. The maximum heart rate is found by subtracting your age from 220 and then multiplying by 85%. What is the maximum heart rate of someone whose age is 25? 36? 48? 55? 76? Round to the nearest one.

20. It costs an oil company $40,000 a day to operate two refineries. Refinery A accounts for 37.5% of the cost, and refinery B for the rest of the cost.

    a) What percent of the cost does it take to run refinery B?

    b) What is the cost of operating refinery A? refinery B?

b   Solve.

21. *Savings Increase.* The amount in a savings account increased from $200 to $216. What was the percent of increase?

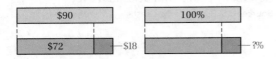

22. *Population Increase.* The population of a small mountain town increased from 840 to 882. What was the percent of increase?

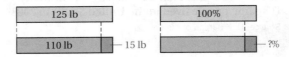

23. During a sale, a dress decreased in price from $90 to $72. What was the percent of decrease?

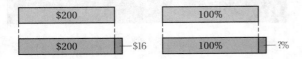

24. A person on a diet goes from a weight of 125 lb to a weight of 110 lb. What is the percent of decrease?

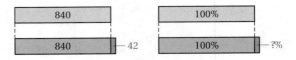

25. *Population Increase.* The population of the state of Nevada increased from 1,201,833 in 1990 to 2,241,154 in 2003. What is the percent of increase?

Source: U.S. Bureau of the Census

26. *Population Increase.* The population of the state of Utah increased from 1,722,850 in 1990 to 2,351,467 in 2003. What is the percent of increase?

Source: U.S. Bureau of the Census

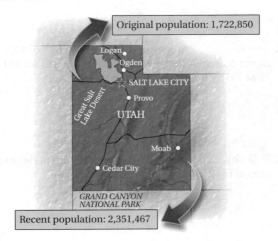

Original population: 1,722,850

Recent population: 2,351,467

27. A person earns $28,600 one year and receives a 5% raise in salary. What is the new salary?

28. A person earns $43,200 one year and receives an 8% raise in salary. What is the new salary?

29. *Car Depreciation.* Irwin buys a car for $21,566. It depreciates 25% each year that he owns it. What is the depreciated value of the car after 1 yr? after 2 yr?

30. *Car Depreciation.* Janice buys a car for $22,688. It depreciates 25% each year that she owns it. What is the depreciated value of the car after 1 yr? after 2 yr?

31. *Doormat.* A bordered coir doormat 42 in. × 24 in. × $1\frac{1}{2}$ in. has a retail price of $89.95. Over the holidays it is on sale for $65.49. What is the percent of decrease?

32. *Business Tote.* A leather business tote retails for $239.99. An insurance company bought 30 totes for its sales staff at a reduced price of $184.95. What was the percent of decrease in the price?

33. *Two-by-Four.* A cross-section of a standard or nominal "two-by-four" board actually measures $1\frac{1}{2}$ in. by $3\frac{1}{2}$ in. The rough board is 2 in. by 4 in. but is planed and dried to the finished size. What percent of the wood is removed in planing and drying?

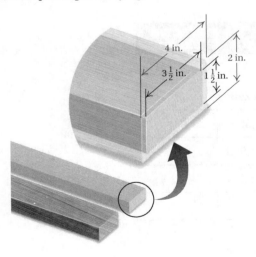

34. *Tipping.* Diners frequently add a 15% tip when charging a meal to a credit card. What is the total amount charged if the cost of the meal, without tip, is $18? $34? $49?

35. ⌨ *Population Decrease.*   Between 1990 and 2000, the population of Detroit, Michigan, decreased from 1,028,000 to 951,000.

a) What is the percent of decrease?

b) If this percent of decrease over a 10-yr period repeated itself in the following decade, what would the population be in 2010?

Source: U.S. Bureau of the Census

36. ⌨ *World Population.*   World population is increasing by 1.14% each year. In 2004, it was 6.39 billion. How much will it be in 2006? 2010? 2015?

Source: *The World Factbook,* 2004

Life Insurance Rates for Smokers and Nonsmokers.   The following table provides data showing how yearly rates (premiums) for a $500,000 term life insurance policy are increased for smokers. Complete the missing numbers in the table.

TYPICAL INSURANCE PREMIUMS (DOLLARS)

	AGE	RATE FOR NONSMOKER	RATE FOR SMOKER	PERCENT INCREASE FOR SMOKER
	35	$ 345	$ 630	83%
37.	40	$ 430	$ 735	
38.	45	$ 565		84%
39.	50	$ 780		100%
40.	55	$ 985		117%
41.	60	$1645	$2955	
42.	65	$2943	$5445	

Source: Pacific Life PL Protector Term Life Portfolio, OYT Rates

Population Increase.   The following table provides data showing how the populations of various states increased from 1990 to 2003. Complete the missing numbers in the table.

	AGE	POPULATION IN 1990	POPULATION IN 2003	CHANGE	PERCENT CHANGE
43.	Alaska	550,043	648,818		
44.	Connecticut	3,287,116		196,256	
45.	Montana		917,621	118,556	
46.	Texas		22,118,509	5,131,999	
47.	Colorado	3,294,394		1,256,294	
48.	Pennsylvania	11,881,643	12,365,455		

Source: U.S. Bureau of the Census

7.4

Sales Tax, Commission, and Discount

EXERCISE SET

a   Solve.

1. *Tennessee Sales Tax.* The sales tax rate in Tennessee is 7%. How much sales tax would be charged on a lawn mower that costs $279?

2. *Arizona Sales Tax.* The sales tax rate in Arizona is 5.6%. How much sales tax would be charged on a lawn mower that costs $279?

3. *Kansas Sales Tax.* The sales tax rate in Kansas is 5.3%. How much sales tax would be charged on a video game, Quest of the Planets, which sells for $49.99?

4. *New Jersey Sales Tax.* The sales tax rate in New Jersey is 6%. How much sales tax would be charged on a copy of John Grisham's novel *A Painted House*, which sells for $27.95?

   Source: Borders Bookstore; Andrea Sutcliffe, *Numbers*

5. *Utah Sales Tax.* The sales tax rate in Utah is 4.75%. How much tax is charged on a purchase of 5 telephones at $69 apiece? What is the total price?

6. *New York Sales Tax.* The sales tax rate in New York is 4.25%. How much tax is charged on a purchase of 5 teapots at $37.99 apiece? What is the total price?

7. The sales tax is $48 on the purchase of a dining room set that sells for $960. What is the sales tax rate?

8. The sales tax is $15 on the purchase of a diamond ring that sells for $500. What is the sales tax rate?

9. The sales tax is $35.80 on the purchase of a refrigerator–freezer that sells for $895. What is the sales tax rate?

10. The sales tax is $9.12 on the purchase of a patio set that sells for $456. What is the sales tax rate?

11. The sales tax on a used car is $100 and the sales tax rate is 5%. Find the purchase price (the price before taxes are added).

12. The sales tax on the purchase of a new boat is $112 and the sales tax rate is 2%. Find the purchase price.

13. The sales tax on a dining room set is $28 and the sales tax rate is 3.5%. Find the purchase price.

14. The sales tax on a portable DVD player is $24.75 and the sales tax rate is 5.5%. Find the purchase price.

15. The sales tax rate in Austin is 2% for the city and county and 6.25% for the state. Find the total amount paid for 2 shower units at $332.50 apiece.

16. The sales tax rate in Omaha is 1.5% for the city and 5% for the state. Find the total amount paid for 3 air conditioners at $260 apiece.

17. The sales tax is $1030.40 on an automobile purchase of $18,400. What is the sales tax rate?

18. The sales tax is $979.60 on an automobile purchase of $15,800. What is the sales tax rate?

b Solve.

19. Katrina's commission rate is 6%. What is the commission from the sale of $45,000 worth of furnaces?

20. Jose's commission rate is 32%. What is the commission from the sale of $12,500 worth of sailboards?

21. Mitchell earns $120 selling $2400 worth of television sets in a consignment shop. What is the commission rate?

22. Donna earns $408 selling $3400 worth of shoes. What is the commission rate?

23. An art gallery's commission rate is 40%. They receive a commission of $392. How many dollars worth of artwork were sold?

24. A real estate agent's commission rate is 7%. She receives a commission of $5600 on the sale of a home. How much did the home sell for?

25. A real estate commission is 6%. What is the commission on the sale of a $98,000 home?

26. A real estate commission is 8%. What is the commission on the sale of a piece of land for $68,000?

27. Bonnie earns $280.80 selling $2340 worth of tee shirts. What is the commission rate?

28. Chuck earns $1147.50 selling $7650 worth of ski passes. What is the commission rate?

29. Miguel's commission is increased according to how much he sells. He receives a commission of 5% for the first $2000 and 8% on the amount over $2000. What is the total commission on sales of $6000?

30. Lucinda earns a salary of $500 a month, plus a 2% commission on sales. One month, she sold $990 worth of encyclopedias. What were her wages that month?

C   Find what is missing.

	MARKED PRICE	RATE OF DISCOUNT	DISCOUNT	SALE PRICE
31.	$300	10%		
32.	$2000	40%		
33.	$17	15%		
34.	$20	25%		
35.		10%	$12.50	
36.		15%	$65.70	
37.	$600		$240	
38.	$12,800		$1920	

39. Find the discount and the rate of discount for the car seat in this ad.

Sale
Car Seat
$149.99
Was $179.99

40. Find the discount and the rate of discount for the wicker chair in this ad.

Best price of the season!
Now only
$90
Was $125

41. Find the marked price and the rate of discount for the stacked tool storage units in this ad.

CLOSEOUT
$349
buys both
SAVE
$200

42. Find the marked price and the rate of discount for the basketball system in this ad.

SAVE $400
Basketball System
Now
$599 99

Algebra: Solving Equations and Problems

8

8.1 Solving Equations:
     The Addition Principle

8.2 Solving Equations:
     The Multiplication Principle

8.3 Using the Principles Together

a   Solve using the addition principle. Don't forget to check!

1. $x + 2 = 6$

Check: $x + 2 = 6$
                  ?

2. $y + 4 = 11$

Check: $y + 4 = 11$
                  ?

3. $x + 15 = -5$

Check: $x + 15 = -5$
                  ?

4. $t + 10 = 44$

Check: $t + 10 = 44$
                  ?

5. $x + 6 = -8$

6. $y + 8 = 37$

7. $x + 5 = 12$

8. $x + 3 = 7$

9. $-22 = t + 4$

10. $t + 8 = -14$

11. $x + 16 = -2$

12. $y + 34 = -8$

13. $x - 9 = 6$

14. $x - 9 = 2$

15. $x - 7 = -21$

16. $x - 5 = -16$

17. $5 + t = 7$

18. $6 + y = 22$

19. $-7 + y = 13$

20. $-8 + z = 16$

21. $-3 + t = -9$

22. $-8 + y = -23$

23. $r + \dfrac{1}{3} = \dfrac{8}{3}$

24. $t + \dfrac{3}{8} = \dfrac{5}{8}$

25. $m + \dfrac{5}{6} = -\dfrac{11}{12}$

26. $x + \dfrac{2}{3} = -\dfrac{5}{6}$

27. $x - \dfrac{5}{6} = \dfrac{7}{8}$

28. $y - \dfrac{3}{4} = \dfrac{5}{6}$

29. $-\dfrac{1}{5} + z = -\dfrac{1}{4}$

30. $-\dfrac{1}{8} + y = -\dfrac{3}{4}$

31. $7.4 = x + 2.3$

32. $9.3 = 4.6 + x$

Solving Equations: The Multiplication Principle

EXERCISE SET

a   Solve using the multiplication principle. Don't forget to check!

1. $6x = 36$ **2.** $4x = 52$ **3.** $5x = 45$ **4.** $8x = 56$

5. $84 = 7x$ **6.** $63 = 7x$ **7.** $-x = 40$ **8.** $50 = -x$

9. $-2x = -10$ **10.** $-78 = -39p$ **11.** $7x = -49$ **12.** $9x = -54$

13. $-12x = 72$ **14.** $-15x = 105$ **15.** $-21x = -126$ **16.** $-13x = -104$

17. $\dfrac{1}{7}t = -9$ **18.** $-\dfrac{1}{8}y = 11$ **19.** $\dfrac{3}{4}x = 27$ **20.** $\dfrac{4}{5}x = 16$

21. $-\dfrac{1}{3}t = 7$ **22.** $-\dfrac{1}{6}x = 9$ **23.** $-\dfrac{1}{3}m = \dfrac{1}{5}$ **24.** $\dfrac{1}{5} = -\dfrac{1}{8}z$

25. $-\dfrac{3}{5}r = \dfrac{9}{10}$ **26.** $\dfrac{2}{5}y = -\dfrac{4}{15}$ **27.** $-\dfrac{3}{2}r = -\dfrac{27}{4}$ **28.** $-\dfrac{5}{7}x = -\dfrac{10}{14}$

Solve. Don't forget to check!

1. $5x + 6 = 31$ **2.** $8x + 6 = 30$ **3.** $8x + 4 = 68$ **4.** $8z + 7 = 79$

5. $4x - 6 = 34$ **6.** $4x - 11 = 21$ **7.** $3x - 9 = 33$ **8.** $6x - 9 = 57$

9. $7x + 2 = -54$ **10.** $5x + 4 = -41$ **11.** $-45 = 3 + 6y$ **12.** $-91 = 9t + 8$

13. $-4x + 7 = 35$ **14.** $-5x - 7 = 108$ **15.** $-7x - 24 = -129$ **16.** $-6z - 18 = -132$

b Solve.

17. $5x + 7x = 72$ **18.** $4x + 5x = 45$ **19.** $8x + 7x = 60$

20. $3x + 9x = 96$ **21.** $4x + 3x = 42$ **22.** $6x + 19x = 100$

23. $-6y - 3y = 27$ **24.** $-4y - 8y = 48$ **25.** $-7y - 8y = -15$

26. $-10y - 3y = -39$ **27.** $10.2y - 7.3y = -58$ **28.** $6.8y - 2.4y = -88$

29. $x + \dfrac{1}{3}x = 8$ **30.** $x + \dfrac{1}{4}x = 10$ **31.** $8y - 35 = 3y$

32. $4x - 6 = 6x$

33. $8x - 1 = 23 - 4x$

34. $5y - 2 = 28 - y$

35. $2x - 1 = 4 + x$

36. $5x - 2 = 6 + x$

37. $6x + 3 = 2x + 11$

38. $5y + 3 = 2y + 15$

39. $5 - 2x = 3x - 7x + 25$

40. $10 - 3x = 2x - 8x + 40$

41. $4 + 3x - 6 = 3x + 2 - x$

42. $5 + 4x - 7 = 4x - 2 - x$

43. $4y - 4 + y + 24 = 6y + 20 - 4y$

44. $5y - 7 + y = 7y + 21 - 5y$

Solve. Clear fractions or decimals first.

45. $\dfrac{7}{2}x + \dfrac{1}{2}x = 3x + \dfrac{3}{2} + \dfrac{5}{2}x$

46. $\dfrac{7}{8}x - \dfrac{1}{4} + \dfrac{3}{4}x = \dfrac{1}{16} + x$

47. $\dfrac{2}{3} + \dfrac{1}{4}t = \dfrac{1}{3}$

48. $-\dfrac{3}{2} + x = -\dfrac{5}{6} - \dfrac{4}{3}$

49. $\dfrac{2}{3} + 3y = 5y - \dfrac{2}{15}$

50. $\dfrac{1}{2} + 4m = 3m - \dfrac{5}{2}$

51. $\dfrac{5}{3} + \dfrac{2}{3}x = \dfrac{25}{12} + \dfrac{5}{4}x + \dfrac{3}{4}$

52. $1 - \dfrac{2}{3}y = \dfrac{9}{5} - \dfrac{y}{5} + \dfrac{3}{5}$

53. $2.1x + 45.2 = 3.2 - 8.4x$

54. $0.96y - 0.79 = 0.21y + 0.46$

55. $1.03 - 0.62x = 0.71 - 0.22x$

56. $1.7t + 8 - 1.62t = 0.4t - 0.32 + 8$

57. $\dfrac{2}{7}x - \dfrac{1}{2}x = \dfrac{3}{4}x + 1$

58. $\dfrac{5}{16}y + \dfrac{3}{8}y = 2 + \dfrac{1}{4}y$

C   Solve.

59. $3(2y - 3) = 27$

60. $4(2y - 3) = 28$

61. $40 = 5(3x + 2)$

62. $9 = 3(5x - 2)$

63. $2(3 + 4m) - 9 = 45$

64. $3(5 + 3m) - 8 = 88$

65. $5r - (2r + 8) = 16$

66. $6b - (3b + 8) = 16$

67. $6 - 2(3x - 1) = 2$

68. $10 - 3(2x - 1) = 1$

69. $5(d + 4) = 7(d - 2)$

70. $3(t - 2) = 9(t + 2)$

71. $8(2t + 1) = 4(7t + 7)$

72. $7(5x - 2) = 6(6x - 1)$

73. $3(r - 6) + 2 = 4(r + 2) - 21$

74. $5(t + 3) + 9 = 3(t - 2) + 6$

75. $19 - (2x + 3) = 2(x + 3) + x$

76. $13 - (2c + 2) = 2(c + 2) + 3c$

77. $0.7(3x + 6) = 1.1 - (x + 2)$

78. $0.9(2x + 8) = 20 - (x + 5)$

79. $a + (a - 3) = (a + 2) - (a + 1)$

80. $0.8 - 4(b - 1) = 0.2 + 3(4 - b)$

81. **D**$_W$ A student begins solving the equation $\frac{2}{3}x + 1 = \frac{5}{6}$ by multiplying by 6 on both sides. Is this a wise thing to do? Why or why not?

82. **D**$_W$ Describe a procedure that a classmate could use to solve the equation $ax + b = c$ for x.

Answers

Exercise Set 1.1

1. 387 **3.** 5198 **5.** 164 **7.** 100 **9.** 8503 **11.** 5266
13. 4466 **15.** 6608 **17.** 34,432 **19.** 101,310
21. 230 **23.** 18,424 **25.** 31,685 **27.** 114 mi
29. 570 ft **31.** D_W **33.** 8 ten thousands
34. Five billion, two hundred ninety-four million,
two hundred forty-seven thousand
35. $1 + 99 = 100, 2 + 98 = 100, \ldots, 49 + 51 = 100$. Then
$49 \cdot 100 = 4900$ and $4900 + 50 + 100 = 5050$.

Exercise Set 1.2

1. $7 = 3 + 4$, or $7 = 4 + 3$ **3.** $13 = 5 + 8$, or $13 = 8 + 5$
5. $23 = 14 + 9$, or $23 = 9 + 14$ **7.** $43 = 27 + 16$, or
$43 = 16 + 27$ **9.** $6 = 15 - 9; 9 = 15 - 6$
11. $8 = 15 - 7; 7 = 15 - 8$ **13.** $17 = 23 - 6; 6 = 23 - 17$
15. $23 = 32 - 9; 9 = 32 - 23$ **17.** 44 **19.** 533
21. 39 **23.** 234 **25.** 5382 **27.** 3831 **29.** 7748
31. 43,028 **33.** 56 **35.** 454 **37.** 3749 **39.** 2191
41. 95,974 **43.** 9989 **45.** 4206 **47.** 10,305 **49.** D_W
51. 1024 **52.** 12,732 **53.** 90,283 **54.** 29,364
55. 1345 **56.** 924 **57.** 22,692 **58.** 10,920
59. Six million, three hundred seventy-five thousand, six
hundred two **60.** 7 ten thousands **61.** 3; 4

Exercise Set 1.3

1. 50 **3.** 470 **5.** 730 **7.** 900 **9.** 100 **11.** 1000
13. 9100 **15.** 32,900 **17.** 6000 **19.** 8000
21. 45,000 **23.** 373,000 **25.** 180 **27.** 5720
29. 220; incorrect **31.** 890; incorrect **33.** 16,500
35. 5200 **37.** $11,200 **39.** $18,900; no **41.** Answers
will vary depending on the options chosen.

Exercise Set 1.4

1. 870 **3.** 2,340,000 **5.** 520 **7.** 564 **9.** 1527
11. 64,603 **13.** 4770 **15.** 3995 **17.** 46,080
19. 14,652 **21.** 207,672 **23.** 798,408 **25.** 20,723,872
27. 362,128 **29.** 20,064,048 **31.** 25,236,000
33. 302,220 **35.** 49,101,136 **37.** $50 \cdot 70 = 3500$

39. $30 \cdot 30 = 900$ **41.** $900 \cdot 300 = 270,000$
43. $400 \cdot 200 = 80,000$ **45.** **(a)** $2,840,000; **(b)** $2,850,000
47. 529,984 sq mi **49.** 8100 sq ft **51.** D_W **53.** 12,685
54. 10,834 **55.** 427,477 **56.** 111,110 **57.** 1241
58. 8889 **59.** 254,119 **60.** 66,444 **61.** 6,376,000
62. 6,375,600 **63.** 247,464 sq ft

Exercise Set 1.5

1. $18 = 3 \cdot 6$, or $18 = 6 \cdot 3$ **3.** $22 = 22 \cdot 1$, or $22 = 1 \cdot 22$
5. $54 = 6 \cdot 9$, or $54 = 9 \cdot 6$ **7.** $37 = 1 \cdot 37$, or $37 = 37 \cdot 1$
9. $9 = 45 \div 5; 5 = 45 \div 9$ **11.** $37 = 37 \div 1; 1 = 37 \div 37$
13. $8 = 64 \div 8$ **15.** $11 = 66 \div 6; 6 = 66 \div 11$ **17.** 12
19. 1 **21.** 22 **23.** Not defined **25.** 55 R 2 **27.** 108
29. 307 **31.** 753 R 3 **33.** 74 R 1 **35.** 92 R 2
37. 1703 **39.** 987 R 5 **41.** 12,700 **43.** 127
45. 52 R 52 **47.** 29 R 5 **49.** 40 R 12 **51.** 90 R 22
53. 29 **55.** 105 R 3 **57.** 1609 R 2 **59.** 1007 R 1
61. 23 **63.** 107 R 1 **65.** 370 **67.** 609 R 15 **69.** 304
71. 3508 R 219 **73.** 8070 **75.** D_W **77.** perimeter
78. equation, inequality **79.** digits, periods
80. additive **81.** dividend **82.** factors, product
83. minuend **84.** associative **85.** 54, 122; 33, 2772;
4, 8 **87.** 30 buses

Margin Exercises, Section 1.6

1. 11,277 adoptions **2.** 8441 adoptions
3. 19,089 adoptions **4.** $1874 **5.** $171 **6.** $5572
7. 9180 sq in. **8.** 378 cartons with 1 can left over
9. 79 gal **10.** 181 seats

Translating for Success

1. E **2.** M **3.** D **4.** G **5.** A **6.** O **7.** F **8.** K
9. J **10.** H

Exercise Set 1.6

1. 33,042 performances **3.** 704 performances
5. 2054 miles **7.** 18 rows **9.** 792,316 degrees;
1,291,900 degrees **11.** 192,268 degrees **13.** $69,277

15. 240 mi   **17.** 168 hr   **19.** 225 squares   **21.** $24,456
23. 35 weeks; 2 episodes left over   **25.** 236 gal
27. 3616 mi   **29.** 12,804 gal   **31.** $14,445   **33.** $247
35. (a) 4200 sq ft; (b) 268 ft   **37.** $29,105,000,000
39. 151,500   **41.** 563 packages; 7 bars left over
43. 384 mi; 27 in.   **45.** 21 columns   **47.** 56 full cartons;
11 books left over. If 1355 books are shipped, it will take
57 cartons.   **49.** 32 $10 bills   **51.** $400
53. 280 min; or 4 hr 40 min   **55.** 525 min, or 8 hr 45 min
57. 106 bones   **59.** 3000 sq in.   **61.** D_W **63.** 234,600
64. 234,560   **65.** 235,000   **66.** 22,000   **67.** 16,000
68. 8000   **69.** 4000   **70.** 320,000   **71.** 720,000
72. 46,800,000   **73.** 792,000 mi; 1,386,000 mi

Exercise Set 1.7

1. 3^4 **3.** 5^2 **5.** 7^5 **7.** 10^3 **9.** 49   **11.** 729
13. 20,736   **15.** 121   **17.** 22   **19.** 20   **21.** 100
23. 1   **25.** 49   **27.** 5   **29.** 434   **31.** 41   **33.** 88
35. 4   **37.** 303   **39.** 20   **41.** 70   **43.** 295   **45.** 32
47. 906   **49.** 62   **51.** 102   **53.** 32   **55.** $94
57. 401   **59.** 110   **61.** 7   **63.** 544   **65.** 708   **67.** 27
69. D_W **71.** 452   **72.** 835   **73.** 13   **74.** 37
75. 2342   **76.** 4898   **77.** 25   **78.** 100
79. 104,286 mi^2 **80.** 98 gal   **81.** 24; $1 + 5 \cdot (4 + 3) = 36$
83. 7; $12 \div (4 + 2) \cdot 3 - 2 = 4$

CHAPTER 2
Margin Exercises, Section 2.1

1. $\frac{5}{11}$, or 5:11   **2.** $\frac{57.3}{86.1}$, or 57.3:86.1   **3.** $\frac{6\frac{3}{4}}{7\frac{2}{5}}$, or $6\frac{3}{4}:7\frac{2}{5}$

4. $\frac{739}{12}$ **5.** $\frac{12}{14}$ **6.** $\frac{71}{214.1}$; $\frac{214.1}{71}$ **7.** $\frac{38.2}{56.1}$ **8.** $\frac{205}{278}$, $\frac{278}{205}$, $\frac{278}{483}$
9. 18 is to 27 as 2 is to 3   **10.** 3.6 is to 12 as 3 is to 10
11. 1.2 is to 1.5 as 4 is to 5   **12.** $\frac{9}{16}$

Exercise Set 2.1

1. $\frac{4}{5}$ **3.** $\frac{178}{572}$ **5.** $\frac{0.4}{12}$ **7.** $\frac{3.8}{7.4}$ **9.** $\frac{56.78}{98.35}$ **11.** $\frac{8\frac{3}{4}}{9\frac{5}{6}}$ **13.** $\frac{4}{1}$
15. $\frac{356}{100,000}$; $\frac{173}{100,000}$ **17.** $\frac{93.2}{1000}$ **19.** $\frac{190}{547}$; $\frac{547}{190}$ **21.** $\frac{60}{100}$; $\frac{100}{60}$
23. $\frac{2}{3}$ **25.** $\frac{3}{4}$ **27.** $\frac{12}{25}$ **29.** $\frac{7}{9}$ **31.** $\frac{2}{3}$ **33.** $\frac{14}{25}$ **35.** $\frac{1}{2}$
37. $\frac{3}{4}$ **39.** $\frac{478}{213}$; $\frac{213}{478}$ **41.** D_W **43.** =   **44.** ≠   **45.** ≠
46. =   **47.** 50   **48.** 9.5   **49.** 14.5   **50.** 152
51. $6\frac{7}{20}$ cm   **52.** $17\frac{11}{20}$ cm   **53.** $\frac{30}{47}$ **55.** 1:2:3

Margin Exercises, Section 2.2

1. Yes   **2.** No   **3.** No   **4.** Yes   **5.** No   **6.** Yes
7. 14   **8.** $11\frac{1}{4}$ **9.** 10.5   **10.** 2.64   **11.** 10.8
12. $\frac{125}{42}$, or $2\frac{41}{42}$

Calculator Corner

1. Left to the student   **2.** Left to the student   **3.** 27.5625
4. 25.6   **5.** 15.140625   **6.** 40.03952941
7. 39.74857143   **8.** 119

Exercise Set 2.2

1. No   **3.** Yes   **5.** Yes   **7.** No   **9.** 0.61; 0.66; 0.69;
0.66; the completion rates (rounded to the nearest
hundredth) are the same for Brees and Roethlisberger
11. 45   **13.** 12   **15.** 10   **17.** 20   **19.** 5   **21.** 18
23. 22   **25.** 28   **27.** $9\frac{1}{3}$ **29.** $2\frac{8}{9}$ **31.** 0.06   **33.** 5
35. 1   **37.** 1   **39.** 14   **41.** $2\frac{3}{16}$ **43.** $\frac{51}{16}$, or $3\frac{3}{16}$
45. 12.5725   **47.** $\frac{1748}{249}$, or $7\frac{5}{249}$ **49.** D_W **51.** quotient
52. sum   **53.** average   **54.** dollars, cents
55. subtrahend   **56.** terminating   **57.** commutative
58. cross products   **59.** Approximately 2731.4
61. (a) Ruth: 1.863 strikeouts per home run; Schmidt: 3.436
strikeouts per home run; (b) Schmidt

Margin Exercises, Section 2.3

1. 445 calories   **2.** 15 gal   **3.** 8 shirts   **4.** 38 in. or less
5. 9.5 in.   **6.** 2074 deer

Translating for Success

1. N   **2.** I   **3.** A   **4.** K   **5.** J   **6.** F   **7.** M   **8.** B
9. G   **10.** E

Exercise Set 2.3

1. 11.04 hr   **3.** 880 calories   **5.** 177 million, or
177,000,000   **7.** 9.75 gal   **9.** 175 bulbs   **11.** 2975 ft^2
13. 450 pages   **15.** (a) 23.63445 British pounds;
(b) $16,450.56   **17.** (a) 21,206 Japanese yen; (b) $29.99
19. (a) About 112 gal; (b) 3360 mi   **21.** 60 students
23. 13,500 mi   **25.** 120 lb   **27.** 64 gal   **29.** 100 oz
31. 954 deer   **33.** 58.1 mi   **35.** (a) 56 games; (b) about
2197 points   **37.** D_W **39.** Neither   **40.** Composite
41. Prime   **42.** Composite   **43.** Prime
44. $2 \cdot 2 \cdot 2 \cdot 101$, or $2^3 \cdot 101$ **45.** $2 \cdot 2 \cdot 7$, or $2^2 \cdot 7$
46. $2 \cdot 433$ **47.** $3 \cdot 31$ **48.** $2 \cdot 2 \cdot 5 \cdot 101$, or $2^2 \cdot 5 \cdot 101$
49. 17 positions   **51.** 2150 earned runs   **53.** CD player:
$150; receiver: $450; speakers: $300

CHAPTER 3
Exercise Set 3.1

1. −7   **3.** −4   **5.** 0   **7.** −8   **9.** −7   **11.** −27
13. 0   **15.** −42   **17.** 0   **19.** 0   **21.** 3   **23.** −9
25. 7   **27.** 0   **29.** 45

Exercise Set 3.2

1. -4 **3.** -7 **5.** -6 **7.** 0 **9.** -4 **11.** -7
13. -6 **15.** 0 **17.** 11 **19.** -14 **21.** 5 **23.** -7
25. -5 **27.** -3 **29.** -23 **31.** -68 **33.** -73
35. 116 **37.** 37 **39.** -62 **41.** 6 **43.** 107 **45.** 219
47. Down 3 ft **49.** $-3°$ **51.** 20,602 ft **53.** $-\$85$
55. 100°F

Exercise Set 3.3

1. -16 **3.** -24 **5.** -72 **7.** 16 **9.** 42 **11.** -120
13. -238 **15.** 1200 **17.** -756 **19.** -720
21. $-30,240$

Exercise Set 3.4

1. -7 **3.** -7 **5.** -334 **7.** 14 **9.** 1880 **11.** 12
13. 8 **15.** -86 **17.** 37 **19.** -1 **21.** -10 **23.** -67
25. -7988 **27.** -3000 **29.** 60 **31.** 1 **33.** 10
35. $-\frac{13}{45}$ **37.** $-\frac{4}{3}$ **39.** $\mathbf{D_W}$

CHAPTER 4

Exercise Set 4.1

1. 1 **3.** $\frac{3}{4}$ **5.** $\frac{3}{2}$ **7.** $\frac{7}{24}$ **9.** $\frac{3}{2}$ **11.** $\frac{19}{24}$ **13.** $\frac{9}{10}$
15. $\frac{29}{18}$ **17.** $\frac{31}{100}$ **19.** $\frac{41}{60}$ **21.** $\frac{189}{100}$ **23.** $\frac{7}{8}$ **25.** $\frac{13}{24}$
27. $\frac{17}{24}$ **29.** $\frac{3}{4}$ **31.** $\frac{437}{500}$ **33.** $\frac{53}{40}$ **35.** $\frac{391}{144}$

Exercise Set 4.2

1. $\frac{2}{3}$ **3.** $\frac{3}{4}$ **5.** $\frac{5}{8}$ **7.** $\frac{1}{24}$ **9.** $\frac{1}{2}$ **11.** $\frac{9}{14}$ **13.** $\frac{3}{5}$ **15.** $\frac{7}{10}$
17. $\frac{17}{60}$ **19.** $\frac{53}{100}$ **21.** $\frac{26}{75}$ **23.** $\frac{9}{100}$ **25.** $\frac{13}{24}$ **27.** $\frac{1}{10}$
29. $\frac{1}{24}$ **31.** $\frac{13}{16}$ **33.** $\frac{31}{75}$ **35.** $\frac{13}{75}$ **37.** $<$ **39.** $>$
41. $<$ **43.** $<$ **45.** $>$ **47.** $>$ **49.** $<$

Exercise Set 4.3

1. $28\frac{3}{4}$ **3.** $185\frac{7}{8}$ **5.** $6\frac{1}{2}$ **7.** $2\frac{11}{12}$ **9.** $14\frac{7}{12}$ **11.** $12\frac{1}{10}$
13. $16\frac{5}{24}$ **15.** $21\frac{1}{2}$ **17.** $27\frac{7}{8}$ **19.** $27\frac{13}{24}$ **21.** $1\frac{3}{5}$
23. $4\frac{1}{10}$ **25.** $21\frac{17}{24}$ **27.** $12\frac{1}{4}$ **29.** $15\frac{3}{8}$ **31.** $7\frac{5}{12}$
33. $13\frac{3}{8}$ **35.** $11\frac{5}{18}$ **37.** $5\frac{3}{8}$ yd **39.** $7\frac{5}{12}$ lb **41.** $6\frac{5}{12}$ in.

CHAPTER 5

Exercise Set 5.1

1. $\frac{3}{5}$ **3.** $\frac{5}{8}$ **5.** $\frac{8}{11}$ **7.** $\frac{70}{9}$ **9.** $\frac{2}{5}$ **11.** $\frac{6}{5}$ **13.** $\frac{21}{4}$
15. $\frac{85}{6}$ **17.** $\frac{1}{6}$ **19.** $\frac{1}{40}$ **21.** $\frac{2}{15}$ **23.** $\frac{4}{15}$ **25.** $\frac{9}{16}$ **27.** $\frac{14}{39}$
29. $\frac{7}{100}$ **31.** $\frac{49}{64}$ **33.** $\frac{1}{1000}$ **35.** $\frac{182}{285}$ **37.** $\frac{3}{8}$ cup

Exercise Set 5.2

1. $\frac{6}{5}$ **3.** $\frac{1}{6}$ **5.** 6 **7.** $\frac{3}{10}$ **9.** $\frac{4}{5}$ **11.** $\frac{4}{15}$ **13.** 4 **15.** 2
17. $\frac{1}{8}$ **19.** $\frac{3}{7}$ **21.** 8 **23.** 35 **25.** 1 **27.** $\frac{2}{3}$ **29.** $\frac{9}{4}$
31. 144

CHAPTER 6

Exercise Set 6.1

1. 334.37 **3.** 1576.215 **5.** 132.560 **7.** 50.0248
9. 40.007 **11.** 977.955 **13.** 771.967 **15.** 8754.8221
17. 49.02 **19.** 85.921 **21.** 2.4975 **23.** 3.397
25. 8.85 **27.** 3.37 **29.** 1.045 **31.** 3.703 **33.** 0.9902
35. 99.66 **37.** 4.88 **39.** 0.994 **41.** 17.802
43. 51.13 **45.** 32.7386 **47.** 4.0622 **49.** 11.65
51. 384.68 **53.** 582.97 **55.** 15,335.3
57. The balance forward should read:
$ 9704.56
9677.12
10,677.12
10,553.17
10,429.15
10,416.72
12,916.72
12,778.94
12,797.82
9997.82
59. $\mathbf{D_W}$

Exercise Set 6.2

1. 60.2 **3.** 6.72 **5.** 0.252 **7.** 0.522 **9.** 237.6
11. 583,686.852 **13.** 780 **15.** 8.923 **17.** 0.09768
19. 0.782 **21.** 521.6 **23.** 3.2472 **25.** 897.6
27. 322.07 **29.** 55.68 **31.** 3487.5 **33.** 50.0004
35. 114.42902 **37.** 13.284 **39.** 90.72 **41.** 0.0028728
43. 0.72523 **45.** 1.872115 **47.** 45,678 **49.** 2888¢
51. 66¢ **53.** $0.34 **55.** $34.45

Exercise Set 6.3

1. 2.99 **3.** 23.78 **5.** 7.48 **7.** 7.2 **9.** 1.143
11. 4.041 **13.** 0.07 **15.** 70 **17.** 20 **19.** 0.4
21. 0.41 **23.** 8.5 **25.** 9.3 **27.** 0.625 **29.** 0.26
31. 15.625 **33.** 2.34 **35.** 0.47 **37.** 0.2134567
39. 21.34567 **41.** 1023.7 **43.** 9.3 **45.** 0.0090678
47. 45.6 **49.** 2107 **51.** 303.003 **53.** 446.208
55. 24.14 **57.** 13.0072 **59.** 19.3204 **61.** 473.188278
63. 10.49 **65.** 911.13 **67.** 205 **69.** $1288.36

CHAPTER 7

Exercise Set 7.1

1. 41%   **3.** 5%   **5.** 20%   **7.** 30%   **9.** 50%
11. 87.5%, or $87\frac{1}{2}$%   **13.** 80%   **15.** $66.\overline{6}$%, or $66\frac{2}{3}$%
17. $16.\overline{6}$%, or $16\frac{2}{3}$%   **19.** 18.75%, or $18\frac{3}{4}$%
21. 81.25%, or $81\frac{1}{4}$%   **23.** 16%   **25.** 5%   **27.** 34%
29. 40%; 18%   **31.** 22%   **33.** 5%   **35.** 9%   **37.** $\frac{17}{20}$
39. $\frac{5}{8}$ **41.** $\frac{1}{3}$ **43.** $\frac{1}{6}$ **45.** $\frac{29}{400}$ **47.** $\frac{1}{125}$ **49.** $\frac{203}{800}$
51. $\frac{176}{225}$ **53.** $\frac{711}{1100}$ **55.** $\frac{3}{2}$ **57.** $\frac{13}{40,000}$ **59.** $\frac{1}{3}$ **61.** $\frac{2}{25}$
63. $\frac{3}{5}$ **65.** $\frac{1}{50}$ **67.** $\frac{7}{20}$ **69.** $\frac{47}{100}$

71.

FRACTION NOTATION	DECIMAL NOTATION	PERCENT NOTATION
$\frac{1}{8}$	0.125	12.5%, or $12\frac{1}{2}$%
$\frac{1}{6}$	$0.1\overline{6}$	$16.\overline{6}$%, or $16\frac{2}{3}$%
$\frac{1}{5}$	0.2	20%
$\frac{1}{4}$	0.25	25%
$\frac{1}{3}$	$0.\overline{3}$	$33.\overline{3}$%, or $33\frac{1}{3}$%
$\frac{3}{8}$	0.375	37.5%, or $37\frac{1}{2}$%
$\frac{2}{5}$	0.4	40%
$\frac{1}{2}$	0.5	50%

73.

FRACTION NOTATION	DECIMAL NOTATION	PERCENT NOTATION
$\frac{1}{2}$	0.5	50%
$\frac{1}{3}$	$0.\overline{3}$	$33.\overline{3}$%, or $33\frac{1}{3}$%
$\frac{1}{4}$	0.25	25%
$\frac{1}{6}$	$0.1\overline{6}$	$16.\overline{6}$%, or $16\frac{2}{3}$%
$\frac{1}{8}$	0.125	12.5%, or $12\frac{1}{2}$%
$\frac{3}{4}$	0.75	75%
$\frac{5}{6}$	$0.8\overline{3}$	$83.\overline{3}$%, or $83\frac{1}{3}$%
$\frac{3}{8}$	0.375	37.5%, or $37\frac{1}{2}$%

Exercise Set 7.2

1. $y = 32\% \times 78$ **3.** $89 = a \times 99$ **5.** $13 = 25\% \times y$
7. 234.6   **9.** 45   **11.** $18   **13.** 1.9   **15.** 78%
17. 200%   **19.** 50%   **21.** 125%   **23.** 40

Exercise Set 7.3

1. About 13,247 wild horses **3.** 3 years: $21,080; 5 years: $17,680 **5.** Overweight: 176.4 million people; obese: 73.5 million people **7.** Acid: 20.4 mL; water: 659.6 mL **9.** About 1808 miles **11.** About 39,867,000 people **13.** 36.4 correct; 3.6 incorrect **15.** 95 items **17.** 25% **19.** 166; 156; 146; 140; 122 **21.** 8% **23.** 20% **25.** About 86.5% **27.** $30,030 **29.** $16,174.50; $12,130.88 **31.** About 27% **33.** 34.375%, or $34\frac{3}{8}$% **35.** **(a)** 7.5%; **(b)** 879,675

Exercise Set 7.4

1. $19.53 **3.** $2.65 **5.** $16.39; $361.39 **7.** 5% **9.** 4% **11.** $2000 **13.** $800 **15.** $719.86 **17.** 5.6% **19.** $2700 **21.** 5% **23.** $980 **25.** $5880 **27.** 12% **29.** $420 **31.** $30; $270 **33.** $2.55; $14.45 **35.** $125; $112.50 **37.** 40%; $360 **39.** $30; 16.7% **41.** $549; 36.4%

CHAPTER 8

Exercise Set 8.1

1. 4 **3.** −20 **5.** −14 **7.** 7 **9.** −26 **11.** −18 **13.** 15 **15.** −14 **17.** 2 **19.** 20 **21.** −6 **23.** $\frac{7}{3}$ **25.** $-\frac{7}{4}$ **27.** $\frac{41}{24}$ **29.** $-\frac{1}{20}$ **31.** 5.1

Exercise Set 8.2

1. 6 **3.** 9 **5.** 12 **7.** −40 **9.** 5 **11.** −7 **13.** −6 **15.** 6 **17.** −63 **19.** 36 **21.** −21 **23.** $-\frac{3}{5}$ **25.** $-\frac{3}{2}$ **27.** $\frac{9}{2}$

Exercise Set 8.3

1. 5 **3.** 8 **5.** 10 **7.** 14 **9.** −8 **11.** −8 **13.** −7 **15.** 15 **17.** 6 **19.** 4 **21.** 6 **23.** −3 **25.** 1 **27.** −20 **29.** 6 **31.** 7 **33.** 2 **35.** 5 **37.** 2 **39.** 10 **41.** 4 **43.** 0 **45.** −1 **47.** $-\frac{4}{3}$ **49.** $\frac{2}{5}$ **51.** −2 **53.** −4 **55.** $\frac{4}{5}$ **57.** $-\frac{28}{27}$ **59.** 6 **61.** 2 **63.** 6 **65.** 8 **67.** 1 **69.** 17 **71.** $-\frac{5}{3}$ **73.** −3 **75.** 2 **77.** $-\frac{51}{31}$ **79.** 2

Appendix

TEENAGE DRINKING AND DRIVING TRENDS
AN INTERDISCIPLINARY MATH PROJECT
MAT 033 BASIC MATHEMATICS

Don Reichman, Instructor   Name _____

Scan the following chart to get a general sense of this project. When you are done, begin to answer the questions that follow. Remember to *use the members of your group as a resource if you don't understand a question.*

Teenage Drunk Driving

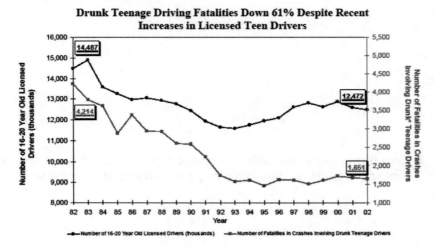

Drunk Teenage Driving Fatalities Down 61% Despite Recent Increases in Licensed Teen Drivers

1. What does the word "thousands" refer to that is written in parenthesis on the side of the vertical axis of the graph?

2. Why did the authors of this graph choose to display the data in "thousands"?

Reprinted from *beerinstitute.org*

3. Create a table with three columns. The first column should display the years 1982 through 2002. The second column should display the approximate number of 16–20 year old licensed drivers (in thousands) from the graph. The third column should show the approximate number of fatalities in crashes that involve teenage drinking.

4. Even if the data in the table was completely accurate, describe two advantages of using the data in the graph vs. using the data in the table.

5. Let's explore what it means for the number of fatalities to go down a given percent. Answer this question: if one year there were 100 automobile deaths in Mercer County, NJ and the next year there were 75, what is the actual decrease in the number of deaths?

6. If we divide the actual decrease in the number of fatalities by the original number of fatalities and convert this to a percent, then we have the percent that the number of deaths has declined. This is also referred to as a *percent decrease* in the number of deaths. Calculate the *percent decrease* in automobile fatalities in Mercer County.

7. Estimate from the graph the percent *increase* in the number of teenage drunk driving fatalities from 1985 to 1986.

8. Estimate the *percent* increase or decrease in the number of licensed teenaged drivers from 1985 to 1986.

9. Explain in two sentences the meaning of the two results you found in question #7 and #8.

10. Visit the following web site:
http://www.ama-assn.org/ama/pub/article/3566-3640.html
and determine what event occurred in the country that might explain these results.

11. Let's examine the heading "Drunk Teenage Driving Fatalities Down 61%". Using the values in the graph above, demonstrate using mathematical operations how the authors of this graph arrived at this percent decrease.

12. Considering the source of the graph and the heading that is described in #11 above, what position on drinking and driving trends do you believe the authors are trying to take?

13. Consider the years 1998 to 2003 from the two lines of the graph on page A-7. Suppose you worked for the **Anti-Beer Institute.** Choose a heading for the graphs from those years that make the opposite argument from that made by the beer institute in their heading. Justify your heading by showing the mathematical operations that support your title.

14. Write a paragraph that summarizes the role that data can play in convincing your audience that your viewpoint on a topic like teenage drinking vs. driving is correct.

This graph is presented so that the students can create their own questions. Brainstorm among yourselves and create five questions you would like answered by members of another group.

Drunk Driving

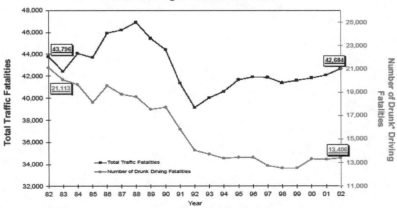

Drunk Driving Fatalities Down 37%

Fatalities in drunk driving crashes decreased 37% from 1982 to 2002, despite fluctuations in the total number of traffic fatalities. A 5% decrease in drunk driving fatalities was noted after 1992, despite a 9% increase in the total number of traffic fatalities.

Source: Data compiled by the National Highway Traffic Safety Administration, 2003.

* Note that "drunk drivers" are defined as those with BACs of 0.08 or higher. These drunk-driving data reflect NHTSA's new methodology in estimating missing BAC test result data, introduced in 2002. All historical numbers have been recalculated using the new methodology, allowing trends to be presented.

Updated 1/10/2004

(source: *http://beerinstitute.org/*)

BEER IS TO BLAME:
AN INTERDISCIPLINARY MATH PROJECT
MAT 033 BASIC MATHEMATICS

Don Reichman, Instructor   Name _____

Read the following article to get a general sense of the project. When you are done reading the article, begin to answer the questions that follow. Remember to *use the members of your group as a resource if you don't understand a question.*

Beer Gets Blame for Violent Crime Rate

Australia's high incidence of violent crime and domestic violence was directly linked to the population's massive beer intake, a crime expert said yesterday. Speaking in Adelaide at the eighth International Symposium on Victimology, Professor Jan van Dijk from the Netherlands said an international study he had made found a link between drinking beer and violent crime. The study found a particular link between beer drinking and sexual and domestic violence.

"There is a direct correlation between beer consumption in countries and levels of violence, so where people drink more beer the rates of violence tend to be higher," he said. "In countries where people drink less, or drink wine, there appears to be less violence.

"We do not fully understand the direct link between these two, but the link is certainly there.

"In typical beer-drinking cultures like Holland, Germany, England, Canada and Australia there is more violence than in Italy or Greece or Spain, where people drink wine."

Professor van Dijk said Australia was a "burglar's paradise" because most people lived in single-storey detached homes rather than high-rise apartments. "It's very difficult to burgle an apartment block in Paris on the sixth floor when there's a concierge on the ground floor," he said. "But in Australia 80 percent of people live in a detached house which is easily accessible from all sides. "This makes it much easier to commit burglaries in Australia." Professor van Dijk said 3.7 percent of Australians were burgled in 1991, 1.8 percent were robbed, 15 percent were victims of non-contact personal theft and 6.7 were victims of violent crimes, including sexual assaults, threats and domestic violence.

Australia generally experienced a higher crime rate than Europe because of its urban nature, high youth unemployment and high car ownership. Professor van Dijk said robberies and muggings were less common in Australia, unlike Africa or Brazil where crime was rife because of the large number of dispossessed people. "But there aren't that many desperate people in Holland

_____
Reprinted from the *Mercury,* August 23, 1994

and Australia because you have social welfare, so that helps to prevent rob-beries." Professor van Dijk's study showed one quarter of crime victims in Australia thought police failed to treat them respectfully or fairly.

But only 5 percent of victims suffered post-traumatic stress and needed professional counselling, he said.

1. The article claims that: *"There is a direct correlation between beer con-sumption in countries and levels of violence, so where people drink more beer the rates of violence tend to be higher."* Paraphrase in a paragraph what this sentence means to you.

2. Both beer consumption and rates of violent crime can be referred to as variables since each have values for a particular country in a particular year.

   a) If we wanted to compare beer consumption and violent crimes in the US to that of say, a small country like Cuba in 2003, is the *total* amount of beer consumed and the *total* amount of violent crime in each coun-try the best variables to use?

   b) If you knew the total amount of beer consumed in the US and the total US population in 2003, how would you compute the average amount of beer consumed per person in the US in 2003?

   c) Why would the average amount of beer consumed per person be a bet-ter variable to use if you wanted to compare beer consumption in the US to that of Cuba?

3. A *direct correlation* between two variables indicates that when one variable increases, so does the other or, when one decreases, so does the other. Describe two variables or ideas that are correlated. For example, one variable might be a person's age; now think of a variable that might have a correlation to age.

4. Reread the italics sentence in #1. Does the sentence imply that a high level of beer consumption *causes* violent behavior? Explain your answer in one or two sentences.

5. Medical research shows that there is a *correlation* between the amount of antibiotics taken by a woman and the probability of her getting breast cancer. However, taking antibiotics *does not cause* breast cancer. What other variables might explain these two sentences?

6. Describe in your own words what you think the difference is between two variables that are *correlated* and one variable that *causes* a change to occur in another variable.

7. From your careful reading of the article, what other variables beside beer consumption could account for the high incidence of violent crime in Australia?

8. The resident population of Australia at the end of 2003 was approximately **20,050,000** (source: *http://www.abs.gov.au/ausstats/*). Assuming that Professor van Dijk's data from the article is correct and can be applied to 2003, calculate the following:

a) The approximate number of Australians that lived in detached houses at the end of 2003.

b) The approximate number of Australians that were victims of violent crimes by the end of 2003.

c) The approximate number of Australians that were robbed by the end of 2003.

d) The article states that "only 5 percent of victims suffered post-traumatic stress and needed professional counselling". Using this statistic, how many victims of:

1) violent crimes suffered post-traumatic stress and needed professional counselling?

2) robbery suffered post-traumatic stress and needed professional counselling?

10 YEAR TREND IN MUSIC CONSUMER TRENDS
PROJECT 1: AN INTERDISPLINARY MATH PROJECT
MAT 033 BASIC MATHEMATICS

Don Reichman, Instructor   Name _____

Scan the following chart to get a general sense of this project. When you are done, begin to answer the questions that follow. Remember to *use the members of your group as a resource if you don't understand a question.*

THE RECORDING INDUSTRY ASSOCIATION OF AMERICA

2002 Consumer Profile

Phone: 202/775-0101   Web: www.riaa.com

	1993	1994	1995	1996	1997	1998	1999	2000	2001	2002	
ROCK	30.2	35.1	33.5	32.6	32.5	25.7	25.2	24.8	24.4	24.7	%
RAP/HIP-HOP[1]	9.2	7.9	6.7	8.9	10.1	9.7	10.8	12.9	11.4	13.8	
R&B/URBAN[2]	10.6	9.6	11.3	12.1	11.2	12.8	10.5	9.7	10.6	11.2	
COUNTRY	18.7	16.3	16.7	14.7	14.4	14.1	10.8	10.7	10.5	10.7	
POP	11.9	10.3	10.1	9.3	9.4	10.0	10.3	11.0	12.1	9.0	
RELIGIOUS[3]	3.2	3.3	3.1	4.3	4.5	6.3	5.1	4.8	6.7	6.7	
JAZZ	3.1	3.0	3.0	3.3	2.8	1.9	3.0	2.9	3.4	3.2	
CLASSICAL	3.3	3.7	2.9	3.4	2.8	3.3	3.5	2.7	3.2	3.1	
SOUNDTRACKS	0.7	1.0	0.9	0.8	1.2	1.7	0.8	0.7	1.4	1.1	
OLDIES	1.0	0.8	1.0	0.8	0.8	0.7	0.7	0.9	0.8	0.9	
NEW AGE	1.0	1.0	0.7	0.7	0.8	0.6	0.5	0.5	1.0	0.5	
CHILDREN'S	0.4	0.4	0.5	0.7	0.9	0.4	0.4	0.6	0.5	0.4	
OTHER[4]	4.6	5.3	7.0	5.2	5.7	7.9	9.1	8.3	7.9	8.1	
FULL LENGTH CDS	51.1	58.4	65.0	68.4	70.2	74.8	83.2	89.3	89.2	90.5	%
FULL LENGTH CASSETTES	38.0	32.1	25.1	19.3	18.2	14.8	8.0	4.9	3.4	2.4	
SINGLES (ALL TYPES)	9.2	7.4	7.5	9.3	9.3	6.8	5.4	2.5	2.4	1.9	
MUSIC VIDEOS/VIDEO DVDS[5]	1.3	0.8	0.9	1.0	0.6	1.0	0.9	0.8	1.1	0.7	
DVD AUDIO[6]	NA	NA	NA	NA	NA	NA	NA	NA	1.1	1.3	
DIGITAL DOWNLOAD[6]	NA	NA	NA	NA	NA	NA	NA	NA	0.2	0.5	
VINYL LPS	0.3	0.8	0.5	0.6	0.7	0.7	0.5	0.5	0.6	0.7	
10-14 YEARS	8.6	7.9	8.0	7.9	8.9	9.1	8.5	8.9	8.5	8.9	%
15-19 YEARS	16.7	16.8	17.1	17.2	16.8	15.8	12.6	12.9	13.0	13.3	
20-24 YEARS	15.1	15.4	15.3	15.0	13.8	12.2	12.6	12.5	12.2	11.5	
25-29 YEARS	13.2	12.6	12.3	12.5	11.7	11.4	10.5	10.6	10.9	9.4	
30-34 YEARS	11.9	11.8	12.1	11.4	11.0	11.4	10.1	9.8	10.3	10.8	
35-39 YEARS	11.1	11.5	10.8	11.1	11.6	12.6	10.4	10.6	10.2	9.8	
40-44 YEARS	8.5	7.9	7.5	9.1	8.8	8.3	9.3	9.6	10.3	9.9	
45+ YEARS	14.1	15.4	16.1	15.1	16.5	18.1	24.7	23.8	23.7	25.5	
RECORD STORE	56.2	53.3	52.0	49.9	51.8	50.8	44.5	42.4	42.5	36.8	%
OTHER STORE	26.1	26.7	28.2	31.5	31.9	34.4	38.3	40.8	42.4	50.7	
TAPE/RECORD CLUB	12.9	15.1	14.3	14.3	11.6	9.0	7.9	7.6	6.1	4	
TV, NEWSPAPER, MAGAZINE AD OR 800 NUMBER	3.8	3.4	4.0	2.9	2.7	2.9	2.5	2.4	3.0	2	
INTERNET[7]	NA	NA	NA	NA	0.3	1.1	2.4	3.2	2.9	3.4	
FEMALE	49.3	47.3	47.0	49.1	51.4	51.3	49.7	49.4	51.2	50.6	%
MALE	50.7	52.7	53.0	50.9	48.6	48.7	50.3	50.6	48.8	49.4	

Total U.S. Dollar Value

The figures below (in millions) indicate the overall size of the U.S. sound recording industry based on manufacturers' shipments at suggested list prices.

1993	$10,046.60
1994	$12,068.00
1995	$12,320.30
1996	$12,533.80
1997	$12,236.80
1998	$13,723.50
1999	$14,584.50
2000	$14,323.00
2001	$13,740.89
2002	$12,614.21

Methodology

Peter Hart Research conducts a national telephone survey of past month music buyers (over 3,000 per year). Data from the survey is weighted by age and sex, and then projected to reflect the U.S. population age 10-and-over. The reliability of the data is +/- 1.8% at a 95% confidence level. With respect to genre, consumers were asked to classify their music purchases; they are not assigned a particular category by Hart Research.

Permission to cite or copy these statistics is hereby granted as long as proper attribution is given to the Recording Industry Association of America.

[1] "Rap": Includes Rap (10.5%) and Hip-Hop (3.3%).
[2] "R&B": Includes R&B, blues, dance, disco, funk, fusion, Motown, reggae, soul.
[3] "Religious": Includes Christian, Gospel, Inspirational, Religious, and Spiritual.
[4] "Other": Includes Ethnic, Standards, Big Band, Swing, Latin, Electronic, Instrumental, Comedy, Humor, Spoken Word, Exercise, Language, Folk and Holiday Music.
[5] 2001 is the first year that music video DVD was recorded separately.
[6] 2001 is the first year that data was collected on DVD audio and digital download purchases.
[7] "Internet": Does not include record club purchases made over the Internet.

Reprinted from *www.riaa.com,* the Recording Industry Association of America Website.

The chart above describes lots of trends in the music industry. Let's try to answer the following question by analyzing the data in the chart: Which musical genre has experienced the greatest growth between 1993 and 2002?

1. To answer this question we first must make sure we understand the question. Write your own definition for the term "musical genre". Next state some examples of musical genre from the chart on page A-19.

2. Write your own definition for the word *growth*.

3. Some students in the class should have a dictionary. Write a dictionary definition for the words *genre* and *growth*.

4. Suppose in a given year your daughter's height changes from 39 inches to 43 inches. How much has she *actually* grown? If your son's height changes from 18 inches to 21 inches, how much has he *actually* grown? Who has grown the most? Rewrite your definition of *growth* based on the work you just did.

5. What if your grandmother actually shrank during the past year. Suppose her height went from 64 inches to 63 inches. Let's call this *negative* growth. Let's agree to say: "*she grew by negative one inch.*" Mathematically, this is written as an *actual* growth of –1 inch. Write the following *actual* changes in height among several people during the previous year as either positive or negative growth. For example, if you grew from 68 inches to 70 inches you would write: 70 inches – 68 inches = +2 inch growth.

a) Your baby brother grew from 30 inches to 35 inches.

b) Your grandfather shrank from 74 inches to 72 inches.

c) Your mother's height remained 66 inches.

d) Kareem Abdul-Jabbar shrank from 7 feet 2 inches to 7 feet.

6. *Percent* growth is defined as the actual growth divided by the original value converted into a percent. For example, your daughter's height (in question #4) actually changed by 4 inches. Since her original height was 39 inches, her *percent* change in height is 4 ÷ 39 = .103 = 10.3%.

Use the information from question #5 to compute the *percent* growth for the following:

a) Your baby brother grew from 30 inches to 35 inches.

b) Your grandfather shrank from 74 inches to 72 inches.

c) Your mother's height remained 66 inches.

d) Kareem Abdul-Jabbar shrank from 7 feet 2 inches to 7 feet.

7a. Describe in a few sentences the difference between *actual growth* and *percent growth*.

7b. Which of the two forms of growth convey the most meaning to you and why?

7c. Give examples from your life of where you might use *actual growth* and where you might use *percent growth*.

8. Fill out the following table for the top ten types of music sales for 2002. Remember actual change is defined as 2002 sales minus 1993 sales. What does it mean if the actual change is a negative number?

Music Type	% Sales in 1993	% Sales in 2002	Actual Change	Percent Change

Source: Saturn

9. Which musical genre has experienced the greatest *percent* growth between 1993 and 2002? Which experienced the least *percent* growth (greatest "shrinkage").

10a. Find the sum of all the musical genres on the table that experienced positive percent growth.

10b. Find the sum of the musical genres that experienced negative percent growth.

10c. The *net* percent growth is the sum of all positive and negative percent growths. Use your results from 10a and 10b to compute the net percent growth of all the musical genres described on the table.

10d. Write a paragraph that convinces me that you correctly computed the net growth in question 10c.

11. In 2 or 3 sentences paraphrase what you have learned by doing this project. Write the sentences as if you were describing the benefit of this project to future students of this course.

10 YEAR TREND IN MUSIC CONSUMER TRENDS PROJECT PART II

1. The table of data displays information in numerical form. In 2 or 3 sentences explain what you like and what you do not like about the way the data is displayed. Is it easy to read? Can you easily compare one genre to another? Can you easily determine which genre has grown the most and which the least?

2. Information in a graph gives us a different view of the data. Take the information for the top 7 genres from the year 2002 and create a pie graph.

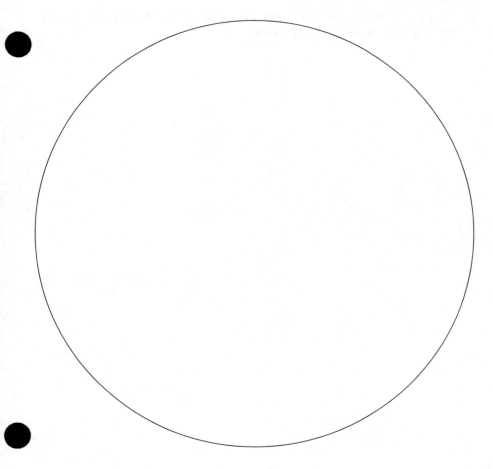

3. Now construct a line graph by plotting the points representing percent vs. year for the top 5 genres.

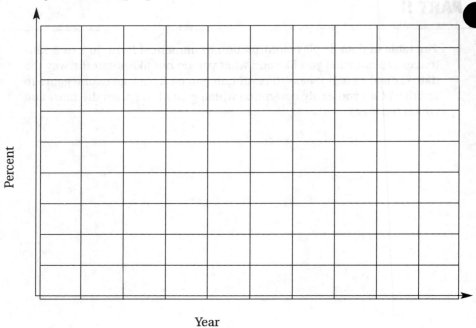

4. Explain in several sentences the strengths and weaknesses of the two types of graphs that you just created.

THE GAMBLING PROJECT
MAT 033 BASIC MATHEMATICS

Don Reichman, Instructor   Name _____

Below is an article and graph that describes the relationship between gambling and family funds. Answer the questions below, remember to discuss your answers with the other members of your group.

Gambling Bites into Family Funds

By KYLIE HANSEN, family reporter VICTORIANS are using housekeeping money to finance an $89 million a week gambling habit.

One of the big winners is Crown Casino, which has attracted 38 percent of Victorians, with 15 percent now regular casino customers.

The Victorian Casino and Gaming Authority's third annual survey of community gambling patterns, released yesterday, shows almost half the gamblers dip into their daily household expenses to finance a flutter.

And about a quarter of regular gamblers adjust the family budget so they can gamble.

The study, conducted in June last year, is the first detailed account of the social impact of gaming since Crown Casino opened. It revealed: GAMBLING attracted 77 percent of Victorians last year. MONEY for housekeeping costs is used for gambling by 45 percent of gamblers.

THE big winners were casinos—patronage is up from 7 percent in 1994 to 21 percent last year. ADULTS spend about $27 a week on gaming—though regular casino patrons spend $73 a week. THE

Reprinted from the *Herald Sun*, February 3, 1996

casino is especially attractive to people born in Asia, those aged in their 20s, low-earning white-collar workers and people earning $35,000 to $50,000. A spokeswoman for the Interchurch Gambling Task Force, Bronwyn Pike, said the churches were extremely worried by the figures.

"Our worst fears are confirmed—a few individuals and the Crown Casino owners are in a gold rush and mining the citizens of this state," Ms. Pike said.

The State Opposition's gaming spokesman, Mr. David White, said: "The casino control authority stands to be condemned for increasing table numbers from 200 to 350 and not taking into account this information and making it public."

But the Victorian Casino and Gaming Authority chairman, John Richards said the figures showed a stabilised gambling population.

A Crown Casino spokesman, Gary O'Neill, said: "It is immediately clear from this research that the impact of the casino has been nothing like the scaremongering by the State Opposition." Victoria's Minister for Gaming, Haddon Storey welcomed the figures and said they showed most Victorians gambled well within their means.

AT A GLANCE VICTORIANS spend about $89 million a week on gambling.

SEVENTY-seven percent of adults have gambled in the past 12 months.

ABOUT 38 percent of Victorians have visited the Melbourne Casino.

CASINO usage is up from seven percent in 1994 to 21 percent in 1995. CASINO users are prepared to spend the most gambling money (average $57 a visit).

THE authority's calculated weekly gambling outlay for adults is $27 ($73 for regular casino patrons).

FORTY-five percent of gamblers said the source of gambling funds was housekeeping or living costs.

SIXTY-three percent said gambling was a serious social problem.

MANY regular gamblers have cut back on leisure and clothing to pay for their habit.

FIFTEEN percent of Victorians are regular casino users (at least once a month).

FIVE percent of Victorians spend more than 25 percent of their gross income on gambling.

1. If the population of Victoria at this time was about 4 million people, how many gambled at some time during the year?

2. What was the change in percent of the patronage at Victoria's gambling casinos from 1994 to 1995?

3. Using the figure found in question #1, what was the change in the actual number of people that gambled in casinos between 1994 and 1995?

4. What is the average amount of money gambled per person per visit to the casino in 1995?

5. Based on the work that you did in question #3 and #4, what was the approximate change in revenue at the casino from 1994 to 1995?

6. In total how much do Victorians spend in a year on gambling?

7. Why do the percentages for Tattslotto, Poker machines, casinos and horse racing in the lower right of the figure add to more than 100%?

8. Write a paragraph that describes if the relative heights of the stacks of chips in the lower left of the figure are appropriate to the percentages they represent.

9. Write a paragraph that describes the visual impact that using a roulette wheel has on the presentation of the pie chart.

THE LEISURE TIME PROJECT
MAT 033 BASIC MATHEMATICS

Don Reichman, Instructor   Name _____

Below is a table that describes the economics of leisure activities from 1990 to 1998. Answer the questions below. Remember to discuss your answers with the other members of your group.

Trends in Leisure Time
1990–1998

No. 420. Motion Pictures and Amusement and Recreation Services—Annual Receipts: 1990 to 1998

[In millions of dollars (39,982 represents $39,982,000,000). For taxable employer and nonemployer firms. Based on the Service Annual Survey; see Appendix III]

Kind of business	1987 SIC code [1]	1990	1994	1995	1996	1997	1998
Motion pictures	78	39,982	53,504	57,184	60,279	62,865	66,229
Production, distribution, and allied services	781, 782	28,888	40,256	43,264	46,274	48,176	50,393
Theaters	783	6,088	6,233	6,530	7,044	7,582	8,298
Video tape rental	784	5,006	7,015	7,390	6,961	7,107	7,538
Amusement and recreation services	79	50,126	68,453	77,452	85,733	92,836	97,512
Dance studios, schools, and halls	791	626	906	947	1,046	1,080	1,138
Theatrical producers (except motion picture), bands, orchestras, and entertainers	792	10,735	16,050	17,479	19,597	20,964	22,401
Bowling centers	793	2,800	2,709	2,681	2,751	2,763	2,764
Commercial sports	794	8,636	11,090	13,056	14,589	16,437	17,711
Professional sports clubs and promoters	7941	3,702	6,138	7,695	8,841	9,983	10,732
Racing, including track operation	7948	4,934	4,952	5,360	5,748	6,454	6,979
Miscellaneous amusement and recreation services [2]	799	27,329	37,698	43,290	47,748	51,594	53,500
Physical fitness facilities	7991	3,623	4,033	4,412	4,975	5,705	6,353
Public golf courses	7992	2,254	3,059	3,584	3,979	4,303	4,619
Coin-operated amusement devices	7993	2,146	2,965	3,254	3,491	3,649	3,750
Amusement parks	7996	4,922	5,858	6,298	6,777	7,312	7,478
Membership sports and recreation clubs	7997	4,825	6,379	6,765	7,427	7,653	7,780

[1] 1987 Standard Industrial Classification code; see text, Section 17, Business.   [2] Includes kinds of businesses, not shown separately.

Source: U.S. Census Bureau, *Current Business Reports, Service Annual Survey: 1998*, BS/98, and earlier issues.

The table above describes how Americans spend money during their leisure time. The two forms of leisure activity it describes are: going to the movies and a variety of amusement and recreation services including bowling, sporting events, golf, amusement parks and fitness facilities among others. The chart lists three major headings: Motion Pictures, Amusement and recreation services and Miscellaneous amusement and recreation services. Each of these categories is broken down into subcategories.

1. What are the annual receipts for all "Motion Pictures" in 1998? Show that the sum of the data for its subcategories in 1998 is equal to this value.

2. Suppose you were thinking of going into business with your sister-in-law. She's thinking of opening one of the following businesses: fitness facility, bowling center, amusement park or a video rental store. Which of these subcategories in the chart appears to be the best business for you and your sister-in-law to begin? Be sure to explain and justify your reasoning by providing calculations from the data in the chart.

3. Calculate the actual change in the annual receipts for each of the businesses described in question #2 by filling in the following chart.

Actual Changes in the Annual Receipts

	1990–94	1994–95	1995–96	1996–97	1997–98
Fitness Facility					
Bowling Center					
Amusement Park					
Video Rental Store					

4. Let's define the *rate* in which the annual receipts change as the ratio of the actual change in receipts to the change in time. For example, if my son grew 6 inches from January 1, 2002 to January 1, 2004 then he grew at a rate of 6 inches/2 years or 3 inches per year. Calculate the rate of growth in the annual receipts for the four businesses described above for the following three intervals: 1990–1994, 1994–1997 and 1997–1998.

THE PIZZA PROJECT
MAT 033 BASIC MATHEMATICS

Don Reichman, Instructor   Name _____

Below is an article that describes the economics of the pizza industry. Answer the questions below. Remember to discuss your answers with the other members of your group.

Dining Out Review: Volume III—
Pizza Restaurants—US—June 2002 ($4025.00)

An American staple, pizza is a $25 billion a year industry in the U.S. It is one of America's most popular foods, appealing to time-crunched families, children and young adults. According to Packaged Facts, each man, woman and child in America eats an average of 46 slices of pizza a year, translating to 23 pounds per person per year. Pizza's versatility, convenience and value-orientation (relative to other casual dining options) makes it a popular choice for many consumers, particularly as at 4:00 p.m. each and every day, millions of dollars hang in balance as people in the U.S. decide what to eat for dinner.

The industry economics are good for the restaurant pizza industry, and business appears to be holding steady despite continued price wars and general slowdowns precipitated by the terrorist attacks of September 11. Food and utility costs are down, labor costs down, and chains are adding new outlets and new products and sprucing up their sites. Increasingly, the pizza industry will be segmented into two distinct spheres—those restaurants with solid growth prospects, and those that are old and tired.

This Mintel report explores the following hypothesis: Over the years 1996–2001, sales at pizza restaurants outpaced the growth of the restaurant industry in general, and despite the slowing of the economy starting mid-way through 2001, have fared relatively well, growing at a rate of nearly 10% per year. It used to be that restaurants and fast food chains were consumer cyclical companies. Now they are becoming consumer staples, posting gains irrespective of economic conditions, because consumers today, led by the Baby Boomers, are restaurant-oriented, and the economy has not changed that. The children of these consumers are also steady customers, and they will be increasingly important customers as they mature. The highly competitive pizza industry is faced with a more discriminating consumer, and one that has more choice than ever in their dining out options.

1. Based on the article, during the years 1996–2001 what was the rate of growth of pizza sold in restaurants?

2. Describe in your own words what "rate of growth" means from the context of this article.

_____

Reprinted from *www.prepared foods.com*

3. Using the 10% growth rate described in the article and that America spent $25 billion dollars on pizza in 2001, approximately how much did Americans spend on pizza in 2002?

4. Use the result in question #3 to approximate the amount of money Americans spent on pizza in 2003.

5. Describe in two sentences how you calculated the solution to the problem described in question #3.

6. Suppose S = the amount America spends on pizza in a year and p = the amount America spent on pizza during the previous year. Use the yearly rate of increase in pizza expenditures found in this article to create a formula to determine the amount spent on pizza in a year (S) as a function of the amount spent on pizza during the previous year (p).

    Your formula should begin with S = .

7. Suppose we call 2001 year 0, 2002 year 1, etc. Draw a graph that displays year 0 to year 10 (2011) on the horizontal axis and the approximate amount that Americans spent or may spend on pizza if the 10% growth rate continues on the y axis.

8. Describe in a paragraph if you believe it is reasonable to expect that the growth in pizza sales will continue at a 10% rate for the next ten years. Include in your answer what events or factors might interfere with this continued growth rate.

MUSIC DOWNLOADS:
AN INTERDISCIPLINARY MATH PROJECT
MAT 033 BASIC MATHEMATICS

Don Reichman, Instructor   Name _____

Read the following article to get a general sense of the project. When you are done reading the article, begin to answer the questions that follow. Remember to *use the members of your group as a resource if you don't understand a question.*

Millions of Europeans Pay for Music Downloads
Tue January 20, 2004 05:18 AM ET

By Bernhard Warner, European Internet Correspondent

LONDON (Reuters)—Europeans purchased over three million song downloads in 2003 from the continent's primary online music store, OD2, raising faint hopes the lacklustre music industry is on the road to recovery.

A few million downloads is not going to immediately turn around an industry bracing for its fourth straight year of declining CD sales.

But the emerging download market offers a glimmer of hope for record label executives who have struggled for years to thwart free file-sharing services like Kazaa.

"I have to believe electronic distribution of music will be an increasingly important part of the business for record labels, but unfortunately I don't think this is an instant cure," Charles Grimsdale, chief executive of Britain's OD2, told Reuters Tuesday.

"The market is growing fast for sure, but new markets take time," said Grimsdale, who co-founded the company with rocker Peter Gabriel.

Still, the volume of downloads is growing 25 percent month on month, Grimsdale said, which would mean download sales should grow more than three-fold in 2004.

The more mature U.S. market is growing even faster. American music fans purchased 30 million download tracks in 2003 as online stores such as Apple Computer's iTunes proved a big hit with consumers.

The success of iTunes, combined with some encouraging reports that online piracy may be tailing off in the U.S., has helped propel shares of EMI, the largest stand-alone music company, more than 40 percent higher since the beginning of the year.

At 4:07 a.m. EST Tuesday, shares in EMI were trading down 0.3 percent at 225.5 pence.

For OD2, which licenses its download service to 30 European retail and Internet partners including HMV and Microsoft's MSN, the volume of downloads picked up in August when it introduced through MSN a tariff scheme allowing users to buy downloads without a subscription.

"Our sales increased in some cases as much as 900 percent at that point," Grimsdale said.

Grimsdale acknowledged competition will be much more fierce in 2004. Industry officials expect the big U.S.-based online stores such as iTunes and Roxio's Napster will make their European debut by summer.

OD2 is the most established player in Europe, having arranged licensing deals with all five major music labels, giving it a catalog of 260,000 songs.

Grimsdale said it was the process of adding to its library several hundred thousands songs it has under license, giving it a catalog of one million songs. "We are furiously trying to fill the gap," he said.

© Reuters 2004. All Rights Reserved.

_____

Reprinted from *www.reuters.com* (Valleo Intellectual Property)

1. Write three sentences that describe the main idea of this article.

2. Write a sentence explaining what you think the following sentence means. *"Still, the volume of downloads is growing 25 percent month on month."*

3. Give a math example that illustrates the sentence above. For example, you might write "suppose we start with 10 million downloads, one month later there would be _____, one month after that there would be _____ etc."

4. Consider the following sentence: *"Shares in EMI were trading down 0.3 percent at 225.5 pence."* Is 0.3 percent more or less than 1 percent?

5. If we **let p = the original selling price of a share of EMI stock**, this analytical model will help you calculate the original price of the stock:

$$p - 0.003p = 225.5$$

a) Why does this model use 0.003?

b) What does the expression **.003p** mean?

c) If you evaluate **p − .003p** when p = 230, do you get 225.5?

d) Since 5p − 2p = 3p, can you determine what 1.000p − .003p is equivalent to?

e) Rewrite the equation p − .003p = 225.5 by replacing the left side of this equation with the results you found in question 5d). Solve this new equation for p. Recall that to solve an equation of the form: 3x = 57, you divide both sides by 3.

6. Let's look at this statement: *"Our sales increased in some cases as much as 900 percent at that point."*

a) A 200 percent increase means to calculate the new price you will first multiply 2.00 times the original value, then add this to the original value. For example, if the price of a $100 pair of shoes increased by 200%, its new value would be equal to:

$$\$100 + 2.00 \times \$100 = \$300$$

Explain in one or two sentences what a 900% increase would mean if original sales were $1,000.

b) Invent a math example that illustrates a 900% increase in the sales of ipods. For example you might begin this math example with the following: "Suppose 1 million ipods were sold last year . . ."

7. Write a paragraph that discusses the mathematical ideas presented in this article.

THE REEBOK PROJECT
MAT 033 BASIC MATHEMATICS

Don Reichman, Instructor   Name _____

Below is an article that describes the economics at Reebok during the fourth quarter in 2003 . Answer the questions below; remember to discuss your answers with the other members of your group.

UPDATE 3-Reebok Fourth-Quarter Profit Jumps Sharply
Wed January 28, 2004 10:38 AM ET

(Adds analyst quote, details, updates stock activity)

NEW YORK, Jan 28 (Reuters) - Reebok International Ltd. (RBK.N: Quote, Profile, Research), the No. 2 U.S. sports shoe maker, said on Wednesday fourth-quarter profit rose 70 percent on its booming U.S. footwear and licensed apparel businesses.

Reebok, ranked behind Nike Inc. (NKE.N: Quote, Profile, Research) in sales, reported fourth-quarter earnings of $28.1 million, or 44 cents a share, up from $16.5 million, or 27 cents a share, a year earlier.

Analysts, on average, expected 41 cents a share, according to Reuters Research, a unit of Reuters Group Plc.

"The real key factor was the strength of its forward order levels. That came in considerably stronger in the U.S. market, particularly for apparel," Wells Fargo Securities analyst John Shanley said.

Total U.S. orders placed in advance for apparel through June jumped 21 percent, while future orders for footwear rose about 8 percent.

"During the quarter, much of the margin improvement came from our U.S. footwear business," Paul Fireman, Reebok's chief executive officer, said in a statement.

Reebok said gross margin was up 50 basis points, while U.S. footwear sales gained 17 percent to $228.4 million from a year earlier.

Reebok's performance was boosted by its Rbk unit, which makes performance and fashion shoes, as well as its classic footwear division, which remained the biggest and most profitable, said Shanley, who rated Reebok shares a "buy" and does not own them.

Net sales climbed 11 percent to $843.6 million. Excluding the effects of foreign currency adjustment, sales rose 6 percent from a year earlier.

U.S. clothing sales rose 7 percent to $155.1 million, led by its licensed athletic apparel unit. Reebok is now the exclusive outfitter for the entire National Football League, as well as 19 teams in the National Basketball Association.

For 2004, Reebok said it expected earnings to rise 15 percent and will be in line with Wall Street's average estimate. Analysts, on average, expected $2.76 a share, according to Reuters Research.

The Canton, Massachusetts-based company also said full-year revenue growth will be in the mid-single-digit range.

Reebok shares were 25 cents higher at $39.74 on Wednesday on the New York Stock Exchange. The company's stock has risen about 18 percent in the past four months.

_____

Reprinted from *www.reuters.com* (Valleo Intellectual Property)

1. The article uses percentages quite frequently. Write down every occurrence of percent you can find in this article and explain its meaning. For example you might write 1) "fourth quarter profit rose by 70% means profit increased during the last 3 months of the year."

2. Consider the following sentence: "Reebok, ranked behind Nike Inc. (NKE.N: Quote, Profile, Research) in sales, reported fourth-quarter earnings of $28.1 million, or 44 cents a share, up from $16.5 million, or 27 cents a share, a year earlier." A company is composed of millions of shares of stock. Ordinary people own these shares.

   a) Suppose we wanted to determine how many shares of Nike stock there are in all. This seems like a difficult problem. Let's try a simpler problem. What if you knew that your pizza pie had 800 slivers of cheese or 100 slivers per slice. Can you determine how many slices there are in the entire pizza?

b) Now apply the same strategy to the following question: Your company earns a total of $1,000 for all its shareholders. This is equivalent to $0.50 per share. How many shares are there in your company?

c) Explain in one or two sentences how you solved this problem.

d) Now determine how many shares there are in Nike from the above information.

3. Consider the following sentence: "Reebok shares were 25 cents higher at $39.74 on Wednesday on the New York Stock Exchange."

a) In one or two sentences explain what this sentence means.

b) Percent increase is defined as the actual change (increase or decrease) in value divided by the original value. What was the original value of Nike stock (that is on Tuesday)? By how much did the value of a share of Nike stock increase? Now determine the percent increase in the value of Nike stock on Wednesday.

4. Write the sentence from the article that describes the percent change in Nike stock over the past four months.

a) Suppose we want to solve the following problem: "If the growth in Nike stock continues at this rate, how much will a share sell for in one year?" First let's determine the annual growth rate (assuming that Nike stock continues to grow as it has). This is a hard problem. Let's try an easier version of the same problem. If the value of my Michael Jordan rookie card increases by $10 in 6 months, how much will it increase in one year (12 months)?

b) Explain in one or two sentences how you solved the problem.

c) Try to use the same method to solve the following problem: What would be the annual rate of growth of Nike stock if it continues to grow as it has over the last 4 months?" Hint: try proportional reasoning.

d) Using your results in 4c) let's attack the problem: "How much will Nike stock sell for in one year?" Again, if the problem seems too hard try a simpler version of the same problem. For example suppose that last year a jacket sold for $100. If the price of the jacket increased by 10% over the year, how much will the jacket cost? Explain what you did to solve this problem. Now use this method to solve the problem at hand.

5. Several times in this project we were faced with difficult problems. The strategy we used was to construct a simpler version of the same type of problem. Describe in one or two sentences the main idea of this strategy.

6. Construct a simpler version of the following problem: "What is the value of 6.88 ounces of gold @ $378.93 per ounce?" Now try to solve the problem.

COMPREHENDING COLLEGE TEXTBOOKS

STEPS TO

UNDERSTANDING

AND REMEMBERING

WHAT YOU READ

3d

EDITION

COMPREHENDING COLLEGE TEXTBOOKS

STEPS TO

UNDERSTANDING

AND REMEMBERING

WHAT YOU READ

Joe Cortina

Janet Elder

Katherine Gonnet

Richland College
Dallas County Community College District

The McGraw-Hill Companies, Inc.
New York St. Louis San Francisco Auckland
Bogotá Caracas Lisbon London Madrid
Mexico City Milan Montreal New Delhi
San Juan Singapore Sydney Tokyo Toronto

COMPREHENDING COLLEGE TEXTBOOKS
Steps to Understanding and Remembering What You Read

Acknowledgments appear on pages 549–550, and on this page by reference.

This book is printed on acid-free paper.

2 3 4 5 6 7 8 9 0 DOC DOC 9 0 9 8 7 6

ISBN 0-07-024058-2

This book was set in Times Roman by Graphic World, Inc.
The editors were Tim Julet, Laura Lynch, and Scott Amerman;
the designer was Robin Hoffmann;
the production supervisor was Louise Karam.
R. R. Donnelley & Sons Company was printer and binder.

Library of Congress Cataloging-in-Publication Data

Cortina, Joe.
   Comprehending college textbooks: Steps to understanding and
remembering what you read / Joe Cortina, Janet Elder, Katherine
Gonnet.—3d ed.
      p.   cm.
   Includes index.
   ISBN 0-07-024058-2
   1. Reading (Higher education)   2. Reading comprehension.
I. Elder, Janet.   II. Gonnet, Katherine.   III. Title.
LB2395.3.C66   1996
428.4'3—dc20   95-9661

ABOUT THE AUTHORS

Joe Cortina

Janet Elder

Katherine Gonnet

All three authors teach basic and advanced reading improvement and study skills courses at Richland College, a member of the Dallas County Community College District. Their combined teaching experience spans elementary, secondary, and undergraduate levels, as well as clinical remediation. Each is trained as a reading specialist.

The authors have worked together as a writing team for more than a decade. *Comprehending College Textbooks,* their first book, was first published in 1989. Their second textbook, *Opening Doors: Understanding College Reading,* was published in 1995. In addition, Dr. Elder and Dr. Gonnet co-authored the reading section of *How to Prepare for the TASP,* a study guide for entering college students who take the Texas Academic Skills Program Test.

DR. JOE CORTINA received his undergraduate degree in English from San Diego State University and master's and doctoral degrees in curriculum and instruction in reading from the University of North Texas. He has taught undergraduate teacher education courses in reading at the University of North Texas and Texas Woman's University. In 1981 he was selected to represent the Dallas County Community College District as a nominee for the Piper Award for Teaching Excellence, and in 1994 he was a recipient of an Excellence Award given by the National Institute for Staff and Organizational Development. In addition to teaching reading courses at Richland College, he has served on interdisciplinary teaching teams for honors English courses and has served as a faculty leader of Richland's Writing Across the Curriculum Program. Dr. Cortina has served as a member of the editorial advisory board of *The Journal of Reading.* He is a frequent speaker at professional meetings.

DR. JANET ELDER was graduated summa cum laude from the University of Texas in Austin with a B.A. in English and Latin. She is a member of Phi Beta Kappa. She was the recipient of a government fellowship for Southern Methodist University's Reading Research Specialist Program, which resulted in a master's degree. Her Ph.D. in curriculum and instruction in reading is from Texas Woman's University where the College of Education presented her the Outstanding Dissertation Award. She established the first comprehensive secondary reading program in the Dallas Independent School District and has conducted extensive staff development training for Dallas area teachers. After teaching reading and study skills courses at Richland for several years, she was asked to develop and implement an honors program for the college. After coordinating the honors program during its first six years, she resumed teaching full time. She has served on a task force that evaluated Richland's college-wide writing program. She received the Extra Mile Award from special services students and has been her division's Piper Award nominee for excellence in teaching, and in 1993 received an Excellence Award from the National Institute for Staff and Organizational Development. Dr. Elder serves as a presenter at many professional conferences.

DR. KATHERINE GONNET's educational background includes a B.S. from Texas Woman's University and a master's degree from Southern Methodist University, where she was awarded a government fellowship in the Reading Research Specialist Program. Her doctorate, from the University of North Texas, is in Higher Education Administration. She served as the chairperson of Richland's Developmental Studies Division for six years before resuming full-time teaching. In recent years, she represented Richland in a district project to revise reading course curricula. She was selected by Richland to attend an international education program in Heidelberg, Germany. In addition to teaching reading and serving on interdisciplinary teaching teams in honors humanities and English courses, she has been a "technology scout" for the college, investigating the use of computers in reading instruction. She was selected as her division's nominee for the Piper Award for Teaching Excellence, and was given an Excellence Award in 1992 by the National Institute for Staff and Organizational Development. Dr. Gonnet has also made numerous presentations at professional meetings.

CONTENTS

To the Instructor   *xi*

To the Student   *xvii*

INTRODUCTION   **1**

1
DETERMINING THE SUBJECT MATTER   **11**

Who or what is this passage about?

Chapter Summary   *35*
Practice Exercises   *37*
Answer Key for Practice Exercises   *45*
Review Test   *47*
Supplemental Exercises   *53*

2
LOCATING DIRECTLY STATED MAIN IDEAS   **67**

What is the most important point the author wants me
to understand about the subject matter?

Locate the sentence that expresses this idea.

Chapter Summary   *79*
Practice Exercises   *81*

Answer Key for Practice Exercises   *93*
Review Test   *97*
Supplemental Exercises   *103*

3
FORMULATING IMPLIED MAIN IDEAS   107

What is the most important point that the author wants me to infer and understand about the subject matter?

Formulate a sentence that expresses the implied main idea.

Chapter Summary   *125*
Practice Exercises   *127*
Answer Key for Practice Exercises   *135*
Review Test   *139*
Supplemental Exercises   *145*

4
IDENTIFYING SUPPORTING DETAILS   149

What additional information does the author want me to know in order to understand more about the main idea?

Chapter Summary   *161*
Practice Exercises   *163*
Answer Key for Practice Exercises   *173*
Review Test   *177*
Supplemental Exercises   *189*

5
RECOGNIZING AUTHORS' WRITING PATTERNS   195

How does the author organize the material he or she is presenting?

Chapter Summary   *231*
Practice Exercises   *235*
Answer Key for Practice Exercises   *243*

Review Test	*245*
Supplemental Exercises	*253*
Textbook Excerpt and Comprehension Quiz:	
"Communicating Interculturally" from *Business*	
Communications Today, 4th ed., by	
Courtland L. Bovée and John V. Thill	*261*

6
APPLYING COMPREHENSION SKILLS TO
LONGER PASSAGES   279

What is the overall main idea of a textbook selection?

Chapter Summary	*297*
Practice Exercises	*301*
Answer Key for Practice Exercises	*313*
Review Test	*315*
Supplemental Exercises	*321*
Textbook Excerpt and Comprehension Quiz:	
"The Primates" from *Anthropology,* 6th ed., by Conrad	
Phillip Kottak	*333*

7
REMEMBERING COLLEGE TEXTBOOK
MATERIAL THROUGH ORGANIZING   348

What techniques can I use to help me
remember what I read?

Chapter Summary	*364*
Practice Exercises: Part A	*366*
Answer Key for Practice Exercises: Part A	*374*
Practice Exercises: Part B	*384*
Answer Key for Practice Exercises: Part B	*394*
Review Test	*402*
Supplemental Exercises	*420*
Textbook Excerpt and Comprehension Quiz:	*439*
"The Nature of Life: An Introduction" from *The Nature*	
of Life, 3d ed., by John H. Postlethwait and Janet L. Hopson	

8
THINKING CRITICALLY AS YOU READ   477

Is the main idea or are any of the supporting details
an opinion?

Based on the information in the passage, what
inference does the author want me to make?

Are there words that reveal the author's point of view?

Chapter Summary   499
Practice Exercises   503
Answer Key for Practice Exercises   515
Review Test   517
Supplemental Exercises   527
Textbook Excerpt and Comprehension Quiz:
    "Ludwig van Beethoven" from *Music: An Appreciation,*
    5th ed., by Roger Kamien   535

Acknowledgments   549

Index   551

TO THE INSTRUCTOR

This book is aimed at the entering college student whose skills are at a precollege level. The *focus* of the book is comprehension, the heart of the reading process. The *theme* of the book is that reading is a form of the thinking process. One's reading ability is related to the quality of one's thinking, the ability to make connections between elements of text and the ability to see the relationship between one's prior knowledge and the content of the text. This book attempts to provide underprepared readers with a systematic way of thinking about and approaching college textbook material.

Unlike most books at this level, this text utilizes a theoretical framework: Reading is viewed as a psycholinguistic, interactive process. The readers bring their knowledge and experience to bear upon the text; their knowledge and experience are modified and enhanced by the content of the text. The readers are as important as the text.

Passages of varying lengths from actual college textbooks have been used in this text. *College text material is used throughout because it is what students will encounter in subsequent college course work.* In the third edition of *Comprehending College Textbooks,* a lengthy textbook excerpt has been added to Chapters 5 through 8. The excerpt in Chapter 7, "Remembering College Textbook Material through Organizing," is a full-length chapter from a biology textbook. Each excerpt is accompanied by a full-length objective quiz over the content, the sort of quiz a content area instructor might give. With appropriate coaching and guidance from the instructor, developmental students should be able to "reach" for these passages so that they have realistic expectations about and experiences with college-level material, the ultimate goal of most developmental reading courses. Moreover, they will not have the disappointing and disheartening experience of completing a reading course only to discover that it truly did not prepare them for "real" college course work.

Many exercises in this text call for subjective responses formulated as complete sentences. Again, this mirrors reality (and serves as a foundation for summarizing and performing well on essay tests). The student's tasks always include identifying the subject matter and main idea since this is what active, efficient readers must do to comprehend well. The emphasis is on direct instruction and time on task, that is, the amount of time students actually spend dealing with passages from college textbooks. Therefore, this book deliberately provides extensive practice and reinforcement.

Often, texts used in developmental reading courses cover a barrage of skills in a superficial manner. In an effort to avoid this shortcoming, we have chosen to treat vocabulary in a restricted way and to focus only on certain essential study skills. The goal is to present the crucial skills that provide the framework for comprehension and to ground the student thoroughly in them. There is abundant repetition and reinforcement.

The primary thrust of this book is helping students grasp the main ideas and supporting details of material they are assigned to read in their college textbooks. In working with college textbook material, however, students will encounter a great deal of new vocabulary, including many specialized terms in each subject. It is important for students to acquire this vocabulary, but it is equally important for students not to let the vocabulary cause them to "miss the forest for the trees." Many underprepared readers tend to concentrate more on words than on ideas. They focus on words in and of themselves rather than giving attention to the words as a means of helping them unlock the ideas being presented.

To minimize this problem, in this book we have simply listed beneath each passage the words that are likely to be new to students or to cause them difficulty and *have defined them according to the way they are used in the passage.* Moreover, the part of speech and pronunciation are given. You may ask students to refer to the lists of words as needed, or you may prefer to direct their attention to them in a more systematic manner. It is impossible to anticipate every word that will be new to students. Consequently, you may find it necessary to add vocabulary beyond what is listed beneath a passage or to have individual students add words as needed.

Since part of the students' task in underlining and annotating college textbook passages is to identify, mark, and define new terms, no vocabulary words are listed or defined in the Supplementary Exercises and Chapter 7, "Remembering College Textbook Material through Organizing." Students should be made to understand that they are responsible for identifying and defining *any* word that blocks their complete comprehension of a passage.

The emphasis in this book is also upon the theoretical construct of *metacomprehension:* creating in the reader an awareness of the function that the sentences and paragraphs fulfill, as well as an awareness of a paragraph's organization (e.g., definition, listing, sequence, comparison-contrast, and cause-effect). The ability to perceive function and organization results not only in increased comprehension but also in enhanced retention.

Chapter 8 deals with critical thinking. Again, we have tried to target essential skills rather than barrage students with a multitude of them. For this reason, we concentrate on distinguishing opinion from fact, making inferences, and recognizing an author's point of view.

Comprehension monitoring is demonstrated and emphasized throughout this book. It is important for students (1) to realize when they are comprehending and when they are not, and (2) to have a repertoire of strategies available to them when they fail to grasp meaning. It is also important for students to learn to isolate the source of their confusion or misunderstanding (such as an unknown term or lack of background information). Research clearly indicates that many less able readers do not see comprehension as part of the reading process; others are unable to judge whether or not they have understood material they are reading. It is essential that whenever a student fails to produce an acceptable response, he or she determines (or is helped to determine) *why*. Most materials provide no feedback other than whether an answer is right or wrong. In this text, however, the initial chapters present several formulations of "acceptable" answers since many unsuccessful readers labor under the impression that there is one right answer and only one correct way to state it. This text provides examples of answers of varying degrees of acceptability so that students can learn to evaluate the quality of their responses.

Materials don't teach, but a good teacher can use this book to help students learn to comprehend college textbook material. Your willingness to become involved with the material, your enthusiasm for acquiring new information (since none of us has had a course in every subject, you may also learn some new things from the college textbook excerpts used in this book!), and your pleasure in learning can be a model for your students. We wish you great success as you help prepare your students to read college textbooks effectively. Toward that end, we have incorporated in the *Instructor's Manual* many of the strategies and approaches for using this book that have proved especially successful in our own classrooms.

The third edition of *Comprehending College Textbooks* features the following:

- Excerpts of varying lengths from college content area textbooks

- A no-nonsense, direct instruction approach that focuses entirely upon comprehension and retention

- Extensive, purposeful practice and reinforcement of basic comprehension techniques

- Metacomprehension (the function of a sentence or paragraph in relation to the entire passage)

- Comprehension monitoring ("What have I understood and how well have I understood? How can I deal with material I don't understand adequately?")

- Longer textbook reading selections with an objective quiz after each reading

- A full-length biology chapter as a reading selection in Chapter 7

Moreover, this book fulfills these goals:

- Anticipates faulty strategies that inefficient readers often use

- Emphasizes and explains "obvious" skills because these are not always obvious to the underprepared reader

- Describes what good readers do in order to read well, because these steps are not clear to underprepared readers

- Explains *why* readers need to know certain techniques, why a strategy works, and why it is important

- Concentrates on *the teaching of comprehension,* because it is the most difficult component of reading instruction to teach

- Addresses the frustration and discouragement college readers may experience and explains how to cope with such feelings

The concepts presented in this text are hardly new. Nearly every text in this field presents the notion of subject matter, main ideas, details, and organization or structure. What is different is that the approach is thorough and is systematic, and incorporates comprehension monitoring and support strategies. Most books do not address the problem of what students are to do when they *don't* comprehend. The instructional methodology also differs in that it is more than just explanations and examples followed by exercises. Rather, the teacher, with the help of the text, actively guides the students deductively through the techniques being introduced. Students move toward autonomy and maturity in their reading in a way that promotes mastery.

The introduction of this book is designed to orient students to the book's content and to give a rationale for the methodology used. To gain full advantage from this book, it is *essential* for the instructor and the students to go over this section together. The introduction is an integral part of this textbook.

In this textbook, we have chosen to use the terms *subject matter* and *topic* interchangeably. Although some instructors prefer to treat the topic as a single *aspect* of a more general subject matter, we believe that making this distinction may unnecessarily confuse students who are using this book. Therefore, we have used the term subject matter throughout this book when referring to what the author is writing about.

ACKNOWLEDGMENTS

We are grateful to Tim Julet, English Editor at McGraw-Hill, for his encouragement and assistance with this edition. Thanks, too, to the editorial and production team at McGraw-Hill, who did such an admirable job of guiding this text from manuscript to bound book: Scott Amerman, editing supervisor; Laura Lynch, associate editor; Robin Hoffmann, designer; and Louise Karam, production supervisor. Special thanks go to Lesley Denton, marketing director, for her continuing support.

Our reviewers served us well with their constructive criticisms, suggestions, and supportive comments. We are grateful to Elaine Carter, Utah Valley Community College; Gwendolyn Gray, Eastern Kentucky University; Stephan Strachman, Hudson Valley Community College; and Sebastian Vasta, Camden County College.

Our students at Richland College offered wonderful suggestions and encouraging comments during the field testing of this book. They have been among our best and most helpful critics.

Our thanks would not be complete without recognizing the continuing contributions of our families. This book has also been a part of their lives for several years. We offer our heartfelt thanks to them for their unwavering interest, patience, and support.

Joe Cortina

Janet Elder

Katherine Gonnet

TO THE STUDENT

Dear Student,

Welcome to the third edition of *Comprehending College Textbooks: Steps to Understanding and Remembering What You Read.*

This is a very special book. Every reading selection in this book was carefully chosen from popular textbooks now in wide use in colleges and universities throughout the United States.

Many students feel unprepared to deal with college textbooks. They know that they have not yet had the opportunity to gain the practice, skill, and confidence to handle college textbooks effectively. Because we want you to have many chances to work with material from actual college textbooks, we have included *only* selections from college textbooks.

This book focuses on what we believe is the single most important ability you can have as a reader: the ability to *comprehend* (understand) your college textbooks. This book presents specific strategies to help you identify and recall the important information and concepts in your textbooks.

We have deliberately selected textbook passages from a variety of subjects: history, biology, computer science, business, government, economics, psychology, humanities, sociology, geology, and philosophy. When you first meet a passage from each of these subjects, you will be given a brief description of what each subject deals with. If you are like most students, you will encounter many subjects in college that are new to you.

Perhaps you will never take an economics course or a computer science course or a biology course, but you *will* have some idea about the subject matter of these courses from the textbook selections you will read in this book. Perhaps *because* you are introduced to a subject in this book and find it interesting, you may even decide to take a course in a subject that you might otherwise not have taken. College is the ideal time to explore *any* area in which you think you may have an interest. You will never know if you are interested in a subject, however, if you don't learn enough about it to make an informed decision.

For the sake of convenience, colleges often divide academic subjects into several broad areas, or "disciplines," as they are called. The *natural sciences* consist of subjects such as astronomy, biology, chemistry, geology, physical science, and physics. Another broad area is referred to as the *social sciences*. These include history, political science (government), sociology, psychology, anthropology, and economics. The *humanities* consist of literature, the fine arts (drama, dance, music, art), and philosophy. Examples of *communications* courses could include composition, foreign languages, and speech. *Business, engineering,* and *technical programs* are other areas in which many colleges offer course work.

The college textbook passages used in this book for illustrations and practice exercises contain a great deal of useful and fascinating information. Please don't view the passages merely as "exercises" to be completed. They are more than that. They are opportunities to acquire valuable background information and introductions to subjects that may be new to you. You may find, in fact, that the information you learn from the passages in this book provides helpful information in other courses you are taking or will be taking.

A word of warning: In this text, there are no shortcuts. You will have to *think* about what you are doing because sometimes the passages will seem difficult. Remember, these passages are from actual college textbooks. As you increase your skill and confidence, you will become more and more adept at comprehending college-level texts. You may need to "reach" a little to understand some of the passages presented in this book, but soon you may be saying, "Hey, I *can* do this. College-level material is manageable after all." We hope you will feel this way as you complete the exercises in this book. "Time on task" (in other words, *practice*) is closely related to how much progress you attain. No one else can do the exercises in this textbook for you. There is nothing any teacher can "do" to you to make you learn. This book is for students who *want* to learn and who are willing to work at improving their comprehension in order to learn in college.

Remember that no book can really "teach" you, but you can learn a great deal from books. *It is what you do with this book* that determines whether learning occurs.

Joe Cortina

Janet Elder

Katherine Gonnet

COMPREHENDING COLLEGE TEXTBOOKS

STEPS TO

UNDERSTANDING

AND REMEMBERING

WHAT YOU READ

INTRODUCTION

1
Determining Subject Matter

2
Locating Directly Stated Main Ideas

3
Formulating Implied Main Ideas

4
Identifying Supporting Details

5
Recognizing Authors' Writing Patterns

6
Applying Comprehension
Skills to Longer Passages

7
Remembering College Textbook
Material through Organizing

8
Thinking Critically as You Read

1

OVERVIEW OF THIS BOOK

Chapter 1: Determining Subject Matter

Determining the subject matter is a skill that focuses your attention on *what a passage is basically about.* Many times in a college textbook passage, determining or deciding upon the subject matter is easy because there may be a boldfaced heading at the beginning of the passage that clearly indicates the subject matter. You will also learn to use other techniques to help you determine the subject matter of the passage when there is no heading.

Chapter 2: Locating Directly Stated Main Ideas

Finding the main idea of a passage focuses your attention on *the most important idea in the passage.* Many times in a college textbook passage, locating the directly stated main idea is easy because the main idea is presented in the first sentence of the paragraph. (What could be easier than that?) However, the main idea sentence may also be found at the end of the paragraph or even in the middle of the paragraph. With practice, you will be able to locate this important idea sentence. The main ideas of textbook paragraphs are often used as the basis for test questions on college exams.

Chapter 3: Formulating Implied Main Ideas

Sometimes a college textbook passage does not have a directly stated main idea sentence. Instead, the author gives you many ideas, facts, or examples, and you must formulate (or infer) a version of the main idea of the passage using your own words. With practice, you will be able to determine *when* there is no directly stated main idea in a passage, and you will be able to formulate a main idea sentence using your own words.

Chapter 4: Identifying Supporting Details

You will find a number of supporting details in textbook passages. These details *support* the main idea. Of course, some of the details are more important than others. In college courses, teachers often base exam questions on these details. Thus it is important to be able to select the significant supporting details. Ultimately, you will be able to determine the relationship between the main idea and its supporting details.

Chapter 5: Recognizing Authors' Writing Patterns

Authors organize their material by using several common writing patterns: listing, sequence, definition, comparison and contrast, and cause and effect. As you learn to recognize these patterns, you will be able to predict what is likely to come next in textbook passages and to recall more easily what you have read.

Chapter 6: Applying Comprehension Skills to Longer Passages

One of the hallmarks of a maturing reader is the ability to deal with increasingly longer textbook passages. You will learn how to apply the skills learned in earlier chapters to determine the overall subject matter and main ideas of longer textbook passages. You will also have practice summarizing these longer passages.

Chapter 7: Remembering College Textbook Material through Organizing

After reading a college textbook passage or series of passages, you will want to remember what you have read well enough to pass a test on it. You will practice using several organizing techniques that enable you to prepare to recite and remember what you have read. These include:

- Memory techniques

- Underlining and annotating textbook passages

- Outlining and mapping

- Making study and vocabulary cards

Chapter 8: Thinking Critically as You Read

Even though you already think critically every day of your life, you may not be accustomed to thinking critically as you read your textbooks. Thinking critically as you read involves going beyond determining the subject matter, main idea, and supporting details. You will learn to distinguish opinions from facts, make inferences based on information in passages, and recognize an author's point of view.

As you gain proficiency in your reading, you will find that you do not need to apply *every* technique presented in this book every time you read your college textbooks. But when you *do* need them, you will know how to use them. Learning and practicing the strategies in this book will prepare you for reading college textbooks.

THE READING PROCESS

Students frequently have misconceptions about the reading process. Since your beliefs can influence your performance, it is important that you understand the following points about the reading process:

1. *Reading makes no unusual or unique demands on a reader.* You often "read" people's faces, get the main idea of what is going on when you observe a situation, draw conclusions about what you've seen, and so forth. The same mental processes are used when you read.

2. *Reading is a form of the thinking process. You read with your brain, not your eyes.* (Blind people read through braille.) Your eyes simply transmit images to the brain. Improving your reading means improving your thinking—not practicing moving your eyes faster or in a different way.

3. *Reading includes three steps: preparing yourself to read* (thinking about what you already know about a subject and setting purposes for reading); *comprehending;* and *reacting* to what you read.

4. *Effective readers are highly interactive readers.* They constantly seek to bring meaning to the text; they take steps to correct the situation when they are not comprehending.

5. *Many comprehension problems are not just reading problems.* If you fail to understand something you are reading, it could be because it is poorly written. More likely, however, you lack the background information needed to comprehend. (That is, you still wouldn't understand if someone read it *aloud* to you.) Try reading another textbook or an easier book on the same subject, and then return to the text that is causing you difficulty. You might also consult your instructor, a classmate, or another knowledgeable person. Sometimes, you may want to prepare questions about the things you don't understand in order to ask about them in class. Often, simply looking up items that you don't understand in an encyclopedia will help you begin to make up for any de-

ficiencies in your background knowledge and help you understand what is being presented.

6. *Good readers are sensitive to the structure of the material they are reading.* By seeing how it is structured (or organized), they improve their comprehension and recall. They not only know the subject matter and main idea of each paragraph, they understand how each paragraph is organized (e.g., sequence, listing, cause and effect, comparison and contrast, and definition).

7. *Speed is a by-product of comprehension.* The more quickly you understand something, the faster you can read it. "Speed" without comprehension is meaningless. Reading is more than just allowing your eyes to pass over lines of print.

Characteristics of College-Level Reading

As you work your way through the exercises in this book, you will begin to notice that there are several characteristics of college-level textbook reading:

1. In college-level reading, there may be *many* ideas or facts packed into a single paragraph. We call this **idea density.** Nearly every sentence seems to contain new or important information. Everything seems important in this type of paragraph!

2. In college-level reading, many new terms will be introduced because each college subject has its own special vocabulary. This is called the **technical vocabulary** for a subject. Remember, though, that textbook authors define and explain many of these new terms. It may take one sentence or several pages to give you the information you need about these new terms. Pay special attention to these terms. You will certainly be asked about these words on tests in your college courses.

3. In college-level reading, there will be **patterns of organization** which you will learn to recognize. For example, in the social sciences, the cause-effect pattern is widely used. This pattern often is found in the natural sciences also. Other patterns you will learn to recognize are the definition pattern, the comparison-contrast pattern, the sequence pattern, and the simple listing pattern.

4. In college-level reading, you will frequently need to stop and ask yourself, "Did I understand what I just read?" Asking yourself this question is the first step in **comprehension monitoring,** a process you will learn in this book.

5. In college-level reading, you may not have adequate background knowledge to understand a subject. It may seem as if you are trying to read another language! Sometimes an author or your instructor may assume that you know more than you actually do. If this is the case, it is still your responsibility to fill in the gaps in your knowledge. You can do this by talking with the instructor, a tutor, or a knowledgeable classmate or friend. You can also do this by reading simpler explanations. You can find simpler explanations in other textbooks or books from the library or bookstore. *Then* return to your more difficult textbook. Although this may seem like more work, it can actually save you time and frustration.

6. In college-level reading you will find that not all textbooks are equally well written. Unfortunately, some are less well organized and less clearly written. Should you encounter a text of this sort, it will still be your responsibility to deal with that textbook by using the skills presented in this book, by obtaining more background knowledge, by getting a simpler book on the same subject, or by talking about the subject with someone who is knowledgeable.

7. In college-level reading, there will be times when you feel very discouraged. This feeling is common to every student at one time or another. We refer to this feeling as **intellectual despair.** Fortunately, you can learn to overcome this discouragement by using the skills presented in this book. These strategies will help you learn how to understand difficult material.

The Importance of Background Knowledge to Reading Comprehension

In well-written paragraphs, the sentences of the paragraph fit together like the pieces of a jigsaw puzzle. You may also have begun to realize that understanding how the "pieces" fit together depends upon how close the match is between your background knowledge and the subject matter. If you do not know enough about the subject matter to make sense of what the author is saying, then you, the reader, must fill the gaps in your background knowledge.

When you lack background knowledge in a subject you are reading—and this happens frequently when students are new to college subjects and college textbooks—you have a comprehension problem. However, this is not simply a *reading* comprehension problem. It is a more *general* comprehension problem; that is, you probably would not understand the material even if someone read it *to* you. This means that you will have to take whatever steps are necessary to obtain the background information you lack. This will enable you to return to the textbook and comprehend it.

Only you can take the necessary steps to correct the problem of inadequate background knowledge. These steps might include reading parts of another textbook or other books (perhaps easier ones) on the same subject, consulting an encyclopedia, or talking with someone knowledgeable about the subject. These steps require effort, and, obviously, there are no shortcuts.

Going the "extra mile" to get more background knowledge is just part of being a responsible and mature learner. You may discover how exciting and how satisfying it is to gain an understanding of new or difficult material through your own efforts. You will find that you feel better about yourself as a student (a "student" is one who *studies*) when you take the initiative for your own learning. In short, you may discover how much joy there can be in learning.

The very fact that you are taking this course indicates that you intend to improve your reading skills and background knowledge. You may be surprised at how much new knowledge you gain from the textbook excerpts in this book since all of them are taken from widely used college textbooks.

MAINTAINING A POSITIVE ATTITUDE

The keys to maintaining a positive attitude are to realize that everyone occasionally feels discouraged, to know that you do not have to give in to these feelings, and to acquire the reading skills needed to handle college textbooks.

What can you do? First, be patient with yourself. Some subjects *will* be harder for you. Plan to spend more time on them; this alone can work wonders. Seek extra help if you need it—from the instructor, from a tutor, from a classmate, or from other, simpler books on the same subject.

Break a big assignment into smaller parts. Decide that you are not going to quit until you read and understand at least *one* section or small part of the assigned chapter. Once you have mastered one small section, your self-esteem will be higher and you will have the confidence and motivation to tackle the next section.

If a particular assignment becomes *too* frustrating, put it down for a while and come back to it later. Study another subject, take a walk, or exercise to clear your mind.

If you don't understand an idea or a concept, try to pinpoint exactly what it is that you don't understand. This sometimes clears it up. At the very least, you will have your questions ready to ask the instructor or someone else who can help.

It might be useful to you to ask successful classmates or the instructor for their suggestions for doing well in the class and for handling the textbook effectively. Sometimes a "study buddy" or a study group can make a dramatic improvement in your grade (and provide a welcome support group). Be sure to choose your study partners carefully—and be sure to uphold your responsibility by coming to the study sessions as prepared as possible and with your questions clearly in mind.

Finally, remember that you don't have to love a subject in order to do well in it (although it makes it more enjoyable). Try to replace your negative self-talk ("I can't do this." "I'm going to fail." "I've never been any good at this stuff.") with positive self-talk ("Even if I can't understand *all* of this assignment, I'll stay with it until I've learned at least one new thing." "Other people have learned this; I can too." "I'm not going to let this defeat me."). A positive attitude, determination, and a willingness to work hard separate successful students from unsuccessful ones. Successful students don't believe that their success comes from luck. Geniuses are rare. If you succeed, it will be because *you* made the effort to succeed. And you can feel very good about that accomplishment.

"BUT I'M NOT INTERESTED IN HISTORY"

(Or Science or English or Math or Government or . . .)

No matter what your major is, you will still be required to take a variety of courses—and some of them may not appeal to you or interest you. Students often say, "If I like a subject, I can concentrate when I read it; but if I *don't* like it, I can't concentrate on it or understand it." They assume they have no control over whether or not they are interested in a subject.

Nothing could be further from the truth. Part of your responsibility as a student is to develop an interest in your courses. As a bonus, you'll find that you will enjoy your courses more.

The more you know about a course, the more you will want to know. This is especially important to remember at the beginning of the semester. You might also ask classmates who like the subject (or who even plan to major in it) what it is that attracts them. You can also ask your instructors (tactfully, of course) what caused them to choose a particular subject for their teaching field.

Try to understand how a course that is not interesting to you relates to your life. What does history have to do with your life? government? math? English? What is it about these subjects that caused colleges and universities to think them important enough to *require* students to take them? It is through these courses that our culture is transmitted to you, the next generation. Don't dismiss a subject without giving it a chance.

Remember that you are responsible for your attitude and your interest in a subject. If you aren't naturally interested in a subject, then you must take whatever steps necessary to *create* interest, such as those described above. Remember, too, the skills presented in this book will help you become interested in a subject because they will help you *understand* more of what you read.

In college you will probably have more freedom than you have ever had before. It may be tempting to skip going to a class that does not interest you. The more classes you miss, the harder it will be to develop interest. Research studies show that class attendance during the first six weeks of the semester is closely related to the final grade you earn in the course. You should plan to attend *every* class but make a special effort not to miss a class during the first part of the semester.

It will be especially tempting to skip a class when you have not read the assignment. This is the worst thing you can do; it will put you even further behind and make the assignment seem harder to read. *Read your assignments. Go to class.* If you never miss, you will never have to catch up.

VOCABULARY

Part of comprehending college textbooks is comprehending the meaning of the words used in them. Since college textbooks contain many specialized terms as well as other words that are new to students, it is important for you to pay close attention to vocabulary.

The focus of this book, of course, is on comprehending the main ideas an author is making and understanding the supporting details that go with each main idea. Although the emphasis of this book is on the *ideas* contained in college textbooks rather than just the words, the words are still important to your understanding and learning.

To help you keep your focus on an author's ideas, vocabulary words are listed and defined in a "mini-glossary" beneath each passage. Although many of the words have more than one meaning, *the words are defined according to the way they are used in the passage.* The words and their definitions are available so that you may refer to them if you need to. Obviously, when you are reading your own college textbooks, you would have to look up unfamiliar words in the dictionary or glossary—unless the author has defined them for you in the passage.

You will also be told what part of speech a word is and how to pronounce it. There is a pronunciation key provided on each page so that you can easily determine the correct pronunciation for each word. You may be pleasantly surprised to discover how many new terms you learn in the process of using this book. You may, in fact, be well on your way to developing a college-level vocabulary by the time you have completed the exercises in this textbook.

In Chapter 7, "Remembering College Textbook Material through Organizing," there are no vocabulary "helps" in the Practice Exercises, the Review Test, or the Supplemental Exercises. At this stage, you will truly by ready to "solo" and to try your own hand at managing new vocabulary terms encountered in college textbook passages.

It will not always be necessary for you to look up an unfamiliar word. Textbook authors usually define important terms for you, and you can often figure out the meaning of an unfamiliar word by the way the word is used in a sentence. Deducing the meaning of a word according to how it is used in the sentence is called *using the context.* Using the context refers to using the surrounding words or sentences to help you determine a word's meaning. Sometimes you will be figuring out a word that is completely new to you; sometimes it will be a familiar word that is used in a way that is new to *you.* Textbook authors generally write in a manner that makes the meaning of unfamiliar words clear to the reader.

As noted above, the focus of this book is on *comprehending ideas.* However, there are many excellent vocabulary materials available that focus on using the context and other vocabulary skills.

CHAPTER

1

DETERMINING SUBJECT MATTER

1

Determining Subject Matter

2

Locating Directly Stated Main Ideas

3

Formulating Implied Main Ideas

4

Identifying Supporting Details

5

Recognizing Authors' Writing Patterns

6

Applying Comprehension Skills to Longer Passages

7

Remembering College Textbook Material through Organizing

8

Thinking Critically as You Read

11

INTRODUCTION

The *subject matter* of a piece of writing is simply what the writer has chosen as the *topic*. The subject matter is the topic of the writing, or, in other words, what the author is writing *about*.

Efficient readers determine the subject matter whenever they read. Once you can correctly determine the subject matter of a passage, you can begin to ask useful questions about the passage. Determining the subject matter is the first step to understanding an entire passage. This chapter is designed to help you learn and practice this skill.

> The **subject matter** is a word or a phrase that tells what the author is writing about. The subject matter is also called the *topic*.

THE IMPORTANCE OF DETERMINING THE SUBJECT MATTER

Why are effective readers concerned about determining the subject matter of a passage? How will this skill help you?

The human mind strives to see the organization or pattern of things because organized information is easier to grasp and to remember. Writers understand this so they try to present ideas in an organized way. Because of this, each sentence and each detail in a well-written paragraph will give you information about the subject matter. If the sentences did not have a common subject matter, they would be merely a collection of unrelated sentences, and not a paragraph. A passage like that might be difficult to understand, and it certainly would be harder to remember.

The subject matter of a paragraph provides you with a convenient way of describing what all the details in the passage pertain to. Determining the subject matter is also a starting point for using each of the skills that you will learn in the remaining chapters of this book.

EXPLANATION AND EXAMPLES

Whenever you read a textbook passage, try to determine the *subject matter* by asking yourself questions such as:

- Who or what is this passage about?

    or

- What is the topic of this passage?

Suppose you can't answer these questions immediately? Don't be discouraged if the subject matter of a passage isn't obvious to you. Realizing that you haven't yet determined the subject matter should alert you to the fact that you must take additional steps in order to identify it. Use the five strategies described in the rest of this section.

The first strategy to help determine the subject matter is the use of headings.

---

1. See if the author identifies the subject matter by using a *heading*.

Many readers do not give headings the attention they deserve. Headings are important, however, because a writer often states the subject matter of the paragraph in the heading. To be an effective reader, you should pay attention to headings.

Here is a sample passage from an economics textbook. (Economics is the study of the development and management of a country's material wealth.) Notice the heading "What Is Inflation?" Read the paragraph. As you read, ask yourself, "Is this paragraph actually about what inflation is?"

What Is Inflation?

Most people associate inflation with price increases on specific goods and services. The economy is not necessarily experiencing an inflation, however, every time the price of a cup of coffee goes up. We must be careful to distinguish the phenomenon of inflation from price increases for specific goods. *Inflation is an increase in the average level of prices, not a change in any specific price.*

The Economy Today
by Bradley R. Schiller

---

inflation (ĭn flā′ shən) n. (The last sentence in the passage defines this word.)

phenomenon (fĭ nŏm′ ə nŏn) n. An unusual fact or occurrence.

ă pat ā pay â care ä father ĕ pet ē be ĭ pit ī tie î pier ŏ pot ō toe
ô paw oi noise o͞o took o͞o boot ou out th thin *th* this ŭ cut û urge
yo͞o abuse zh vision ə *a*bout, it*e*m, ed*i*ble, gall*o*p, circ*u*s

Yes, the subject matter of this paragraph is inflation (an increase in the average level of prices). The author has helped the reader determine the subject matter by identifying it in the heading.

A second strategy to help determine the subject matter is the use of **bold print** within a passage.

---

2. **See if a word, name, or phrase appears in *bold print* within a passage.**

Here is an example of a passage taken from a sociology textbook. (Sociology is the study of human behavior.) You can see that the word *status* is in boldface. As you read, ask yourself, "Is this paragraph actually about status?"

> When we speak of an individual's "status" in casual conversation, the term usually conveys connotations of influence, wealth, and fame. However, sociologists use **status** to refer to any of the full range of socially defined positions within a large group of society—from the lowest to the highest position. Within American society, a person can occupy the status of president of the United States, fruit picker, son or daughter, violinist, teenager, resident of Minneapolis, dental technician, or neighbor.
>
> *Sociology*
> by Richard Schaefer

---

status (stā′ təs, stăt′ əs) n. (The phrase "to refer to" indicates that the author is defining the term for you.)

The subject matter of this passage, of course, is status.

Although you may have been able to *identify* the subject matter of this passage easily, you may still not know what status means. Identifying the subject matter is an important step toward comprehension, but you must be sure that you understand the meaning of the word or phrase

---

ă pat ā pay â care ä father ĕ pet ē be ĭ pit ī tie î pier ŏ pot ō toe
ô paw oi noise o͞o took o͞o boot ou out th thin *th* this ŭ cut û urge
yo͞o abuse zh vision ə *a*bout, it*e*m, ed*i*ble, gall*o*p, circ*u*s

that is the subject matter. In this paragraph the author explains that status refers to "socially defined positions," that is, various positions and roles defined by a society. You will find many new terms (such as status and inflation) in college textbooks. Your professors expect you to learn what these words and phrases mean as they are used in that course.

Now, here is third strategy for determining the subject matter.

---

3. **See if a *word, name, or phrase appears more than once* in a passage.**

Here is an example taken from a biology textbook. (Biology is the study of living things.) As you read this passage, ask yourself, "What is this passage about?"

Osmosis

The diffusion of water across a selectively permeable membrane has been given a special term: it is called *osmosis*. **Osmosis is defined as the net movement of water molecules from the area of greater concentration of water to the area of lesser concentration of water across a selectively permeable membrane.**

Inquiry into Life
by Sylvia Mader

---

osmosis (ŏs mō′ səs) n. (The phrase "is defined as" tells you that the author is explaining the meaning of the term in the passage.)

molecule (mŏl′ ə kyōōl) n. The simplest structural unit that displays the characteristic physical and chemical properties of a compound.

concentration (kŏn sən trā′ shən) n. The amount of specified substance in a unit amount of another substance.

permeable (pûr′ mē ə bəl) adj. Capable of being penetrated; having openings that something can spread through.

diffusion (dĭ fyōō zhən) n. The process of spreading out or dispersing.

ă pat ā pay â care ä father ĕ pet ē be ĭ pit ī tie î pier ŏ pot ō toe
ô paw oi noise ŏŏ took ōō boot ou out th thin *th* this ŭ cut û urge
yōō abuse zh vision ə *a*bout, it*e*m, ed*i*ble, gall*o*p, circ*u*s

It is easy to see that the subject matter of this passage is osmosis. The word *osmosis* appears twice in the passage, as well as in the heading. You may have noticed that the phrase "selectively permeable membrane" also appears twice in the passage. Couldn't this phrase be the subject matter? How can you decide?

There are important clues that tell you that osmosis is the correct subject matter. First, the word *osmosis* is used as the heading. Second, *osmosis* appears in both sentences and is the word being defined in the passage. Notice the phrase, "Osmosis is defined as . . . ."

Here is another example, taken from a philosophy textbook. (Philosophy is the study of the nature of things based on logical reasoning.) Try reading this philosophy passage *aloud*. Often, certain types of writing will seem easier to understand when you read them aloud. As you read this passage, notice the phrase "being responsible" is repeated many times throughout the passage.

In ethics, being responsible for our behavior means that we understand what we are doing, that we are aware of a moral rule which tells us to behave in a certain way, and that we have chosen to obey or disobey that moral rule. If we deliberate over whether to tell the truth and then choose instead to make a false promise, we are responsible for that action because it is the product of our choice. Being responsible means also that it is appropriate that we should be blamed for our actions. But being responsible is not limited to "bad" behavior only. We can also be responsible for "good" actions. In this case, being responsible means that it is appropriate that we should be praised for our behavior. It would not be appropriate, nor would it make any sense, to blame or punish or to praise anyone for those actions for which he is not responsible, that is, for actions which are not the result of his choice. There are many other ways to use the word "responsible," but our concern is with its ethical meaning. In ethics, being responsible focuses on our capacity to deliberate and to choose and therefore on our capacity to originate our actions. It is because these actions are our actions that we are said to be responsible for them.

Elements of Philosophy
by Samuel Stumpf

---

ethics (ĕth′ ĭks) n. pl. The study of the general nature of morals and of the specific moral choices to be made by the individual in his relationship with others.

moral (môr′ əl) adj. Being or acting in accordance with standards and precepts of goodness or with established codes of behavior.

deliberate (dĭ lĭb′ ə rāt) v. To take careful thought; reflect.

originate (ə rĭj′ ə nāt) v. To bring into being; create.

The subject matter of this passage is "being responsible." The sentences in the passage *explain* what "being responsible" means as the term is used in the field of ethics.

Now, you try to find the subject matter in a passage by applying the three strategies you have learned.

Comparable Worth

Because so-called women's work is undervalued, women's groups have argued for **comparable worth:** jobs which require similar education and training and which entail similar responsibility should pay the same. This would end the practice of paying female "cleaning women" less than male "custodians," even though the two jobs are comparable, and of paying female teachers, librarians, and nurses less than male ambulance drivers and window cleaners. Most of the male-dominated uniformed services (the police, fire fighters, and sanitation workers) oppose this idea, while teachers, social workers, librarians, and nurses are in favor of it. The Democratic Party's leadership in Congress has endorsed it, as did its 1984 presidential ticket. The Reagan administration, on the other hand, opposed it strongly. William Niskanen, a White House economist, called it "a truly crazy proposal," and the chairman of the Civil Rights Commission, Clarence Pendleton, said that it was "the looniest idea since looney tunes." In 1985 the Equal Employment Opportunity Commission ruled that federal law does not require equal pay for jobs of comparable worth.

American Politics and Government
by Richard Pious

ă pat ā pay â care ä father ĕ pet ē be ĭ pit ī tie î pier ŏ pot ō toe
ô paw oi noise o͝o took o͞o boot ou out th thin *th* this ŭ cut û urge
y o͞o abuse zh vision ə *a*bout, it*e*m, ed*i*ble, gall*o*p, circ*u*s

comparable (kŏm′ pər ə bəl) adj. Able to be compared; similar or equivalent. (Many people mispronounce this word; notice that the accent is on the *first* syllable.)

male-dominated (māl dŏm′ ə nā təd) adj. Having many more men than women; something that is controlled by men. (The examples of "male-dominated uniformed services"—the police, fire fighters, and sanitation workers—provide a context clue about the meaning of the phrase "male-dominated.")

endorse (ĕn dôrs′) v. To give approval or support.

ticket (tĭk′ ĭt) n. A list of candidates proposed or endorsed by a political party; a slate of candidates.

- Who or what is this passage about? The answer to this question will be the subject matter. Write the subject matter here:

The words *comparable worth* appear both in the passage and in the heading. Also, each sentence in the passage is *about* comparable worth. Therefore, comparable worth is the subject matter of this passage.

Now, read another passage to determine its subject matter. This selection is from a business textbook. It has no heading or no bold print words. You must read it and ask yourself, "Who or what is this passage about?"

The electronic nature of computers gives them several important attributes. First, computers are extremely fast at processing instructions, that is, at performing calculations and at making logical comparisons. Second, computers are extremely accurate in their processing; rarely does a computer make an electronic mistake that it does not catch itself and signal to the computer operator. Almost all errors in computer data processing are caused by faulty programs prepared by humans. Third, computers are extremely reliable; being primarily electronic and without moving parts, they seldom have failures.

Principles of Management Information Systems
by George M. Scott

ă pat ā pay â care ä father ĕ pet ē be ĭ pit ī tie î pier ŏ pot ō toe
ô paw oi noise o͞o took o͞o boot ou out th thin *th* this ŭ cut û urge
yo͞o abuse zh vision ə *a*bout, it*e*m, ed*i*ble, gall*o*p, circ*u*s

---

attribute (ăt′ rə byo͞ot) n. A quality or characteristic of a person or thing.

- Who or what is the passage about? The answer to this question will be the subject matter. Write the subject matter here:

Perhaps you chose *computers* as the subject matter of this passage. If so, you were on the right track! However, the passage does not discuss everything there is to know about computers. Instead, it deals only with *the electronic nature of computers,* which gives them the advantages of speed, accuracy, and reliability. Therefore, the subject matter of the passage is the electronic nature of computers.

Often, writers do not repeat the word or phrase that is the subject matter. Instead they use words such as *it, he, she,* or *they* to stand for the subject matter.

What can you do if there *isn't* a word or phrase that appears more than once in a passage? Try this fourth strategy:

---

4. **See if the passage** *begins with a word or phrase that is then referred to throughout the passage* **by a pronoun (he, she, it, or they) or by other words.**

For example, here is a passage from a psychology textbook. (Psychology is the study of human mental processes and behavior.) Read this passage and ask yourself, "Who or what is this passage about?"

> The brain stem is responsible for many basic functions. It takes in information from several senses through sensory regions for vision, hearing, taste, balance, and touch in the facial area. It controls involuntary activity of the tongue, the larynx, the eyes, and the facial

---

ă pat ā pay â care ä father ĕ pet ē be ĭ pit ī tie î pier ŏ pot ō toe
ô paw oi noise o͝o took o͞o boot ou out th thin *th* this ŭ cut û urge
yo͞o abuse zh vision ə *a*bout, it*e*m, ed*i*ble, gall*o*p, circ*u*s

> muscles through specific motor neurons for these areas. It controls levels of sleep and arousal through the reticular formation, nestled within its central core, and it coordinates the motor neurons in the spinal cord that control such activities as walking, breathing, and the beating of our hearts.
>
> *Psychology*
> by Diane Papalia and Sally Olds

---

sensory (sĕn′ sər ē) adj. Of or pertaining to the senses.

involuntary (ĭn vŏl′ ən tĕr ē) adj. Not performed willingly; not subject to control.

larynx (lăr′ ĭngks) n. The upper part of the respiratory (breathing) tract that controls the vocal cords. (Many people mispronounce the last syllable of this word.)

arousal (ə rou′ zəl) n. Being awakened from sleep; the act of stirring up, exciting, or stimulating.

The entire passage tells about functions of the brain stem although the brain stem is mentioned only at the beginning of the passage. The word *it* is then used throughout the passage to refer to the brain stem. Because of this, you know that the subject matter of this passage is the brain stem and its functions.

Here is another example. It is taken from a section on art in a humanities textbook. (Humanities is the study of human culture as expressed in philosophy, literature, and the fine arts.) As you read, ask yourself, "Who or what is this passage about?"

> **Tempera** is an opaque, watercolor medium whose use spans recorded history. It was employed by the ancient Egyptians, and is still used today by such familiar painters as Andrew Wyeth. Tempera refers to ground pigments and their color binders such as gum or

---

ă pat ā pay â care ä father ĕ pet ē be ĭ pit ī tie î pier ŏ pot ō toe
ô paw oi noise o͞o took o͞o boot ou out th thin *th* this ŭ cut û urge
yo͞o abuse zh vision ə *a*bout, it*e*m, ed*i*ble, gall*o*p, circ*u*s

glue, but is best known in its egg tempera form. It is a fast-drying medium that virtually eliminates brush strokes and gives extremely sharp and precise detail. Colors in tempera paintings appear almost gemlike in their clarity and brilliance.

Perceiving the Arts
by Dennis Sporre

---

tempera (tĕm′ pər ə) n. (The words "is" and "refers to" tell you that the author is explaining the meaning of this term in the passage.)

opaque (ō pāk′) adj. Not reflecting light; without luster; dull.

medium (mē′ dē əm) n. A type of artistic technique.

pigment (pĭg′ mənt) n. Dry coloring matter, usually a powder, to be mixed with water, oil, or another base to produce paint.

binder (bīn′ dər) n. A material used to ensure uniform consistency or adhesion to a surface.

virtually (vûr′ chōō ə lē) adv. Essentially; practically; in fact or to all purposes.

- Who or what is the passage about? The answer to this question will be the subject matter. Write the subject matter here:

The subject matter of this passage is tempera, a type of watercolor paint. In the passage, tempera is often referred to as "it."

Now, you try to find the subject matter in this passage from an American history textbook. Remember to look for words such as *he, she, it, they, this, himself,* or *herself* throughout the passage. One of these words may lead you to the subject matter of the passage. Now read the passage, focusing on who or what this passage is about.

ă pat ā pay â care ä father ĕ pet ē be ĭ pit ī tie î pier ŏ pot ō toe
ô paw oi noise ōō took ōō boot ou out th thin th this ŭ cut û urge
yōō abuse zh vision ə about, item, edible, gallop, circus

Geraldine Ferraro

What enthusiasm there was for the [1984] Democratic ticket arose from Mondale's historic selection of Congresswoman Geraldine Ferraro as his vice-presidential running mate. Feminists hailed this choice, as did numerous women and men throughout the country. She showed herself to be an intelligent, indefatigable campaigner who won the respect of even her opponents.

A People and a Nation
by Mary Beth Norton et al.

---

hail (hāl) v. To welcome or acclaim enthusiastically.

indefatigable (ĭn dĭ fat′ ə gə bəl) adj. Tireless; untiring; not easily fatigued. (The root word "fatigue" gives you a clue to this word's meaning.)

● Who or what is this passage about? The answer to this question will be the subject matter. Write the subject matter here:

The subject matter of this passage is *Geraldine Ferraro,* or *the selection of Geraldine Ferraro as Mondale's vice-presidential running mate in 1984.* Did you identify the words *herself, this choice,* and *her* used to refer to the selection of Geraldine Ferraro in the paragraph?

In this passage, the author gave *two* clues to the subject matter: the heading and several words used throughout the passage to refer to Geraldine Ferraro. Many times, the author gives you *several* clues to the subject matter of a passage.

There is still another way, a fifth way, to determine the subject matter. You can determine the subject matter by seeing what the other sentences in the passage *illustrate, explain,* or *describe.*

ă pat ā pay â care ä father ĕ pet ē be ĭ pit ī tie î pier ŏ pot ō toe
ô paw oi noise ŏŏ took ōō boot ou out th thin th this ŭ cut û urge
yōō abuse zh vision ə *a*bout, it*e*m, ed*i*ble, gall*o*p, circ*u*s

> **5. When reading a passage,** *see what subject the sentences have in common.*

Here is an example taken from a government textbook. As you read this passage, try to understand what subject each sentence has in common.

The statistics were grim. Over the next year, 45,000 Americans would die in traffic accidents. Nearly 10,000 of those fatalities would be accounted for by persons under age twenty-five involved in alcohol-related accidents. "Raising the drinking age will reduce fatalities among the younger drivers of this country," claimed an official of the National Highway Traffic Safety Administration. A study conducted for the insurance industry estimated that 1,250 lives a year could be saved if a minimum drinking age of twenty-one were established. In July 1984 Congress passed legislation requiring states either to impose a minimum age of twenty-one for the purchase of alcohol or to lose their share of federal funds for highway construction.

The American Democracy
by Thomas E. Patterson

fatality (fa tăl′ ĭ tē) n. An accidental death.

● Who or what is this passage about? Write the subject matter here:

The subject matter of this passage is *the minimum drinking age and traffic fatalities.* All sentences in this passage refer to this topic.

ă pat   ā pay   â care   ä father   ĕ pet   ē be   ĭ pit   ī tie   î pier   ŏ pot   ō toe
ô paw   oi noise   o͞o took   o͞o boot   ou out   th thin   *th* this   ŭ cut   û urge
yo͞o abuse   zh vision   ə *a*bout, it*e*m, ed*i*ble, gall*o*p, circ*u*s

Now try this passage from an American history textbook. Read to see what the sentences in this passage have in common.

> In May 1983, the Labor Department announced that for the first time in United States history, more than half (50.5 percent) of all women aged twenty and older held jobs. Some were blue-collar workers, including 9,000 new female carpenters and 29,000 new female truck drivers who had joined the work force since 1970. Nevertheless, in 1985 half of all working women still occupied only 20 of the 441 job categories of the United States census, mostly at the low end of the pay scale. Eighty percent worked in such "female" occupations such as clerking, selling, teaching, nursing, and waitressing.
>
> *A People and a Nation*
> by Mary Beth Norton et al.

blue-collar (blo͞o kŏl′ ər) adj. Of or pertaining to wage earners in jobs performed in rough clothing and often involving manual labor, especially when such workers are regarded as a social class. (The examples of blue-collar workers—carpenters and truck drivers—help make the meaning clear.)

- Who or what is the passage about? Write the subject matter here:

_____

All of these sentences talk about working women; therefore, that is the subject matter. Each sentence in the passage describes something about women's role in the work force.

Now read this passage from a psychology textbook. Read to see what subject matter the sentences have in common.

> Sleep patterns undergo changes for most people between early adulthood and late middle ages. By age 60, people who used to wake up once during the night are now waking up six times, and their sleep

ă pat ā pay â care ä father ĕ pet ē be ĭ pit ī tie î pier ŏ pot ō toe
ô paw oi noise o͝o took o͞o boot ou out th thin *th* this ŭ cut û urge
yo͞o abuse zh vision ə *a*bout, it*e*m, ed*i*ble, gall*o*p, circ*u*s

is much lighter than it used to be. Women's sleep patterns do not change as dramatically as those of men and resemble the sleep of men ten years younger.

> *Psychology*
> by Diane Papalia and Sally Olds

---

undergo (ŭn dər gō′) v. To go through; to experience; to be subjected to.

Remember that authors sometimes mention the subject only once and then use the other sentences to illlustrate, explain, or describe the subject. The sentences in the passage illustrate changes in sleep patterns. Therefore, *changes in sleep patterns* is the subject matter of the passage.

Perhaps your first response was sleep or sleep patterns. You were on the right track, but you must be more precise. The sentences illustrate *changes* in sleep patterns.

Effective readers are careful to state the subject matter in such a way that it is broad enough to cover all the important information in the passage (changes in sleep patterns), yet not so broad that it could include information beyond that discussed in the passage (sleep).

You can evaluate your own accuracy in determining the subject matter by asking yourself, "What is the *entire* passage about?" and then checking to see if your answer is precise rather than too broad or too narrow.

Read this passage from a sociology textbook. As you read, carefully consider the heading and how the sentences in the passage relate to it.

Age Segregation/Nursing Homes

For the older American, age segregation is most obvious in nursing homes. Currently, 11.5 million elderly persons, or about 6 percent of the aged population of the United States, live in nursing homes or

---

ă pat ā pay â care ä father ĕ pet ē be ĭ pit ī tie î pier ŏ pot ō toe
ô paw oi noise o͞o took o͞o boot ou out th thin *th* this ŭ cut û urge
yo͞o abuse zh vision ə *a*bout, it*e*m, ed*i*ble, gall*o*p, circ*u*s

other institutionalized settings. About one in five Americans will stay in such a home at some point in his or her life. Entering a nursing home means becoming part of a total institution. Activities are determined by the institution and are rarely tailored to the individual preferences of residents. Most of one's personal possessions must be left behind, since available space is limited. The majority of the elderly enter such institutions in their late seventies and early eighties, when their health is failing or they lack financial resources needed to live on their own (Frank, 1981; Neuhaus and Neuhaus, 1982; 155–179).

Sociology
by Richard Schaefer

institutionalized (ĭn stə tōō shə nə līzd) adj. Like an institution or place of confinement.

tailor (tā′ lər) v. To make, alter, or adapt for a particular purpose or end.

- Who or what is the passage about? Write the subject matter here:

You will notice that the first sentence mentions age segregation that occurs when older Americans are placed in nursing homes. These two ideas together form the complete subject matter of this passage. Therefore, the subject matter is *age segregation and nursing homes*. Again and again, we see how helpful headings can be in understanding college textbooks.

If the wording you use to describe the subject matter is too general or too specific, it is unacceptable. *Too general* (too broad) means that the topic chosen as the subject matter goes beyond what is discussed in the passage. *Too specific* (too narrow) means that the topic chosen as the subject matter is too limited to cover all that is discussed in this passage. Consider these acceptable and unacceptable versions of the subject matter for the preceding passage:

ă pat ā pay â care ä father ĕ pet ē be ĭ pit ī tie î pier ŏ pot ō toe
ô paw oi noise ŏŏ took ōō boot ou out th thin *th* this ŭ cut û urge
yōō abuse zh vision ə *a*bout, it*e*m, ed*i*ble, gall*o*p, circ*u*s

Too General	Acceptable	Too Specific
Age segregation	Age segregation in nursing homes	Nursing homes
This is too broad because this passage concerns *only* the segregation of older Americans in nursing homes.	*or* Age segregation and nursing homes	This is too narrow because this passage is concerned with *more* than just nursing homes.

A word of warning: Not every heading does a good enough job of telling you the subject matter! A heading may be too brief or too broad. In the example that follows, you will read a passage with a heading that is too broad. It is not precise enough. Read this paragraph from a psychology textbook. Ask yourself, "Who or what is this passage about?"

Enhancing Creativity

A major reason for exploring creativity is the desire to encourage individuals to be more inventive in all aspects of life, both for the good of society and the fulfillment of the individual. To this end, many programs have been devised over the past fifty years, but the results have been generally disappointing. High hopes had been held for such tactics as brainstorming (group problem-solving techniques in which participants are encouraged to produce as many new and original ideas as possible, without evaluating any until the end of the session); so-called productive thinking, and specific problem-solving strategies. Most studies, however, show that specific strategies that can be used on problems similar to those presented during instruction can be learned, especially in highly technical fields such as mathematics, engineering, and product design, but that creative problem solving that applies to many different skills does not appear to be teachable (Mayer, 1983).

Psychology
by Diane Papalia and Sally Olds

---

enhance (ĕn hăns′) v. To increase or make greater.

devise (dĭ vīz′) v. To form or arrange in the mind; plan.

tactics (tăk′ tĭks) n. Techniques for achieving a goal.

To correctly determine the subject matter of this paragraph, you need to understand what each sentence in the passage means.

The first sentence tells us that we are interested in *creativity* because being inventive is good for the individual and society.

The second sentence tells us that many *creativity* programs have been devised, but the results were disappointing.

The third sentence tells us that there had been hope that tactics such as brainstorming, productive thinking, and problem-solving strategies could build *creativity*.

The last sentence tells us that perhaps *creative* problem solving that applies to many different skills cannot be taught.

By examining the sentences in the passage, you can see that the last three sentences are about *attempts* at enhancing creativity or efforts to improve creativity. The first sentence is simply an introduction.

Consider the acceptable and unacceptable versions of the subject matter for the above passage:

Too General	Acceptable	Too Specific
Enhancing creativity	Attempts at enhancing creativity	Problem solving
This is too broad because this passage focuses on the unsuccessful *attempts* to improve creativity.	*or* Efforts to improve creativity	This is too narrow because this was only *one* of the unsuccessful attempts the authors mentioned.

ă pat ā pay â care ä father ĕ pet ē be ĭ pit ī tie î pier ŏ pot ō toe
ô paw oi noise ŏŏ took ōō boot ou out th thin *th* this ŭ cut û urge
yōō abuse zh vision ə *a*bout, it*e*m, ed*i*ble, gall*o*p, circ*u*s

As you can see, you cannot always rely on the heading of a passage to tell you the precise subject matter. Pay attention to the heading, but read the passage carefully to determine whether the heading is an accurate indication of the subject matter.

Incidentally, in longer passages the subject matter of each paragraph can often be combined into one, overall subject matter. Understanding the overall subject matter can make a long passage easier to comprehend and remember. Here is a passage selected from a psychology textbook. The subject matter of each paragraph has been written in the margin. Now read the passage.

How Do We Remember?

Your memory works through four basic steps: First you have to perceive something—to see it, hear it, or become aware of it through some other sense. Second, you have to get it into your memory. Third, you put it away. And finally, you have to be able to find it so you can take it out.

Perception, the first step in this process, may be involuntary. You see or hear something, and it makes an impression on you. Or it may involve a deliberate effort to pay close attention to information so that your perception will be keener.

The second step requires you to encode whatever you want to remember. Encoding is the process of classifying information. You need to get information ready for storage by organizing it in some meaningful way. One way is by coding letters of the alphabet into words, coding words into sentences, and coding sentences into ideas. We also encode material by sound and meaning. Only encoded information can be remembered. Third, you store the material so that it stays in memory.

Subject Matter

Paragraph 1

four basic steps of memory

Paragraph 2

perception

Paragraph 3

encoding and storing material

> The final, crucial step in this sequence is retrieval, or getting the remembered information out of storage. The thoroughness with which we prepare information for memory and store it determines the efficiency with which we retrieve it.
>
> *Psychology*
> by Diane Papalia
> and Sally Olds

Paragraph 4

retrieval
_____

perceive (pər sēv′) v. To see, hear, or become aware of something through one of the other senses. [The noun form of perceive is *perception.* The authors have defined the word. Here the use of a dash (—) tells you that you are receiving a definition.]

involuntary (ĭn vŏl′ ən tĕr ē) adj. Not subject to control. (Here the prefix *in* means "not." Involuntary means not voluntary.)

encode (ĕn cōd′) v. To classify information for storage by organizing it.

classify (klăs′ ə fī) v. To arrange or organize according to class or category.

retrieval (rĭ trē′ vəl) n. Getting remembered information out of storage. (The authors tell you the sense in which they are using the word.)

Who or what is the *entire* passage about? The overall subject matter is *the four basic steps of the memory process* or *how we remember.* After the first paragraph, the authors simply provide more information about each of the four steps in memory.

Now read another longer passage taken from a business textbook. Begin by determining the subject matter of each paragraph and write each one in the margin.

ă pat ā pay â care ä father ĕ pet ē be ĭ pit ī tie î pier ŏ pot ō toe
ô paw oi noise o͝o took o͞o boot ou out th thin *th* this ŭ cut û urge
yo͞o abuse zh vision ə *a*bout, it*e*m, ed*i*ble, gall*o*p, circ*u*s

The Rise of Computers

Until the twentieth century almost all data processing was done manually. Clerical personnel used paper, pen, and pencil to maintain records. Such data processing was the ultimate in labor intensiveness. Frequent clerical errors caused transactions to be misrecorded and company records to be misrepresented. Information was often received too late to serve any but historical and custodial purposes.

During the first half of the twentieth century electromechanical data processing equipment became widely employed. These machines are both electrical and mechanical—they employ electricity for their functioning, and mechanical movement within the machines processes the data. Punched-card machines are examples of electromechanical devices that were used throughout this period and are still in use. Electromechanical data processing equipment represented a great advance over manual data processing because it was faster and more accurate. Also, unlike humans, these machines never grew tired, although they did have frequent mechanical failures. Electromechanical equipment still required a substantial amount of labor and still allowed tremendous opportunity for clerical mistakes.

Electronic computer data processing began after World War II. A landmark in its development was the Eniac, a 20-ton vacuum tube computer completed in 1946 by Mauchley and Eckert, professors of electrical engineering at the University of Pennsylvania. The Eniac now reposes in the Smithsonian Institution. In 1981, a party was held to celebrate the thirty-fifth

Subject Matter

Paragraph 1

_____

_____

_____

Paragraph 2

_____

_____

_____

Paragraph 3

_____

_____

_____

birthday of the Eniac and the computer age. The Eniac was dusted off, plugged in, and assigned a set of calculations to perform. The same request was made of a Radio Shack TRS-80 microcomputer. The 30-lb microcomputer completed the task about 5 times as fast as the 20-ton behemoth Eniac, a startling indication of the tremendous advances made in computing technology in just 35 years.

Principles of Management
Information Systems
by George M. Scott

---

clerical (klĕr′ ĭ kəl) adj. Of or pertaining to clerks or office workers.

intensiveness (ĭn tĕn′ sĭv nəs) n. Exceptionally great concentration, power, or force.

custodial (kŭs tō′ dē əl) adj. Pertaining to being kept.

repose (rĭ pōz′) v. To rest or remain.

startling (stär′ tlĭng) adj. Surprising; causing a mild shock or surprise.

The subject matter of the first paragraph is manual data processing. The subject matter of the second paragraph is electromechanical data processing. The subject matter of the third paragraph is electronic computer data processing. Who or what is the *entire* passage about? Write the overall subject matter of this passage here:

Compare your answer with these acceptable and unacceptable versions of the overall subject matter of the passage:

ă pat   ā pay   â care   ä father   ĕ pet   ē be   ĭ pit   ī tie   î pier   ŏ pot   ō toe
ô paw   oi noise   o͞o took   o͞o boot   ou out   th thin   *th* this   ŭ cut   û urge
yo͞o abuse   zh vision   ə *a*bout, it*e*m, ed*i*ble, gall*o*p, circ*u*s

Too General	Acceptable	Too Specific
Computers	The history of data processing	Manual data processing
Data processing	*or*	Electromechanical data processing
	The rise of computers	Electronic computer data processing
	or	Eniac
	The history of computers	

COMPREHENSION MONITORING

You can monitor, or check, your effectiveness as you read. Monitoring your comprehension will become a habit if you do it regularly. When you monitor your effectiveness in determining the subject matter, you will be able to *know* when you are understanding what you read. Monitoring your own comprehension will also help you remember what you read.

"How well am I understanding what I am reading?" is a question you should ask yourself as you read. If you are not understanding what you are reading, *stop*. Ask yourself, "Why?" Ask yourself:

"Are there words that I do not know?"

"Am I concentrating as I read? Is my mind wandering?"

"Is the topic difficult because it is completely new to me?"

If there are words that you do not know:

- Try to use the rest of the sentence or paragraph to figure out the meaning of those words.

- Check a glossary or a dictionary.

- Ask someone.

ă pat ā pay â care ä father ĕ pet ē be ĭ pit ī tie î pier ŏ pot ō toe
ô paw oi noise o͝o took o͞o boot ou out th thin *th* this ŭ cut û urge
yo͞o abuse zh vision ə *a*bout, it*e*m, ed*i*ble, gall*o*p, circ*u*s

If you are not concentrating:

- Identify what is bothering you and take some action (i.e., write it down or decide not to worry or think about it until later).

- Make a conscious decision to concentrate on what you are reading.

If the topic is difficult because it is new:

- Reread the passage.

- Read the passage aloud.

- Read ahead to see if it becomes clearer.

- Read supplemental material or simpler material on the same topic (perhaps an encyclopedia, another textbook, or a book from the library).

- Ask for a brief explanation from someone who is knowledgeable about this topic.

Keep in mind that you may sometimes have difficulty understanding a passage because it is not clearly written.

1

DETERMINING SUBJECT MATTER
Chapter Summary

The **subject matter** is a word or phrase that tells what the author is writing about. The subject matter is also called the *topic*.

Whenever you read, determine the ***subject matter*** by asking yourself questions such as:

- Who or what is this passage about?

    or

- What is the topic of this passage?

It may be necessary for you to use some of these strategies, as well. Ask yourself:

1. Does the author identify the subject matter by using *headings?*

2. Is there a word, name, or phrase that appears in *bold print* in the passage?

3. Does a certain *word, name, or phrase appear more than once* in the passage?

4. Does the passage begin with a word or phrase that is then *referred to throughout the passage by a pronoun or other words?*

5. What subject do all the sentences in the passage *have in common?*

Remember, once you have correctly determined the subject matter of a college textbook passage, you can begin to ask useful questions about the subject matter in order to comprehend correctly and exactly what you are reading. You will also be ready to identify the *main idea* of the passage, something you will learn about in Chapter 2.

DETERMINING SUBJECT MATTER
Practice Exercises

Determine the subject matter of the passages below. As you read and after you read, ask yourself, "Who or what is the passage about?" Be careful to state the subject matter in such a way that it is broad enough to include all the important information in the passage, yet not so broad that it could include material beyond what is discussed in the passage. Remember to write just a *word or a phrase,* not a sentence.

1. This passage comes from a business textbook.

> Electronic computers now pervade business data processing as well as other areas in our society. The entire computer revolution has come about during the lifetime of today's middle- and senior-level managers, almost none of whom studied computers as part of their formal education because computer technology either did not exist or was not widely used for business data processing. Business data processing has been extensively taught in colleges and universities only since about 1970.
>
> *Principles of Management Information Systems*
> by George M. Scott

pervade (pər vād′) v. To spread throughout.

• Who or what is the passage about? On the line below, write a *word or phrase* that tells the subject matter:

ă pat ā pay â care ä father ĕ pet ē be ĭ pit ī tie î pier ŏ pot ō toe
ô paw oi noise o͝o took o͞o boot ou out th thin *th* this ŭ cut û urge
yo͞o abuse zh vision ə *a*bout, it*e*m, ed*i*ble, gall*o*p, circ*u*s

2. This passage comes from a psychology textbook.

> There are a number of different theories about the function of sleep. People deprived of sleep show some relatively minor physiological symptoms including hand tremors, double vision, and lowered pain threshold. Sleep loss especially affects the ability to do complex or difficult tasks. People totally deprived of sleep are apt to become confused and irritable although their personality is likely to remain intact. People awakened during REM (rapid eye movement) sleep become anxious and irritable and have trouble concentrating. They "catch up" on REM sleep when they are allowed to sleep uninterrupted.
>
> > *Psychology*
> > by Diane Papalia and Sally Olds

---

deprive (dĭ prīv′) v. To take something away from.

physiological (fĭz ē ə lŏj′ ĭ kəl) adj. Of or pertaining to the normal functioning of a living organism.

- Who or what is the passage about? On the line below, write a *word or phrase* that tells the subject matter:

---

3. This passage comes from a humanities textbook.

> **Fresco** is a wall-painting technique in which pigments suspended in water are applied to fresh, wet plaster. Michelangelo's Sistine Chapel frescoes are, of course, the best-known examples of this technique. Since the end result becomes part of the plaster wall rather than being painted on, fresco provides a long-lasting work. However, it is an extremely difficult process, and once the pigments are applied, no change can be made without replastering the entire section of the wall.
>
> > *Perceiving the Arts*
> > by Dennis Sporre

ă pat   ā pay   â care   ä father   ĕ pet   ē be   ĭ pit   ī tie   î pier   ŏ pot   ō toe
ô paw   oi noise   o͞o took   o͞o boot   ou out   th thin   *th* this   ŭ cut   û urge
yo͞o abuse   zh vision   ə *a*bout, it*e*m, ed*i*ble, gall*o*p, circ*u*s

---

fresco (frĕs′ kō) n. (The word *is* tells you that the author is explaining the meaning of the term in the passage.)

Michelangelo (mī kəl ăn′ jə lō) 1475-1564. Italian sculptor, painter, architect, and poet of the high Renaissance. (Don't forget that you can find out information about famous people in the dictionary too.)

Sistine Chapel (sĭs′ tēn chăp′ əl) A chapel in Rome, Italy, in the Vatican, the home of the Roman Catholic pope.

- Who or what is the passage about? On the line below, write a *word or phrase* that tells the subject matter:

---

4. This passage comes from a biology textbook.

> Cells are not static; they are dynamic. Drawings of cells and even microscopic slides of cells give us the impression that cells are inactive; actually, cells are constantly active. Pinocytotic and phagocytotic vesicles are constantly being formed, organelles are moving about, and division may be taking place. A vital part of this activity is constantly occurring chemical reactions, which collectively are termed the **metabolism** of the cell.
>
> *Inquiry into Life*
> by Sylvia Mader

---

static (stăt′ ĭk) adj. Having no motion; at rest; quiescent.

dynamic (dī năm′ ĭk) adj. Characterized by continuous change.

vesicle (vĕs′ ĭ kəl) n. A small bladderlike cell or cavity.

organelle (ôr gə nĕl′) n. A specialized part of a cell that resembles and functions as an organ.

metabolism (mə tăb′ ə lĭz əm) n. The set of constantly occurring chemical reactions within the cells of the body. (The phrase "are termed" tells you the author is giving you a definition. She has also boldfaced the word metabolism.)

ă pat ā pay â care ä father ĕ pet ē be ĭ pit ī tie î pier ŏ pot ō toe
ô paw oi noise ŏŏ took ōō boot ou out th thin *th* this ŭ cut û urge
yōō abuse zh vision ə *a*bout, it*e*m, ed*i*ble, gall*o*p, circ*u*s

●   Who or what is this passage about? On the line below, write a *word or phrase* that tells the subject matter:

_____

5. This passage comes from an economics textbook. Economics is defined for you in the passage.

> Given that wants are unlimited and resources are scarce, economics can be defined as *the science concerned with the problem of using or administering scarce resources (the means of producing) so as to attain the greatest or maximum fulfillment of society's unlimited wants (the goal of producing).* Economics is concerned with "doing the best with what we have." If our wants are virtually unlimited and our resources are scarce, we cannot satisfy all society's material wants. The next best thing is to achieve the greatest possible satisfaction of these wants. Economics is a science of efficiency—efficiency in the use of scarce resources.
>
> *Economics*
> by Campbell R. McConnell

_____

economics (ĕk ə nŏm′ ĭks) n. (The phrase "can be defined as" tells you that the author is explaining the meaning of the term. As a further help, the entire definition appears in italics and is stated again in the last sentence.)

material (mə tîr′ ē əl) adj. Pertaining to or affecting the enjoyment of physical well-being.

_____

●   Who or what is the passage about? On the line below, write a *word or phrase* that tells the subject matter:

_____

6. This passage comes from a U.S. government textbook.

Maternity Policy

Until recently, many companies refused to hire women because they might become pregnant and quit their jobs. Some companies

_____

ă pat   ā pay   â care   ä father   ĕ pet   ē be   ĭ pit   ī tie   î pier   ŏ pot   ō toe
ô paw   oi noise   o͝o took   o͞o boot   ou out   th thin   *th* this   ŭ cut   û urge
yo͞o abuse   zh vision   ə *a*bout, it*e*m, ed*i*ble, gall*o*p, circ*u*s

required women to remain single and fired them if they married. These policies have not been in effect since the 1950's but vestiges of the attitudes behind them remain. Until recently, on some airlines female flight attendants who became pregnant lost their seniority or their jobs. The Supreme Court has ruled that discriminatory policies against women of childbearing age violate the Civil Rights Act of 1964 and has ordered reinstatement and back pay for these women.

American Politics and Government
by Richard Pious

maternity (mə tûr′ nə tē) adj. Associated with pregnancy or childbirth.

vestige (věs′ tĭj) n. A trace or evidence of something that no longer exists.

seniority (sĕn yôr′ ə tē) n. Being higher in position than others of the same rank by reason of a longer span of service.

discriminatory (dĭs krĭm′ ə nə tôr ē) adj. Marked by or showing prejudice; biased.

reinstatement (rē ĭn stāt′ mənt) n. Restoring to a previous condition or position. (Here, giving women back the jobs they had been fired from.)

- Who or what is this passage about? On the line below, write a *word or phrase* that tells the subject matter:

7. This passage comes from a sociology textbook.

Organized crime is a secret, conspiratorial activity that generally evades law enforcement. Although precise information is lacking, a presidential commission estimated that organized crime operates in 80 percent of all cities with more than 1 million residents (President's Commission on Law Enforcement and Administration of Justice, 1976:191). Organized crime takes over legitimate businesses, gains

ă pat   ā pay   â care   ä father   ĕ pet   ē be   ĭ pit   ī tie   î pier   ŏ pot   ō toe
ô paw   oi noise   o͞o took   o͞o boot   ou out   th thin   *th* this   ŭ cut   û urge
y o͞o abuse   zh vision   ə *a*bout, it*e*m, ed*i*ble, gall*o*p, circ*u*s

influence over labor unions, corrupts public officials, intimidates witnesses in criminal trials, and even "taxes" merchants in exchange for "protection" (National Advisory Commission on Criminal Justice, 1976).

Sociology
by Richard Schaefer

---

conspiratorial (kən spîr ə tôr′ ē əl) adj. Of or pertaining to an agreement to perform together an illegal, treacherous, or evil act.

evade (ĭ vād′) v. To escape or avoid by cleverness or deceit.

legitimate (lə jĭt′ ə mĭt) adj. In compliance with the law.

intimidate (ĭn tĭm′ ə dāt) v. To frighten by threats.

- Who or what is this passage about? On the line below, write a *word or phrase* that tells the subject matter:

_____

8. This passage comes from a geology textbook. Geology is the scientific study of the origin, the history, and the structure of the earth.

Evolution is one of the most powerful of man's ideas, for it has revolutionized our way of thinking about natural and even social phenomena. Among great books, Darwin's *Origin of Species* probably ranks second only to the Bible in its impact on Western thought. After 1859, the basic concept of evolution, or change from one form into another through time, was also applied beyond biology. For example, studies of heat energy in the nineteenth century led physicists toward an evolutionary view of the physical realm. Today, science views nature as a whole as evolutionary, thus constantly changing in a series of linked but unique (nonrepeating) historic events.

Evolution in the Earth
by Robert Dott and Roger Batten

ă pat ā pay â care ä father ĕ pet ē be ĭ pit ī tie î pier ŏ pot ō toe
ô paw oi noise o͝o took o͞o boot ou out th thin *th* this ŭ cut û urge
yo͞o abuse zh vision ə *a*bout, it*e*m, ed*i*ble, gall*o*p, circ*u*s

evolution (ĕv ə lōo′ shən) n. (The words set off by commas after the word *evolution* tell you that the author is explaining the meaning of the term in this passage.)

revolutionize (rĕ və lōo′ shən īz) v. To bring about a radical change in.

phenomena (fĭ nŏm′ ə nə) n. (plural of phenomenon) Occurrences or facts directly perceptible by the senses.

origin (ôr′ ə jĭn) n. The source or cause.

species (spē′ shēz) n. A category of organisms capable of interbreeding.

concept (kŏn′ sĕpt) n. A thought or notion; a general idea or understanding, especially one derived from specific instances or occurrences.

• Who or what is this passage about? On the line below, write a *word or phrase* that tells the subject matter:

_____

ă pat   ā pay   â care   ä father   ĕ pet   ē be   ĭ pit   ī tie   î pier   ŏ pot   ō toe
ô paw   oi noise   ōō took   ōō boot   ou out   th thin   *th* this   ŭ cut   û urge
yōō abuse   zh vision   ə *a*bout, it*e*m, ed*i*ble, gall*o*p, circ*u*s

DETERMINING SUBJECT MATTER
Answer Key for Practice Exercises

Compare your answers for the practice exercises on pages 37–43 with the acceptable and unacceptable answers below.

Acceptable	Unacceptable (and Why)	
	Too General	**Too Specific**
1. Managers' lack of knowledge of business data processing	Computers Electronic computers	Business data processing Middle- and senior-level managers
2. Effects of sleep deprivation *or* Effects of sleep loss	Sleep Sleep deprivation Sleep loss	Physiological symptoms Personality and sleep loss REM sleep
3. Fresco *or* Definition of fresco *or* Fresco technique	Painting Painting technique	Sistine Chapel frescoes Difficulty of fresco painting
4. Cell activity *or* The dynamic nature of cells	Cells Metabolism	Cell metabolism Pinocytotic vesicles Phagocytotic vesicles

Acceptable	Unacceptable (and Why)	
	Too General	**Too Specific**
5. The definition of economics *or* The meaning of economics	Economics Social science	Unlimited wants Scarce resources
6. Discriminatory policies against women of childbearing age *or* Unfair maternity policies	Maternity policy Attitudes toward women Hiring policies	Civil Rights Act Female flight attendants
7. Organized crime	Conspiratorial activity Crime	Corrupting public officials Intimidation of witnesses
8. The concept of evolution *or* The impact of the notion of evolution *or* The power of the idea of evolution	Evolution	Darwin's *Origin of Species* Social phenomena

DETERMINING SUBJECT MATTER
Review Test

Determine the subject matter of the passages below.

1. This passage comes from a government textbook.

> ### What Is Government?
>
> *A Definition*
>
> Politics take place everywhere, but the focus of this text is on politics in government. We have so many governments in our own country—thousands of municipal and county governments—that the Census Bureau had to come up with a definition when counting them so that it would know what to include and what to leave out. Its definition: If an organization can make law or collect a tax, it is a government.
>
> *American Politics and Government*
> by Richard Pious

---

government (gŭv′ ĕrn mənt) n. (The subtitle "A Definition" tells you that the author is explaining the meaning of the term in the passage.)

municipal (myōō nĭs′ ə pəl) adj. Of or pertaining to a city or its government.

census (sĕn′ səs) n. An official count of the number of people in a population that is done at periodic intervals of time.

- Who or what is this passage about? On the line below, write a *word or phrase* that tells the subject matter:

ă pat ā pay â care ä father ĕ pet ē be ĭ pit ī tie î pier ŏ pot ō toe
ô paw oi noise ōō took ōō boot ou out th thin *th* this ŭ cut û urge
yōō abuse zh vision ə *a*bout, it*e*m, ed*i*ble, gall*o*p, circ*u*s

2. This passage comes from a sociology textbook.

Victimless Crimes

In white-collar or index crimes, people's economic or personal well-being is endangered against their will (or without their direct knowledge). Sociologists use the term **victimless crimes** to describe the willing exchange among adults of widely desired, but illegal, goods and services (Schur, 1965:169). Many Americans view gambling, prostitution, public drunkenness, and use of marijuana as victimless crimes in which there is no "victim" other than the offender. As a result, there has been pressure from some groups to decriminalize various activities which fall into the category of victimless crimes.

white-collar crime n. Crimes committed by salaried or professional individuals or corporations in the course of their daily activities (such as tax evasion, consumer fraud, bribery, etc.).

index crime n. The eight types of crimes reported annually by the FBI in the *Uniform Crime Report*. They are murder, rape, robbery, assault, burglary, theft, motor vehicle theft, and arson.

victimless crime n. (The phrase "Sociologists use the term" tells you that the author is explaining this term in the passage.)

decriminalize (dē krĭm′ ə nə līz) v. To make legal an activity that was formerly illegal.

- Who or what is this passage about? On the line below, write a *word or phrase* that tells the subject matter:

ă pat ā pay â care ä father ĕ pet ē be ĭ pit ī tie î pier ŏ pot ō toe
ô paw oi noise o͝o took o͞o boot ou out th thin *th* this ŭ cut û urge
yo͞o abuse zh vision ə *a*bout, it*e*m, ed*i*ble, gall*o*p, circ*u*s

3.   This passage comes from a U.S. history textbook.

Social Darwinism

   Defenders of business thus eagerly embraced the doctrine of Social Darwinism, which seemed to justify aggression in human society. Developed by English philosopher Herbert Spencer and preached in the United States by Yale professor William Graham Sumner, Social Darwinism loosely adapted Charles Darwin's theory of the origin of species to the principles of laissez-faire. Human society had evolved naturally, the Social Darwinists reasoned, and any interference with existing institutions would only hamper progress and aid the weak. In a free society operating according to the principle of survival of the fittest, power would flow naturally to the most capable. Property holding and acquisition were therefore sacred rights, and wealth was a mark of well-deserved power and responsibility. Civilization depended on this system, explained Sumner. "If we do not like the survival of the fittest," he wrote, "we have only one possible alternative, and that is survival of the unfittest." Clergymen, journalists, and popular writers also proclaimed the doctrine of Social Darwinism, assuring the public that progress would result only from natural evolution.

A Nation and a People
by Mary Beth Norton et al.

---

embrace (ĕm brās′) v. To take up; adopt; accept eagerly.

doctrine (dŏk′ trĭn) n. A principle or body of principles taught or presented for acceptance or belief.

Social Darwinism n. The application of Charles Darwin's theory of natural selection to society, that those who are best able to adapt to their environment prevail.

laissez-faire (lĕs ā fâr′) n. The doctrine that government should not interfere with commerce. [This is a French phrase that means "to allow (them) to do."]

ă pat   ā pay   â care   ä father   ĕ pet   ē be   ĭ pit   ī tie   î pier   ŏ pot   ō toe
ô paw   oi noise   ŏŏ took   ōō boot   ou out   th thin   *th* this   ŭ cut   û urge
yōō abuse   zh vision   ə *a*bout, it*e*m, ed*i*ble, gall*o*p, circ*u*s

hamper (hăm′ pər) v. To prevent the free movement, action, or progress of; impede.

acquisition (ăk wə zĭsh′ ən) n. The act of gaining possession of something.

- Who or what is this passage about? On the line below, write a *word or phrase* that tells the subject matter:

_____

4. This passage comes from a philosophy textbook.

Being Aware of Others

As in most ethical situations, making a true or false promise involves other people. Almost every time we ask "What should I do?" we are aware that other people are involved in our behavior. Why should someone ask himself "Is it right?" before making a false promise? It may be that he is afraid of being found out. He may, however, wonder whether it is fair to the other person. How we relate ourselves to others or how our behavior affects others makes up most of the subject matter of ethics. Being aware of others is more than wondering how our actions will affect them; we are also concerned about how the behavior of others will affect us. There is no satisfactory way for us to avoid the presence of other people. The most we can do is to try to arrange the rules of behavior, of ethics, in order to reduce the amount of friction and conflict and thereby achieve the greatest amount of harmony. Whether our actions are right and good will depend to a great extent on the effect they will have on others. Actions such as telling a falsehood, stealing, injuring, and killing are considered wrong most of the time because they result in varying degrees of harm to someone. They also produce reactions from the victims, who in effect say, "If it is right for you to do that to me, then I will not hesitate to do the same thing to you."

Elements of Philosophy
by Samuel Stumpf

ă pat ā pay â care ä father ĕ pet ē be ĭ pit ī tie î pier ŏ pot ō toe
ô paw oi noise ōō took ōō boot ou out th thin *th* this ŭ cut û urge
yōō abuse zh vision ə *a*bout, it*e*m, ed*i*ble, gall*o*p, circ*u*s

ethical (ĕth′ ĭ kəl) adj. Pertaining to principles of right and wrong. (In the passage, right and wrong *behavior*.)

friction (frĭk′ shən) n. Conflict or clash of dissimilar people, ideas, or interests obliged to coexist. (The word *conflict* in the same sentence is a clue.)

harmony (här′ mə nē) n. Agreement in feeling; pleasing interaction. (Here, the opposite of "friction.")

- Who or what is this passage about? On the line below, write a *word or phrase* that tells the subject matter:

5. This passage comes from a biology textbook.

Sexual Reproduction

Plants also reproduce sexually. This may come as a surprise to those who never thought of plants as being male and female. Sexual reproduction is properly defined as reproduction that requires gametes, often an egg and a sperm. In flowering plants, the sex organs are located in the flower.

Inquiry into Life
by Sylvia Mader

sexual reproduction n. (The words "is properly defined as" tell you that the author is explaining the meaning in the passage.)

gamete (gă′ mēt) n. A cell, from which a new organism can develop, that is capable of participating in fertilization. (In the passage, the author gives you a clue to the meaning when she mentions "an egg and a sperm.")

- Who or what is this passage about? On the line below, write a *word or phrase* that tells the subject matter:

ă pat ā pay â care ä father ĕ pet ē be ĭ pit ī tie î pier ŏ pot ō toe
ô paw oi noise o͞o took o͞o boot ou out th thin *th* this ŭ cut û urge
yo͞o abuse zh vision ə *a*bout, it*e*m, ed*i*ble, gall*o*p, circ*u*s

DETERMINING SUBJECT MATTER
Supplemental Exercises

Determine the subject matter of the passages below.

1. This passage is taken from an art appreciation book.

> **Design for the Suburbs: The Mall**
>
> "I shop; therefore I am." This witty paraphrase of René Descartes'
> famous philosophical statement ("I think, therefore I am") sums up
> the essence of the mall. Once upon a time people shopped only when
> they needed something. Now people visit the mall as an integral part
> of life, as entertainment. The mall has become the equivalent of the
> village green, a gathering place as comprehensive as the old medieval
> cathedral. Even if you don't need anything, even if you aren't going
> to shop today—come to the mall.
>
> *Living with Art*
> by Rita Gilbert and William McCarter

- Who or what is this passage about? On the line below, write a *word or phrase* that tells the subject matter:

_____

2. This selection comes from an American history textbook.

> Television changed the leisure habits of the American people, made
> them better informed on the news and issues of the day, and even mod-
> ified the patterns of American politics. In 1947 fewer than 10,000 peo-
> ple owned television sets with which they could view programs a few
> hours a day from a handful of stations. A decade later over 40,000,000
> sets in homes, hotels, and bars were tuned in to 457 stations.
>
> *The Essentials of American History Since 1865*
> by Richard Current et al.

- Who or what is this passage about? On the line below, write a *word or phrase* that tells the subject matter:

_____

3.   This passage is from a textbook on logic, a branch of philosophy.

> In criminal law the limits of permissible behavior are laid down. Crimes are defined, and punishments may be specified. A crime is an offense against the *public* order; the dispute in criminal proceedings is therefore between the state, the accuser, and the defendant, the accused. Murder, for example, is defined in the Federal Criminal Code as "the unlawful killing of a human being with malice aforethought." Charged with murder, a defendant on trial may deny that he was the killer, or he may admit the killing but contend that it was excusable, or he may deny the killing was premeditated, or he may contend that it was not malicious but accidental. Typically, a crime will involve both a wrongful *deed* and a wrongful *intention* or state of mind in the actor.
>
> *Introduction to Logic*
> by Irving Copi and Carl Cohen

- Who or what is this passage about? On the line below, write a *word or phrase* that tells the subject matter:

_____

4.   This passage is from a psychology textbook.

> The average number of hours that a healthy young adult sleeps nightly is $7\frac{1}{2}$. About 95 percent of us sleep somewhere between $6\frac{1}{2}$ to $8\frac{1}{2}$ hours. For the remaining 5 percent, some are short sleepers, requiring less than $6\frac{1}{2}$ hours, and some are long sleepers, requiring more than $8\frac{1}{2}$ hours.
>
> *Introduction to Psychology*
> by Ron Plotnik

- Who or what is this passage about? On the line below, write a *word or phrase* that tells the subject matter:

_____

5. This passage also comes from a psychology textbook. Write a word or a phrase that tells the subject matter of *each section.*

Gate Control Theory Stubbing a toe is guaranteed to produce a sharp pain. Gently rubbing the stubbed toe often lessens the pain. The theory that explains why rubbing helps is called the gate control theory (Melzack & Wall, 1965). According to this theory, your experience of pain depends upon the relative difference in activity between large-diameter sensory nerves, which carry pressure sensations, and small-diameter sensory nerves, which carry pain sensations. Presumably, when you stub your toe you feel pain because the small-diameter sensory nerves are primarily active. If you rub your toe, however, you activate the large-diameter nerves which inhibit or "close the gate" on the small-diameter ones. As a result, pain impulses are prevented from reaching the brain and your toe seems to feel better. The next time you experience pain from a mild bump or bruise, try gently rubbing the area to reduce the pain.

Attention and Emotion One of the co-authors of the gate control theory, Ronald Melzack, explains why football players sometimes play for hours with a broken bone (Warga, 1987). The football player's intense attentional and emotional state causes the brain to send impulses to the spinal cord. These impulses close the gate at the spinal cord so that incoming messages about the broken bone do not reach the brain. When the game is over, the player's attention is no longer on football and his emotional state calms down. This

Subject Matter

_____

_____

_____

_____

_____

_____

_____

_____

_____

_____

_____

decreases some of the brain's impulses to the spinal cord. The result is that the gate is opened, messages about the broken bone reach his brain, and he feels pain.

Besides attentional and emotional factors, the gate in the spinal cord can be closed by a number of conscious behaviors, thoughts, and images. For example, it is well documented that a person's perception of mild pain can be reduced if he or she focuses on some pleasant image (McCaul & Malott, 1984). This means that the next time you stub a toe, imagining a scene from your favorite movie will help decrease your pain.

Endorphins   In 1975, neuroscientists made a stunning discovery: the human body naturally produces chemicals with the same properties as morphine, the powerful pain-killing drug. These chemicals, called **endorphins** (en-DOOR-fins), are secreted by the pituitary gland in response to situations that evoke great fear and anxiety. In the laboratory, subjects showed increased secretion of endorphins when fear and anxiety were maximized, such as when receiving painful electric shock or holding their hands in ice water (Millan, 1986). In real life, patients showed increases in endorphins when having their tooth pulp touched, which is very painful, or when having their bandages removed from badly burned areas of the body (Szyfelbein et al., 1985). These and other studies indicate that one of the major functions of endorphins is to reduce pain.

Acupuncture   One kind of treatment for pain is **acupuncture.** During this procedure, the therapist inserts thin needles into various points on the body's surface, points often far removed from the site of pain. The needles are manually twirled or electrically stimulated. Ten to 20 minutes later, patients report an average of 50–80 percent reduction in pain. In comparison, patients reported an average of 30–35 percent reduction in pain produced by placebo conditions, such as having needles inserted without any stimulation.

There is considerable evidence that acupuncture may relieve acute or short-lived pain and, in some cases, chronic or long-lasting pain (Richardson & Vincent, 1986; Kreitler et al., 1987). One way that acupuncture works is by increasing the secretion of endorphins, which we know can reduce pain (Chen et al., 1986).

_____

_____

_____

_____

Behavioral and Cognitive Programs
Some people who suffer from chronic pain, such as that produced by a back injury, may get only limited or temporary relief from drugs or acupuncture. In these cases, psychologists have developed a number of behavioral and cognitive programs to help reduce pain. One behavioral program teaches the patient to monitor his or her muscle tension. As muscle tension increases, so does pain. Patients are taught relaxation techniques that reduce tension and thus reduce pain. Some chronic pain sufferers have learned that their com-

_____

_____

_____

_____

plaints often result in attention, administration of a drug, or avoidance of some unwanted social, family, or occupational responsibility. These kinds of complaints are called *pain behaviors.* Pain behaviors focus the patient's attention on his or her pain. A behavioral program can decrease the patient's pain behaviors by increasing the performance of *well behaviors.* Well behaviors, which include taking walks, exercising, relaxing, and doing hobbies, direct the patient's attention away from feelings of pain.

Besides encouraging well behaviors, therapists explain to chronic pain sufferers how stress can increase bodily arousal and thus increase their pain. Patients learn how to identify or monitor stressors in their environment. Once a stressor is identified, the patient learns behavioral or cognitive methods to cope with it rather than getting upset. Behavioral methods might include practicing relaxation techniques, which calm the body. Cognitive methods might include substituting positive self-statements, such as "I can do something about my pain," for negative ones, such as "Nothing I do helps my pain." A combination of behavioral and cognitive programs have proved very successful in reducing pain in chronic sufferers (Corey et al., 1987; Keefe & Gil, 1986; Shaw & Ehrlich, 1987).

Introduction to Psychology
by Ron Plotnik

6. This passage comes from an economics textbook.

> The 1987 World Series between the Minnesota Twins and the St. Louis Cardinals was played with Japanese gloves, Haitian baseballs, and Mexican bats. Most of the players were wearing shoes made in Korea, and all of them were playing on artificial grass made in Taiwan. Baseball, it seems, has become something less than the "all-American" game. In that same year, [American] consumers spent a lot of their income on French racing bikes, Japanese stereo equipment, Italian sweaters, Swiss chocolates, Colombian coffee, Scotch whiskey, and Venezuelan oil. Most of these goods could have been produced in the United States, and many were. Why did we purchase them from other countries? For that matter, why did the rest of the world buy computers, tractors, chemicals, airplanes, and wheat from us rather than produce such products for themselves? Is there some advantage to be gained from international trade? If so, what is the nature of that advantage, and who reaps the benefits?
>
> *The Economy Today*
> by Bradley Schiller

- Who or what is this passage about? On the line below, write a *word or phrase* that tells the subject matter:

_____

7. This passage comes from an information systems (computer science) textbook.

Computer Crime

Another very important area of the computer's impact on society is **computer crime.** Several sensational computer crimes have been uncovered. Most experts, however, maintain that the computer crime discovered thus far is only the tip of the iceberg; most of it remains hidden. A computer system that is not well controlled provides almost unlimited opportunities for a person wanting to steal funds or goods and conceal the theft. The amount of money taken in an average armed robbery is very small compared with the amounts taken through computer theft. Often, those who perpetrate a computer crime are not prosecuted when they are caught. Managers sometimes feel that the organization would be embarrassed if the public learned of the crime. Perhaps the public would lose confidence in the firm's ability to function effectively.

Information Systems in Business: An Introduction
by James O. Hicks, Jr.

- Who or what is this passage about? On the line below, write a *word or phrase* that tells the subject matter:

_____

8. This passage also comes from a business information systems textbook. Write a word or a phrase that tells the subject matter of *each section.*

Voice Mail

Since the human voice can be *digitized,* stored, and transmitted by computers, many firms have installed voice-mail capabilities. **Voice mail** has the same advantages as electronic mail. A voice message may be stored or routed to many people on a distribution list. However, voice mail has one major advantage over electronic mail. Voice mail is easier to use because typing skills are not necessary and it is faster to talk than it is to type a message. Voice mail is often installed as a part of digital switches, which are computer-based telephone networks where voice, image, text, and data are transmitted and stored by the digital network. This digital network is, in effect, a computer network.

These systems provide other capabilities, such as camping on a person's phone. Camping on is useful when you are trying to reach someone by phone, but the line is busy. With camping on, the telephone digital switch rings both the caller and receiver's phone simultaneously once the receiver's phone becomes free.

Subject Matter

_____

_____

_____

_____

Computer and Video Conferencing

Computer conferencing is a type of electronic mail. A number of individuals can exchange information, data, and comments interactively over a computer network, thus removing the necessity for long-distance travel to a conference. These conferences may occur over a specified short period of time, or they may last for days or even weeks.

Another form of long-distance conferencing is **video conferencing,** where two-way TV systems are set up among all sites of the conference. Thus, individuals can interact both verbally and visually with the other participants. Many firms have their own video-conferencing facilities. Others rent them from hotels and telephone companies.

Electronic Calendaring

Office automation systems also provide **electronic calendaring** capabilities. The appointment calendars of employees and resources, such as conference rooms, are kept on the computer so that they can be accessed by people throughout the organization. Through workstations, personnel can reserve conference rooms and schedule employees to attend meetings.

Facsimile Transmission

Facsimile transmission (usually called **fax**) has been in existence since the 1960s. In the late 1970s and 1980s it became more popular as the capabilities of fax machines increased and their costs decreased. These machines, costing as little as $500, scan a document bit by bit and transmit a complete image of the document (including photos, graphics, and text) to remote locations over standard telephone networks. At the receiving end, the facsimile machine creates an exact copy of the document transmitted. Typical transmission rates are one page per minute, but these are increasing. Facsimile machines are as easy to operate as a copying machine and enable the transmission of documents anywhere in the world that has telephone lines and a receiving fax machine. Personal computers can also transmit text and images directly to a receiving fax machine.

Fax machines have been a factor in increasing the number of people who work at home. With a fax machine, a personal computer, and a copier, many people can perform their office work at home.

Image Storage and Retrieval

One of the most difficult problems in an office is storage of paper documents. Paper files can get very voluminous, and the time necessary to retrieve and refile documents can be substantial. Copies of paper documents are often called **images.** Companies have long used microfiche and microfilm images to reduce the volume of paper storage. However, retrieving and reading microfiche and microfilm can be slow and expensive. Microfiche systems are being combined with computer retrieval of microfiche images to decrease the time and expense of image retrieval and refiling.

In addition, systems are now available that will scan documents and convert them to digital code (digitize them) so that their images can be stored on regular computer disks rather than on microfiche. These documents can be quickly retrieved and displayed on high-resolution graphics terminals. This digital image storage and retrieval of documents is certainly the direction of the future in this area. Eventually, very few paper documents will be stored.

Forms Processing

Companies have traditionally used forms for a great deal of their internal transmission of data from one person to another. Thus, employees feel very comfortable filling out forms. In recent years, **forms-processing** software has become available that automates filling out forms as well as the transmission and storage processes. Forms that look very much like paper forms can be created on computer workstations, and employees can fill them out.

Forms-processing systems can be front ends to data-base management systems, where the input data are captured and processed by data-base management systems in a traditional way. Or, the forms can be transmitted and stored as if they were paper forms.

Forms-processing systems are an example of a concept known as direct manipulation of objects of interest. Under this concept, computers allow personnel to directly manipulate objects in a fashion similar to the way they did these tasks prior to computers. Thus, forms-processing systems allow personnel to directly manipulate forms or directly use forms on the computer. Human/computer interfaces are moving toward this concept of direct manipulation of objects of interest.

Information Systems in Business:
An Introduction
James O. Hicks, Jr.

9.   This passage is taken from a computer science textbook.

In November 1988 a computer virus spread across the United States affecting the performance of thousands of computers. Included were computers in a nuclear weapons lab, the Pentagon, and several major universities. Very little information was lost, but the virus inconvenienced many thousands of computer users. A **computer virus** is a program that is hidden in other programs in the system. The virus is written by a programmer who intends to corrupt or interfere with users of computer systems. Usually the virus program is hidden on a network that many computer users access regularly.

Understanding Computers
by Don Cassel

●   Who or what is this passage about? On the line below, write a *word or phrase* that tells the subject matter:

10. This passage comes from an art appreciation textbook.

> Who is creative? Are artists more creative than other people? If so, how did they get that way? What is creativity? Does everyone start out having it and do some people then lose it? Is there any way to get it if you don't have it? Can a person become more creative? Less creative? These are fascinating questions to which, unfortunately, there are no definite answers. We can approach the problem by looking at examples and perhaps gain some insight, but nobody will ever write the rules of creativity.
>
> *Living with Art*
> by Rita Gilbert and William McCarter

- Who or what is this passage about? On the line below, write a *word or phrase* that tells the subject matter:

_____

CHAPTER

2

LOCATING DIRECTLY STATED MAIN IDEAS

1

Determining Subject Matter

2

Locating Directly Stated Main Ideas

3

Formulating Implied Main Ideas

4

Identifying Supporting Details

5

Recognizing Authors' Writing Patterns

6

Applying Comprehension
Skills to Longer Passages

7

Remembering College Textbook
Material through Organizing

8

Thinking Critically as You Read

INTRODUCTION

As you learned in Chapter 1, when you read a paragraph in a college textbook, you should determine its subject matter. To do this, you learned to ask yourself, "Who or what is the passage about?" and to use clues to help you determine the subject matter: a heading, a word in the passage in bold print, or a word or phrase that is used more than once in the passage. Moreover, you learned that a passage might begin with a word or phrase that is then referred to throughout the passage by a pronoun or other words. Finally, you learned you could ask yourself what subject all the sentences in the passage have in common.

Once you have determined who or what the paragraph is about—its subject matter—you must then ask yourself, "What does the author want me to know or *understand* about the subject matter?" The answer to this question is the *main idea* of the paragraph.

The mental processes you use in determining the main idea of a paragraph are the same mental processes you see in other aspects of your daily life. For example, if you walk up to some friends who are talking, you immediately ask yourself.

"What's going on?"

"Who or what are they talking about?"

In other words, what is the subject matter?

"What is it they have to say *about* that person or thing?"

In other words, what is the main idea?

Your friends might, for example, be discussing last Saturday's football game (the subject matter). They were disappointed that the team played so badly (the main idea, or what it is they have to say about the football team.) The ***stated main idea*** of a paragraph is the most important point the author wants you to understand about the subject matter of the paragraph. You may hear a stated main idea sentence referred to as a *topic sentence*. The main idea sentence and the topic sentence are the same thing.

Effective readers always seek the main ideas when they are reading textbooks. They do this in order to identify the most important idea in each paragraph. It also helps them understand how the information in the other sentences relates to the main idea of the paragraph. In this chapter, you will learn to locate the main idea when it is directly stated as one of the sentences of the paragraph. (Later, in Chapter 3, you will learn what to do

> A **stated main idea** is the sentence that tells the most important point the author wants you to understand about the subject matter of the paragraph. The stated main idea sentence is also called the *topic sentence*.

68

when the main idea sentence is expressed indirectly. That is, you will learn how to combine ideas to formulate the main idea in your own words.)

THE IMPORTANCE OF DETERMINING THE MAIN IDEA

Why are skillful readers concerned about determining the main idea of each paragraph? How can determining the main idea help you as a reader? *The main idea is the one central idea the author wants you to understand about the subject matter.*

There are several additional advantages to determining the main ideas of the paragraphs you are reading. First, actively seeking main ideas will help you focus your concentration on what you are reading. This will make you less likely to be distracted since you will have a purpose for reading. Second, since the main idea is the "glue" that holds the details of the paragraph together, you will be able to recall many more of the details that support the main idea. Third, you will find that determining the main idea is an aid in studying. For example, you will be able to identify and mark important information in your textbooks. You will be able to take effective notes and outline material more efficiently. Identifying the main ideas of separate paragraphs will also enable you to write effective summaries of longer selections. Finally, you may discover that you can write more complete and intelligent answers on essay tests, since essay questions are often based on a textbook's main points.

EXPLANATION AND EXAMPLES

Writers present their ideas paragraph by paragraph, with one main idea in each paragraph.

In a paragraph, there is usually one sentence which *states* the main idea. When there is such a sentence, the reading task is easier for the reader, but the reader must still determine *which* sentence states the main idea. The main idea sentence is often at the beginning of the paragraph, but it may be at the end of the paragraph or even somewhere in between.

How can you determine if there is a stated main idea sentence? Follow these steps:

1. Read the paragraph carefully.

2. Determine the subject matter of the paragraph by asking yourself, "Who or what is the passage about?"

3. Ask yourself: "What is it that the author wants me to *understand* about this subject?"

4. Search for a single sentence in the paragraph that answers the question, "What is it the author wants me to *understand* about this subject?" A sentence that answers that question is the main idea of the paragraph.

Occasionally you will find it a challenge to locate the stated main idea sentence. Even experienced college-level readers sometimes struggle to determine the main idea of a difficult paragraph. Not even the most skillful readers are able to immediately identify the main idea of *every* paragraph they read. Once they realize that they are not understanding the author's main point, though, they stop to *think* about what they have read. If necessary, they reread the paragraph and take additional time to try to determine the main idea.

Rather than feeling discouraged and giving up, successful readers try again. Rather than saying to themselves, "I'm no good at reading" or "I'm no good at main ideas," they say, "I'm having difficulty getting the main idea of *this* paragraph, and I'll have to take some extra steps to figure it out." When you are having trouble with a difficult paragraph, don't give up!

Locating a Main Idea Sentence at the Beginning of the Paragraph

Often, the first sentence of the paragraph states the main idea. Here is a paragraph whose subject matter is the *Charlie the tramp costume created by the actor Charlie Chaplin.* The paragraph is taken from a textbook on understanding films. Since we have already told you the subject matter, you can now read the paragraph and ask yourself, "What does the author want me to *understand* about Charlie Chaplin's tramp costume?" The sentence that answers that question will be the main idea sentence of the paragraph.

> Perhaps the most famous costume in film history is Chaplin's Charlie the tramp outfit. The costume is an indication of both class and character conveying the complex mixture of vanity and dash that makes Charlie appealing. The moustache, derby hat, and cane all

suggest the fastidious dandy. The cane is used to give the impression of self-importance as Charlie swaggers confidently before a hostile world. But the baggy trousers several sizes too large, the oversized shoes, the too-tight coat—all these suggest Charlie's insignificance and poverty. Chaplin's view of mankind is symbolized by that costume: vain, absurd, and—finally—poignantly vulnerable.

Understanding Movies
by Louis Giannetti

complex (kəm plĕks′) adj. Consisting of interconnected parts; involved or intricate; complicated.

dash (dăsh) n. Spirited style; vigor; verve.

fastidious (făs stĭd′ ē əs) adj. Careful in all details; exacting; meticulous.

dandy (dăn′ dē) n. A man who affects extreme elegance in his clothes and manners.

swagger (swăg′ ər) v. To walk or conduct oneself with an insolent air; to strut; to brag or bluster.

poignantly (poin′ yənt lē) adv. Appealingly, touchingly.

vulnerable (vŭl′ nər ə bəl) adj. Unprotected from danger; susceptible to injury.

You will notice that the author's *first sentence* states the most important point that he wants you to understand about Charlie Chaplin's Charlie the tramp costume. All the other sentences in the paragraph pertain to the costume, what it symbolized to Chaplin, and the reason for its fame. Therefore, the main idea of the paragraph is: *Perhaps the most famous costume in film history is Chaplin's Charlie the tramp outfit.*

Here is a passage from a business textbook that was presented earlier. Its subject matter is the electronic nature of computers. To determine the main idea of the paragraph, ask yourself: What does the author want me to *understand* about the electronic nature of computers?

ă pat ā pay â care ä father ĕ pet ē be ĭ pit ī tie î pier ŏ pot ō toe
ô paw oi noise o͞o took o͞o boot ou out th thin th this ŭ cut û urge
yo͞o abuse zh vision ə about, item, edible, gallop, circus

The electronic nature of computers gives them several important attributes. First, computers are extremely fast at processing instructions, that is, at performing calculations and at making logical comparisons. Second, computers are extremely accurate in their processing; rarely does a computer make an electronic mistake that it does not catch itself and signal to the computer operator. Almost all errors in computer data processing are caused by faulty programs prepared by humans. Third, computers are extremely reliable; being primarily electronic and without moving parts, they seldom have failures.

Principles of Management Information Systems
by George M. Scott

attribute (ăt′ rə byo͞ot) n. A quality or characteristic belonging to a person or thing; a distinctive feature.

processing (prŏs′ ĕs ĭng) v. Completing the steps of a procedure.

program (prō′ grăm) n. A procedure for solving problems that is coded for a computer.

- What is the most important point the author wants you to *understand* about the subject matter? Locate the main idea *sentence* that answers this question and copy the sentence here:

_____

_____

_____

_____

As you already know, the subject matter of this passage is *the electronic nature of computers*. The first sentence states the most important point the author wants you to understand about the electronic nature of computers: *The electronic nature of computers gives them several important attributes.* This is the main idea of this paragraph.

ă pat ā pay â care ä father ĕ pet ē be ĭ pit ī tie î pier ŏ pot ō toe
ô paw oi noise o͝o took o͞o boot ou out th thin *th* this ŭ cut û urge
yo͞o abuse zh vision ə *a*bout, it*e*m, ed*i*ble, gall*o*p, circ*u*s

Locating a Main Idea Sentence at the End of the Paragraph

Sometimes the *last sentence* in a paragraph states the main idea, as in this sample paragraph from a psychology textbook. The subject matter is *forgetting*. Read the paragraph, and ask yourself, "What does the author want me to *understand* about forgetting?"

> How much do you remember of what you learned over the past academic year? How many of your high school classmates could you call by name right now? How many times a week do you forget appointments, chores, and other details of everyday life? Before you groan in self-disgust, take heart at how normal you are. We all forget all kinds of things all the time.
>
> *Psychology*
> by Diane Papalia and Sally Olds

---

academic (ăk ə dĕm´ ĭk) adj. Pertaining to a school.

In this paragraph, the beginning sentences give examples of the types of things people forget. In the last sentence, the authors express the main point that they are making: *We all forget all kinds of things all the time.* Therefore, it is the main idea of the paragraph.

Here is a biology passage you encountered earlier. The subject matter is *osmosis*. What does the author want you to *understand* about osmosis? Read the passage to locate a sentence that answers this question.

> The diffusion of water across a selectively permeable membrane has been given a special term: it is called *osmosis*. **Osmosis is defined as the net movement of water molecules from the area of greater concentration of water to the area of lesser concentration of water across a selectively permeable membrane.**
>
> *Inquiry into Life*
> by Sylvia Mader

ă pat ā pay â care ä father ĕ pet ē be ĭ pit ī tie î pier ŏ pot ō toe
ô paw oi noise o͞o took o͞o boot ou out th thin *th* this ŭ cut û urge
yo͞o abuse zh vision ə *a*bout, it*e*m, ed*i*ble, gall*o*p, circ*u*s

---

permeable (pûr′ mē ə bəl) adj. Capable of being penetrated; having openings that something can spread through.

osmosis (ŏs mō′ səs) n. (The words "is defined as" tell you that the author is explaining the meaning of the term in the passage.)

net (nĕt) adj. Total.

molecule (mŏl′ ə kyo͞ol) n. The simplest structural unit that displays the characteristic physical and chemical properties of a compound.

concentration (kŏn sən trā′ shən) n. The amount of specified substance in a unit amount of another substance.

- What is the most important point the author wants you to *understand* about the subject matter? Locate the main idea *sentence* that answers this question and copy the sentence here:

_____

_____

_____

_____

The last sentence of the paragraph states the most important point the author wants you to *understand* about osmosis—its definition: *Osmosis is defined as the net movement of water molecules from the area of greater concentration of water to the area of lesser concentration of water across a selectively permeable membrane.* The first sentence simply introduces the term osmosis. The second sentence focuses on what osmosis is, and is a *complete* definition.

When the Last Sentence of a Paragraph Is a Stated Conclusion

At the end of a paragraph, authors sometimes state an important ***conclusion*** that is based on the information in the paragraph. This information is so important that they want to be sure that all readers recognize it and understand it. When a paragraph contains a stated conclusion, it typically appears at the end of the paragraph. This important conclusion is

---

ă pat   ā pay   â care   ä father   ĕ pet   ē be   ĭ pit   ī tie   î pier   ŏ pot   ō toe
ô paw   oi noise   o͞o took   o͞o boot   ou out   th thin   *th* this   ŭ cut   û urge
yo͞o abuse   zh vision   ə *a*bout, it*e*m, ed*i*ble, gall*o*p, circ*u*s

often the main idea of the paragraph, so you should pay special attention to it.

To help you recognize a stated conclusion, authors frequently use certain signal words. These are some of the words and phrases that indicate a conclusion at the end of a paragraph:

- In conclusion
- Consequently
- Therefore
- Finally

- Thus
- As a result
- So
- For these reasons

Consider this passage from an economics textbook.

Energy in its various forms, from heat to gasoline, plays a larger part in the budget of poor families than well-to-do families. This is because energy is largely used for essentials. For families in the lowest ten percent of households, energy accounts for a full third of household expenditures; whereas for households in the top ten percent, it absorbs only five percent of household expenses. Therefore, a jump in energy costs will penalize the poor much more severely than the rich.

Five Economic Challenges
by Robert Heilbroner and Lester Thurow

As you can see, the subject matter of this paragraph is the *effect of energy costs on poor and rich families.* The last sentence, the main idea, states the most important point the authors want you to *understand* about the effects of energy costs on poor and rich families: *Therefore, a jump in energy costs will penalize the poor much more severely than the rich.* This main idea sentence is also the authors' stated conclusion and is easily identified as a conclusion by the signal word "therefore."

Locating a Main Idea Sentence within the Paragraph

Occasionally, the main idea sentence is neither the first nor the last sentence but one of the other sentences in the paragraph. In this example from a sociology textbook, the subject matter is *victimless crimes.* (You will recognize this passage from Chapter 1.) Read the paragraph again, and ask yourself, "What does the author want me to *understand* about victimless crimes?"

> In white-collar or index crimes people's economic or personal well-being is endangered against their will (or without their direct knowledge). Sociologists use the term **victimless crimes** to describe the willing exchange among adults of widely desired, but illegal, goods and services (Schur, 1965:169). Many Americans view gambling, prostitution, public drunkenness, and use of marijuana as victimless crimes in which there is no "victim" other than the offender.
>
> *Sociology*
> by Richard Schaefer

---

white-collar crime n. Crimes committed by salaried or professional individuals or corporations in the course of their daily activities (such as tax evasion, consumer fraud, bribery, etc.)

index crime n. The eight types of crimes reported annually by the FBI in the *Uniform Crime Report.* They are murder, rape, robbery, assault, burglary, theft, motor vehicle theft, and arson.

victimless crime n. (The phrase "Sociologists use the term" tells you that the author is explaining this word in the passage.)

The author wants you to understand the term *victimless crime* as sociologists define it. The second sentence states the main idea: *Sociologists use the term* **victimless crimes** *to describe the willing exchange among adults of widely desired, but illegal, goods and services.*

How can you be sure that you have correctly identified a main idea sentence? One way is to see what purpose each of the other sentences in the paragraph serves. The first sentence in the passage above merely describes two other types of crimes (white collar and index crimes) that victimless crimes are contrasted with. The last sentence simply lists types of victimless crimes. These sentences support the main idea.

ă pat ā pay â care ä father ĕ pet ē be ĭ pit ī tie î pier ŏ pot ō toe
ô paw oi noise ŏŏ took ōō boot ou out th thin *th* this ŭ cut û urge
yōō abuse zh vision ə *a*bout, it*e*m, ed*i*ble, gall*o*p, circ*u*s

Here is another passage from a sociology textbook that you read in Chapter 1. The subject matter of this passage is *status*. What does the author want you to *understand* about status? Read the paragraph to locate the main idea sentence that answers this question.

> When we speak of an individual's "status" in casual conversation, the term usually conveys connotations of influence, wealth, and fame. However, sociologists use *status* to refer to any of the full range of socially defined positions within a large group or society—from the lowest to the highest position. Within American society, a person can occupy the status of president of the United States, fruit picker, son or daughter, violinist, teenager, resident of Minneapolis, dental technician, or neighbor.
>
> *Sociology*
> by Richard Schaefer

---

status (stā′ təs, stăt′ əs) n. Any of the full range of socially defined positions within a large group or society, from the lowest to the highest position. (The phrase "to refer to" tells you that the author is defining the term.)

- What is the most important point the author wants you to *understand* about the subject matter? Locate the main idea *sentence* that answers this question and copy the sentence here:

_____

_____

_____

_____

The second sentence of the paragraph states the most important point the author wants you to *understand* about status: *However, sociologists use* **status** *to refer to any of the full range of socially defined positions within a large group or society—from the lowest to the highest position.* The other sentences in the paragraph explain more about status.

ă pat ā pay â care ä father ĕ pet ē be ĭ pit ī tie î pier ŏ pot ō toe
ô paw oi noise o͞o took o͞o boot ou out th thin *th* this ŭ cut û urge
y o͞o abuse zh vision ə *a*bout, it*e*m, ed*i*ble, gall*o*p, circ*u*s

CHAPTER 2

LOCATING DIRECTLY STATED MAIN IDEAS
Chapter Summary

The **stated main idea** is the sentence that tells you the most important point the author wants you to understand about the subject matter of the paragraph. The stated main idea sentence is also called the *topic sentence*.

When you read, locate the ***stated main idea*** of a paragraph by asking yourself these questions in order:

1. What is the subject matter? In other words, who or what is the passage about

2. What does the author want me to *understand* about the subject matter? (The answer to this question is the main idea.)

3. Does the first or last sentence of the paragraph answer the question, "What does the author want me to *understand* about the subject matter?"

    At the end of a paragraph, watch for signal words that may introduce an important stated conclusion. This conclusion may also be the stated main idea sentence. Some signal conclusion words are:

    - In conclusion
    - Consequently
    - Therefore
    - Finally
    - Thus
    - As a result
    - So
    - For these reasons

4. If neither the first sentence nor the last sentence states the main idea, is there a sentence within the body of the paragraph that states the main idea?

How can you check to see if you have actually located the stated main idea sentence? You should do the following:

- Check to be sure the sentence contains the subject matter.

- Check to be sure the sentence states the most important point about the subject matter.

- Check to see that the sentence you selected is general enough to cover *all* the important information in the paragraph.

Don't assume you can take a shortcut to finding the main idea sentence by glancing only at the first and last sentences of a paragraph. Also, don't assume that the final sentence is the main idea sentence merely because it contains one of the conclusion signal words listed above. You must read the *entire* paragraph in order to make an accurate determination of the main idea. Unless you read the entire paragraph, you may miss the stated main idea sentence within the paragraph.

You may be tempted to select a sentence as the main idea sentence merely because it has a boldface word in it. The main idea sentence *may* contain a boldface word; however, terms are often boldface because they are being introduced and defined for the first time—not because they appear in the main idea sentence. It is necessary, of course, to understand these terms before you can understand the main idea.

When a passage seems difficult, you may be tempted to select a sentence as a main idea just because it contains familiar or interesting information. But these are not the right reasons for selecting a sentence as the main idea sentence. To be the main idea, a sentence must always answer the question, "What does the author want me to *understand* about the subject matter?"

CHAPTER 2

LOCATING DIRECTLY STATED MAIN IDEAS
Practice Exercises

For each passage, determine the subject matter and then locate the main idea sentence. *Copy the complete main idea sentence exactly as it appears in the paragraph.*

1. This paragraph comes from a management textbook.

Robert Owen

One of the most successful industrialists of the early nineteenth century, Robert Owen was an outstanding pioneer of management. During the period 1800 to 1828, Owen carried out what was then regarded as an unprecedented experiment in the group of textile mills he managed in Scotland. It is not without good reason that he has been referred to as "the father of modern personnel management."

Management
by Harold Koontz et al.

---

pioneer (pī ə nîr′) n. An innovator; one who begins or introduces something new.

unprecedented (ŭn prĕs′ ə dĕn tĭd) adj. Without precedent; without previous occurrence.

textile (tĕks′ tĭl, tĕks′ tīl) adj. Pertaining to weaving or woven fabrics or their manufacture.

ă pat   ā pay   â care   ä father   ĕ pet   ē be   ĭ pit   ī tie   î pier   ŏ pot   ō toe
ô paw   oi noise   ŏŏ took   ōō boot   ou out   th thin   *th* this   ŭ cut   û urge
yōō abuse   zh vision   ə *a*bout, it*e*m, ed*i*ble, gall*o*p, circ*u*s

- Who or what is the passage about? On the line below, write a *word or phrase* that tells the subject matter:

_____

- What is the most important point the authors want you to *understand* about the subject matter? Locate the main idea *sentence* that answers this question and copy the sentence here:

_____

_____

_____

_____

2. The source of this paragraph is a sociology textbook.

> In American society, newspapers, television, and radio are the usual sources of information about certain groups and their problems. However, while the basic function of journalists is to report the news, sociologists bring a different type of understanding to such issues. The perspective of sociology involves seeing through the outside appearance of people's actions and organizations.
>
> *Sociology*
> by Richard Schaefer

_____

perspective (pər spĕk′ tĭv) n. The relationship of different parts of a subject to each other and to a whole.

_____

- Who or what is the passage about? On the line below, write a *word or phrase* that tells the subject matter:

_____

ă pat ā pay â care ä father ĕ pet ē be ĭ pit ī tie î pier ŏ pot ō toe
ô paw oi noise o͝o took o͞o boot ou out th thin *th* this ŭ cut û urge
yo͞o abuse zh vision ə *a*bout, it*e*m, ed*i*ble, gall*o*p, circ*u*s

- What is the most important point the author wants you to *understand* about the subject matter? Locate the main idea *sentence* that answers this question and copy the sentence here:

_____

_____

_____

_____

3. This paragraph comes from a philosophy textbook.

Why do we engage in philosophy? What is there about human beings that leads us to engage in reflective thought, thinking about questions which do not appear to produce practical results? It could be argued that in the long run philosophical thought does produce widespread practical consequences. In the political realm, for example, the writings of John Locke significantly influenced the development of American democracy, while the theories of Karl Marx have brought into being a radically new form of government. It could also be said that what separates us from the animal world and from uncivilized human beings is just this intellectual endeavor, which could be justified as valuable even if only for its own sake. But there is a deeper reason for engaging in philosophy, and that is that we simply cannot turn away from certain questions which constantly confront us.

Elements of Philosophy
by Samuel Stumpf

_____

reflective (rĭ flĕk′ tĭv) adj. Pertaining to careful consideration.

consequence (kŏn′ sə kwĕns) n. An effect; result.

endeavor (ĕn dĕv′ ər) n. A concerted effort; an earnest attempt.

justify (jŭs′ tə fī) n. To show to be right or valid.

ă pat ā pay â care ä father ĕ pet ē be ĭ pit ī tie î pier ŏ pot ō toe
ô paw oi noise ōō took ōō boot ou out th thin *th* this ŭ cut û urge
yōō abuse zh vision ə *a*bout, it*e*m, ed*i*ble, gall*o*p, circ*u*s

constitution (kŏn stə tŌŌ′ shən) n. The composition of something made of a number of parts; makeup.

predispose (prē dĭs pōz′) v. To put into a certain frame of mind for something.

• Who or what is the passage about? On the line below, write a *word or phrase* that tells the subject matter:

_____

• What is the most important point the author wants you to *understand* about the subject matter? Locate the main idea *sentence* that answers this question and copy the sentence here:

_____

_____

_____

_____

4. This selection comes from an economics textbook.

The Meaning of Inflation

What is inflation? *Inflation is a rising general level of prices.* This does not mean, of course, that *all* prices are necessarily rising. Even during periods of rather rapid inflation, some specific prices may be relatively constant and others actually falling. For example, although the United States experienced high rates of inflation in the 1970s and the early 1980s, the prices of such products as video recorders, digital watches, and personal computers actually declined. Indeed, as we shall see momentarily, one of the major sore spots of inflation lies in the fact that prices tend to rise very unevenly. Some spring upward; others ascend at a more leisurely pace; others do not rise at all.

Economics: Principles, Problems, and Policies
by Campbell McConnell and Stanley Brue

ă pat ā pay â care ä father ĕ pet ē be ĭ pit ī tie î pier ŏ pot ō toe
ô paw oi noise ŌŌ took ŌŌ boot ou out th thin *th* this ŭ cut û urge
yŌŌ abuse zh vision ə *a*bout, it*e*m, ed*i*ble, gall*o*p, circ*u*s

inflation (ĭn flā′ shən) n. (The word "is" in the second sentence tells you that the authors are defining the term in the passage.)

ascend (ə sĕnd′) v. To go or come up; to rise.

- Who or what is the passage about? On the line below, write a *word or phrase* that tells the subject matter:

_____

- What is the most important point the authors want you to *understand* about the subject matter? Locate the main idea *sentence* that answers this question and copy the sentence here:

_____

_____

_____

_____

5. This passage is taken from a music appreciation textbook.

Music in the Middle Ages (450–1450)

A thousand years of European history are spanned by the phrase *Middle Ages*. The "dark ages"—a time of migration, upheavals, and wars—began about 450 with the disintegration of the Roman Empire. But the later Middle Ages (until about 1450) were a period of cultural growth: romanesque churches and monasteries (1000–1150) and Gothic cathedrals (1150–1450) were constructed, towns grew, and universities were founded.

Music: An Appreciation
by Roger Kamien

ă pat ā pay â care ä father ĕ pet ē be ĭ pit ī tie î pier ŏ pot ō toe
ô paw oi noise o͞o took o͞o boot ou out th thin *th* this ŭ cut û urge
yo͞o abuse zh vision ə *about, item, edible, gallop, circus*

- Who or what is the passage about? On the line below, write a *word or phrase* that tells the subject matter:

  _____

- What is the most important point the author wants you to *understand* about the subject matter? Locate the main idea *sentence* that answers this question and copy the sentence here:

  _____

  _____

  _____

  _____

  _____

6. This paragraph comes from a geology textbook.

An Artist Saw the Way

The most important early record of a careful interpretation of fossils was that left by the Italian genius Leonardo da Vinci, one of the most original natural philosophers of the early Renaissance. About A.D. 1500 he recognized that fossil shells in northern Italy represented ancient marine life even though found in strata many miles from the nearest seashore. In opposition to the popular view that fossils had been washed in by the biblical Deluge, he argued that clams could not travel hundreds of kilometers in 40 days. Many of the shells certainly could not have been washed inland great distances because they were too fragile. He also pointed out that the associations or assemblages of different kinds of fossils found in these ancient strata were still intact and resembled living communities of organisms that he observed at the coast. Leonardo further noted that there were many distinct layers that were fossil-rich and that these were separated by completely barren, unfossiliferous ones. This suggested to him, by reasoning from seasonal flooding of rivers, that there were many events recorded rather than a single, worldwide deluge.

Evolution of the Earth
by Robert Dott and Roger Batten

fossil (fŏs′ əl) n. A remnant or trace of an organism of a past geological age, such as a skeleton, footprint, or leaf imprint embedded in the earth's crust.

Renaissance (rĕn′ ə säns) n. The revival of classical art, literature, and learning that originated in Italy in the fourteenth century and later spread throughout Europe.

marine (mə rēn′) adj. Of or pertaining to the sea.

strata (strā′ tə, stră′ tə) pl. n. Layers of rock having the same composition throughout.

deluge (dĕl′ yōoj) n. A great flood; heavy downpour.

assemblage (ə sĕm′ blĭj) n. A collection of things.

barren (băr′ ən) adj. Empty; lacking.

unfossiliferous (ŭn fŏs ə lĭf′ ər əs) adj. Not containing fossils.

- Who or what is the passage about? On the line below, write a *word or phrase* that tells the subject matter:

_____

- What is the most important point the authors want you to *understand* about the subject matter? Locate the main idea *sentence* that answers this question and copy the sentence here:

_____

_____

_____

_____

7. This passage is also taken from a psychology textbook.

Thinking about Motives

One contemporary approach to motivation focuses on the role of our thoughts, expectations, and understanding of the world. We

ă pat ā pay â care ä father ĕ pet ē be ĭ pit ī tie î pier ŏ pot ō toe
ô paw oi noise ŏŏ took ōō boot ou out th thin *th* this ŭ cut û urge
yōō abuse zh vision ə *a*bout, it*e*m, ed*i*ble, gall*o*p, circ*u*s

develop sophisticated explanations for the causes behind other
people's behavior, and these explanations have an important
impact on our own subsequent behavior. In short, each of us
develops our own, personal motivational theories, based on our
understanding of the world, in an effort to explain reasons for
others' behavior.

Understanding Psychology
by Robert Feldman

cognitive (kŏg' nə tĭv) adj. Pertaining to the mind; mental.

contemporary (kən tĕm' pə rĕr ē) adj. Current; modern.

subsequent (sŭb' sə kwənt) adj. Following in time or order;
succeeding.

- Who or what is the passage about? On the line below, write a *word or
  phrase* that tells the subject matter:

  _____

- What is the most important point the author wants you to *understand*
  about the subject matter? Locate the main idea *sentence* that answers
  this question and copy the sentence here:

  _____

  _____

  _____

  _____

  _____

ă pat ā pay â care ä father ĕ pet ē be ĭ pit ī tie î pier ŏ pot ō toe
ô paw oi noise o͞o took o͞o boot ou out th thin *th* this ŭ cut û urge
yo͞o abuse zh vision ə *a*bout, it*e*m, ed*i*ble, gall*o*p, circ*u*s

8. This passage is taken from an American history textbook.

By the 1980s Asians had surpassed Hispanics in numbers of legal immigrants. By eliminating the national origins quota system, the Immigration Act of 1965 opened the door on a first-come, first-qualified basis, making possible the influx of people from China and Taiwan, Korea, Japan, the Philippines, Vietnam, Cambodia, Laos, Thailand, and India. As of 1990 about 6.5 million Asian-Americans lived in the United States. Like some earlier immigrants from Europe, those from the Pacific rim came in waves. Some, like the Vietnamese "boat people" of the late 1970s, were driven from their homes by economic or political turmoil; others were drawn to reunite families or realize greater opportunities in the Western Hemisphere. Professional and educated Asian Indians emigrated in search of better jobs in the United States. Doctors and nurses constituted a large percentage of the early Korean immigrants. But letters home to relatives and other nationals soon attracted a more diverse population, which concentrated in small businesses.

Nation of Nations
by James W. Davidson et al.

---

influx (ĭn′ flŭks) n. A mass arrival or incoming.

turmoil (tŭr′ moil) n. Utter confusion; extreme agitation; commotion.

emigrate (ĕm′ ə grāt) v. To leave one country or region to settle in another.

constitute (kŏn′ stə to͞ot) v. To be the elements or parts of; to make up; to compose.

- Who or what is the passage about? On the line below, write a *word or phrase* that tells the subject matter:

ă pat ā pay â care ä father ĕ pet ē be ĭ pit ī tie î pier ŏ pot ō toe
ô paw oi noise o͞o took o͞o boot ou out th thin *th* this ŭ cut û urge
yo͞o abuse zh vision ə about, item, edible, gallop, circus

- What is the most important point the author wants you to *understand* about the subject matter? Locate the main idea *sentence* that answers this question and copy the sentence here:

_____

_____

_____

_____

9.   This passage is from a music appreciation textbook.

Mozart's Music

Mozart was among the most versatile of all composers and wrote masterpieces in all the musical forms of his time—symphonies, concertos, chamber music, operas. All his music sings and conveys a feeling of ease, grace, and spontaneity as well as balance, restraint, and proportion. Yet mysterious harmonies contrast with its lyricism, and it fuses elegance with power. Not only do his compositions sound effortless; they were created with miraculous ease and rapidity—for example, he completed his last three symphonies in only six weeks.

Music: An Appreciation
by Roger Kamien

versatile (vŭr′ sə təl) adj. Capable of turning completely from one task, subject, or occupation to another; having a generalized aptitude.

spontaneity (spŏn tə nē′ ə tē) n. The condition of being unconstrained and unstudied in manner.

lyricism (lĭr′ ə sĭz əm) n. Intense outpouring of exuberant emotion, especially in the arts.

fuse (fyo͞oz) v. To mix together by melting or as if by melting; to blend.

ă pat   ā pay   â care   ä father   ĕ pet   ē be   ĭ pit   ī tie   î pier   ŏ pot   ō toe
ô paw   oi noise   o͝o took   o͞o boot   ou out   th thin   *th* this   ŭ cut   û urge
yo͞o abuse   zh vision   ə *a*bout, it*e*m, ed*i*ble, gall*o*p, circ*u*s

- Who or what is the passage about? On the line below, write a *word or phrase* that tells the subject matter:

_____

- What is the most important point the author wants you to *understand* about the subject matter? Locate the main idea *sentence* that answers this question and copy the sentence here:

_____

_____

_____

_____

10. This selection is drawn from a government textbook.

> By tradition, the choice of the vice-presidential nominee rests with the presidential nominee. His decision can reflect any number of considerations, including the experience, reputation, political beliefs, ethnic background, and home region of a possible running mate. Mondale in 1984 chose Geraldine Ferraro, the first female vice-presidential nominee of a major party, because his private polls indicated that a woman would be a stronger addition to the ticket than any of the available men.
>
> *The American Democracy*
> by Thomas Patterson

- Who or what is the passage about? On the line below, write a *word or phrase* that tells the subject matter:

_____

- What is the most important point the author wants you to *understand* about the subject matter? Locate the main idea *sentence* that answers this question and copy the sentence here:

_____

_____

_____

_____

2

LOCATING DIRECTLY
STATED MAIN IDEAS
Answer Key for Practice Exercises

Compare your answers for the practice exercises on pages 81–91 with the answers below. The subject matter and main idea sentence are given for each paragraph.

1. The subject matter of the paragraph is *Robert Owen.*

    The main idea sentence is: "One of the most successful industrialists of the early nineteenth century, Robert Owen was an outstanding pioneer of management." (first sentence)

    The rest of the paragraph tells why Robert Owen was regarded as an outstanding pioneer of personnel management.

2. The subject matter of the paragraph is *the perspective of sociology.*

    The main idea sentence is: "The perspective of sociology involves seeing through the outside appearances of people's actions and organizations." (last sentence of the paragraph)

    The rest of the paragraph contrasts the perspective (point of view) of sociologists with that of journalists who also provide information about such groups.

3. The subject matter of the paragraph is *the reason for engaging in (studying) philosophy.*

    The main idea sentence is: "But there is a deeper reason for engaging in philosophy, and that is that we simply cannot turn away from certain questions which constantly confront us." (last sentence of the paragraph)

    The preceding sentences in the passage describe other (less important) reasons people study philosophy.

4. The subject matter of the paragraph is *the meaning (definition) of inflation.*

    The main idea sentence is: "Inflation is a rising general level of prices." (second sentence)

Copyright © 1996 by The McGraw-Hill Companies, Inc.

93

The rest of the paragraph gives additional information about the meaning of inflation. Notice that the authors have begun the paragraph by asking a question. Often authors will do that, and then answer their own question. The answer to the question is usually the main idea of the paragraph. Notice also that in this paragraph the authors have printed the answer to the question (the main idea sentence) in italics in order to emphasize it.

5. The subject matter of the paragraph is *the Middle Ages (not <u>music</u> in the Middle Ages).*

    The main idea sentence is: "A thousand years of European history are spanned by the phrase *Middle Ages.*" (first sentence)

    The second sentence tells about the first part of the Middle Ages, which was known as the "dark ages." The last sentence describes the cultural growth that occurred during the later Middle Ages.

    You may have written "<u>music</u> in the Middle Ages" as the subject matter. But this particular paragraph does not mention anything about *music* in the Middle Ages. The paragraph, however, was the first paragraph in a section of the textbook that discussed music in the Middle Ages. Be careful of merely jotting down a heading as the subject matter without reading the paragraph carefully to see whether the heading accurately describes the topic of the paragraph.

6. The subject matter of the paragraph is *da Vinci's interpretation of fossils.*

    The main idea sentence is: "The most important early record of a careful interpretation of fossils was that left by the Italian genius Leonardo da Vinci, one of the most original natural philosophers of the early Renaissance." (first sentence)

    The rest of the sentences explain why da Vinci made the interpretation he did.

7. The subject matter of the paragraph is *how we develop our own, personal theories about people's motives* (or you could have used the heading "Thinking about Motives")

    The main idea sentence is: "In short, each of us develops our own, personal motivational theories, based on our understanding of the world, in an effort to explain reasons for others' behavior." (last sentence)

    The words "in short" alert the careful reader to the important information in the last sentence. The earlier sentences in the paragraph provide an introduction to the subject of how we create our own theories of motives.

8. The subject matter of the paragraph is *reasons for the influx of Asian immigrants.*

   The main idea sentence is: "By the 1980s Asians had surpassed Hispanics in numbers of legal immigrants." (first sentence)

   All of the remaining sentences in the paragraph discuss reasons more Asian immigrants came to this country.

9. The subject matter of the paragraph is *Mozart's music.*

   The main idea sentence is: "Mozart was among the most versatile of all composers and wrote masterpieces in all the musical forms of his time—symphonies, concertos, chamber music, operas." (first sentence)

   The rest of the paragraph explains not only that Mozart was able to compose all different types of music, but also why his compositions were considered masterpieces.

10. The subject matter of the paragraph is *the choice of the vice-presidential nominee.*

    The main idea sentence is: "By tradition, the choice of the vice-presidential nominee rests with the presidential nominee." (first sentence)

    The second sentence lists some of the factors that the presidential nominee takes into consideration when selecting a running mate. The last sentence gives a specific example, Walter Mondale's selection of Geraldine Ferraro.

LOCATING DIRECTLY
STATED MAIN IDEAS
Review Test

Determine the subject matter and locate the main idea sentence for each of these paragraphs. *Write the subject matter. Then copy the complete main idea sentence exactly as it appears in the paragraph.*

1.   This paragraph comes from a composition (writing) textbook.

> Readers are perverse creatures who, if given the slightest opportunity, will manage to get lost when they are reading. If they encounter a gap between one point and the next, they lose track of the narrative or argument. If they don't get clear directional signals to guide them between sentences and between paragraphs, they will head off in the wrong direction. If the author does not put in the right word to show the relationship between ideas, they will put in the wrong one. And if they cannot sense an underlying pattern in a piece of writing, they are likely to get confused and quit reading.
>
> *Contemporary Composition*
> by Maxine Hairston

---

perverse (pər vŭrs′) adj. Directed away from what is right or good.

encounter (ĕn koun′ tər) v. To meet or come upon, especially unexpectedly.

•   Who or what is the passage about? On the line below, write a *word or phrase* that tells the subject matter:

ă pat ā pay â care ä father ĕ pet ē be ĭ pit ī tie î pier ŏ pot ō toe
ô paw oi noise o͞o took o͞o boot ou out th thin *th* this ŭ cut   û urge
yo͞o abuse zh vision ə *about, item, edible, gallop, circus*

- What is the most important point the author wants you to *understand* about the subject matter? Locate the main idea *sentence* that answers this question and copy the sentence here:

_____

_____

_____

_____

_____

2. This passage is taken from a psychology textbook.

> How soon can we determine a child's intelligence? Until recently, most psychologists would have answered that it is not until a child is 3 or 4 years of age that accurate predictions can be made. However, a growing number of psychologists now feel that relatively accurate estimates of adult intelligence can be made in children as young as 6 months.
>
> *Understanding Psychology*
> by Robert Feldman

- Who or what is the passage about? On the line below, write a *word or phrase* that tells the subject matter:

_____

- What is the most important point the author wants you to *understand* about the subject matter? Locate the main idea *sentence* that answers this question and copy the sentence here:

_____

_____

_____

_____

_____

3. This paragraph is excerpted from a psychology textbook.

> We come up with similar findings when we look at adults. Creative people tend to be relatively intelligent, but beyond a certain level, higher IQs do not predict creativity. When groups of architects, mathematicians, and research scientists (all of whom were well above average in intelligence, with IQs ranging from 120 to 140) were divided into groups that had made distinguished contributions to their fields and other competent practitioners who had not, no differences in IQ showed up between the two groups (McKinnor, 1968). Nor were school grades related to later creativity.
>
> *Psychology*
> by Diane Papalia and Sally Olds

competent (kŏm′ pə tənt) adj. Properly or well qualified; capable.

practitioner (prăk tĭsh′ ən ər) n. One who practices an occupation, profession, or technique.

*   Who or what is the passage about? On the line below, write a *word or phrase* that tells the subject matter:

_____

*   What is the most important point the authors want you to *understand* about the subject matter? Locate the main idea *sentence* that answers this question and copy the sentence here:

_____
_____
_____
_____
_____

ă pat ā pay â care ä father ĕ pet ē be ĭ pit ī tie î pier ŏ pot ō toe
ô paw oi noise o͝o took o͞o boot ou out th thin th this ŭ cut û urge
yo͞o abuse zh vision ə about, item, edible, gallop, circus

4.   This paragraph is taken from an economics textbook.

> By **full production** we simply mean that resources should be allo-
> cated efficiently; that is, employed resources should be utilized so as
> to make the most valuable contribution to total output. We should
> avoid allocating astrophysicists to farming and experienced farmers
> to our space research centers! Nor do we want Iowa's farmland
> planted to cotton and Alabama's to corn when experience indicates
> that the opposite assignment would provide the nation substantially
> more of both products from the same amount of land.
>
> *Economics*
> by Campbell R. McConnell

full production (fo͞ol prə dŭk′ shən) n. (The words "we simply mean" tell
you that the author is explaining the term in the passage.)

allocate (ăl′ ō kāt) v. To designate for a special purpose; set apart.

substantially (səb stăn′ shəl ē) adv. Considerably more in amount.

- Who or what is the passage about? On the line below, write a *word or phrase* that tells the subject matter:

  _____

- What is the most important point the author wants you to *understand* about the subject matter? Locate the main idea *sentence* that answers this question and copy the sentence here:

  _____

  _____

  _____

  _____

ă pat ā pay â care ä father ĕ pet ē be ĭ pit ī tie î pier ŏ pot ō toe
ô paw oi noise o͞o took o͞o boot ou out th thin *th* this ŭ cut û urge
yo͞o abuse zh vision ə *a*bout, it*e*m, ed*i*ble, gall*o*p, circ*u*s

5. A history textbook is the source of the following paragraph.

> The Europeans' greatest impact on the Americans was, however, unintended. Diseases carried from the Old World to the New by the alien invaders killed hundreds of thousands, even millions, of Native Americans, who had no immunity to germs that had infested Europe, Asia, and Africa for centuries. The greatest killer was smallpox, which was spread by direct human contact. The epidemic that hit Tenochtitlan in 1520 had begun in Hispaniola two years earlier. Pizarro easily conquered the Inca partly because their society had been devastated by the epidemic shortly before his arrival. Smallpox was not the only villain; influenza, measles, and other diseases added to the destruction.
>
> *A People and a Nation*
> by Mary Beth Norton et al.

alien (āʹ lē ən) adj. Foreign.

epidemic (ĕp ə dĕmʹ ik) n. A contagious disease that spreads rapidly.

● Who or what is the passage about? On the line below, write a *word or phrase* that tells the subject matter:

_____

● What is the most important point the authors want you to *understand* about the subject matter? Locate the main idea *sentence* that answers this question and copy the sentence here:

_____

_____

_____

_____

ă pat ā pay â care ä father ĕ pet ē be ĭ pit ī tie î pier ŏ pot ō toe
ô paw oi noise o͞o took o͞o boot ou out th thin *th* this ŭ cut û urge
yo͞o abuse zh vision ə *a*bout, it*e*m, ed*i*ble, gall*o*p, circ*u*s

6. This paragraph is excerpted from a biology textbook.

> The body of a flowering plant is divided into two portions, the **root system** and the **shoot system.** The roots, which lie below ground level, anchor the plant and absorb water and minerals. Within the shoot system, the stem lifts the leaves to catch the rays of the sun. The leaves receive water and minerals that are sent from the roots up through the stem and take in carbon dioxide from the air.
>
> *Inquiry into Life*
> by Silvia Mader

- Who or what is the passage about? On the line below, write a *word or phrase* that tells the subject matter:

_____

- What is the most important point the author wants you to *understand* about the subject matter? Locate the main idea *sentence* that answers this question and copy the sentence here:

_____

_____

_____

_____

LOCATING DIRECTLY
STATED MAIN IDEAS
Supplemental Exercises

1. The following selection comes from a psychology textbook.

> At some point in your life, you will face death—certainly your own, and probably the deaths of friends and loved ones. Although there is nothing more certain in life than death, it remains a frightening, emotion-laden topic. In fact, there may be nothing more stressful than the death of a loved one or the contemplation of your own imminent death, and preparing for death will likely represent one of your most crucial developmental tasks.
>
> *Understanding Psychology*
> by Robert Feldman

- Who or what is the passage about? On the line below, write a *word or phrase* that tells the subject matter:

_____

- What is the most important point the author wants you to *understand* about the subject matter? Locate the main idea *sentence* that answers this question and copy the sentence here:

_____

_____

_____

_____

_____

_____

_____

2. An economics text is the source of this passage.

> **Oligopoly** is a situation in which only a few firms have a great deal of power in a product market. An oligopoly may exist because only a few firms produce a particular product or because a few firms account for most, though not all, of a product's output. In either case, firms in an oligopoly are highly *interdependent*, because of their very small number. Changes in the price or output of one oligopolist immediately affect the others.
>
> *The Economy Today*
> by Bradley Schiller

- Who or what is the passage about? On the line below, write a *word or phrase* that tells the subject matter:

  _____

- What is the most important point the author wants you to *understand* about the subject matter? Locate the main idea *sentence* that answers this question and copy the sentence here:

  _____

  _____

  _____

  _____

3. This passage comes from a government textbook.

> **Second-Term Blues**
>
> Second terms have been hard on many popular presidents, especially those reelected by wide margins. For George Washington it was factionalism that marred his second term; for Thomas Jefferson, the embargo; for Franklin Roosevelt, the Court-packing plan; for Lyndon Johnson, the Vietnam War; and for Richard Nixon, Water-

gate. So too Ronald Reagan suffered a precipitous drop in his political fortunes as scandals racked his administration.

Nation of Nations
by James W. Davidson et al.

- Who or what is the passage about? On the line below, write a *word or phrase* that tells the subject matter:

_____

- What is the most important point the authors want you to *understand* about the subject matter? Locate the main idea *sentence* that answers this question and copy the sentence here:

_____

_____

_____

_____

4. A business information systems textbook is the source of this passage.

If computers do displace significant numbers of workers, will society support the retraining of these workers? Will there be enough alternative jobs? It seems there will. There is always something to be done, regardless of how many tasks are performed by computers and machines. And usually the new jobs are more interesting. The computer often does the dull and routine jobs such as assembly-line and clerical work. The bottom line, though, is that anytime we can replace a human being with a machine at a cheaper cost, society as a whole benefits because the standard of living rises.

Information Systems in Business: An Introduction
by James O. Hicks, Jr.

- Who or what is the passage about? On the line below, write a *word or phrase* that tells the subject matter:

_____

- What is the most important point the author wants you to *understand* about the subject matter? Locate the main idea *sentence* that answers this question and copy the sentence here:

_____

_____

_____

_____

5. This passage comes from a psychology textbook. Write a word or phrase that tells the subject matter for *each paragraph.* Next, locate and copy the main idea sentence of *each paragraph.*

You Are What You Drink: Thirst

The stimuli that motivate us to drink are mainly internal; the dry mouth that accompanies thirst is a symptom of the need for water rather than the cause. Actually, two primary internal mechanisms produce thirst. First, the salt concentration of the cells of the body varies as a function of the amount of internal fluid, and when the concentration reaches a certain level, it triggers the hypothalamus to act, thereby resulting in the experience of thirst. The second major mechanism that induces thirst is a decrease in the total volume of fluid in the circulatory system. For instance, a person who loses a significant amount of blood through an injury subsequently experiences a powerful sense of thirst.

An increase in body temperature or a significant energy expenditure also produces thirst. This increase is probably due to a rise in the salt concentration in the body, which occurs as a consequence of increased sweating.

Understanding Psychology
by Robert Feldman

Subject Matter

_____

Main Idea

_____

_____

_____

Subject Matter

_____

Main Idea

_____

_____

_____

FORMULATING IMPLIED MAIN IDEAS

1

Determining Subject Matter

2

Locating Directly Stated Main Ideas

3

Formulating Implied Main Ideas

4

Identifying Supporting Details

5

Recognizing Authors' Writing Patterns

6

Applying Comprehension
Skills to Longer Passages

7

Remembering College Textbook
Material through Organizing

8

Thinking Critically as You Read

INTRODUCTION

In Chapter 1, you learned that an important first step in understanding a college textbook passage is to determine its **subject matter.** You learned to ask the question, "Who or what is this passage about?" The answer to that question is the subject matter of the passage. To help you find the subject matter, you learned to look for (1) a heading, (2) bold-faced words in the passage, (3) a word, name, or phrase used more than once in a passage, (4) a word or phrase that is mentioned at the beginning of a passage that is then referred to throughout the passage by a pronoun or other words, and (5) the subject all the sentences in the passage have in common.

In Chapter 2, you learned that the next step in understanding a passage is to locate the **main idea** of each paragraph. First you determined the subject matter; then you asked yourself, "What does the author want me to *understand* about the subject matter?" (What point is he or she trying to make?) The answer to your question leads you to the main idea of the paragraph. You learned that the main idea is always a complete sentence and that it is often the first sentence of a paragraph. However, you also learned that the sentence that states the main idea may be found elsewhere in the paragraph.

The first two chapters of this book provided you with extensive practice in determining the subject matter and locating a directly stated main idea of a paragraph. Even though students generally encounter fewer paragraphs that have indirectly expressed (implied) main ideas, they often find such paragraphs more challenging. You are now ready to learn how to approach that kind of paragraph: a paragraph that has a main idea that has been **implied,** or **expressed indirectly.** Although most paragraphs contain directly stated main ideas, you will encounter paragraphs that do not have a single sentence that expresses the complete main idea.

PARAGRAPHS WITH IMPLIED MAIN IDEAS

In a paragraph with an implied (or indirectly expressed) main idea, there is no single sentence that states the main idea completely. Instead, the sentences of the paragraph present facts, examples, descriptions, or explanations that "add up to" or suggest the main idea the author wants you to understand. When a paragraph contains a stated main idea, your task is simply to *locate* the sentence that states it. But when a paragraph has a main idea that is expressed indirectly, your task is to *formulate* (that is, *think out* or *create*) a main idea sentence for that paragraph. Remember that you are seeking the *author's* main idea. Be careful not to formulate a main idea that is based solely on your own experience or information.

You may wonder why authors write paragraphs that have implied main ideas. You may ask, "Isn't it easier for the reader when there is one single sentence that states the main idea?" The answer is yes, it is often easier for the reader when the main idea is stated directly. However, authors may assume that the main ideas of some paragraphs are so obvious that it is unnecessary to state them directly. When authors are dealing with complex material, they often choose not to state the main idea in a single sentence. They may believe it might oversimplify the point they want to make. Authors also vary their writing by implying their main ideas in different ways.

When the author does not state the main idea directly, he or she is nevertheless expressing it *indirectly.* Remember, every paragraph must have a main idea, even though there is no single sentence that states it directly. The important facts, examples, and explanations in a well-written paragraph should always *add up to, support,* or *suggest* the main idea. When an author *suggests* a main idea without stating it directly, he or she is *implying* it. (When a reader comprehends an implied main idea, he or she is *inferring* it or making an inference.) When authors present an implied main idea, it is up to the reader to create, or formulate, a main idea sentence. You can learn to do this by using the techniques presented in this chapter.

> An **implied main idea** is a main idea that the author does not state directly as a single sentence within the paragraph. Therefore, you must *formulate* a main idea sentence that expresses the author's most important point.

THE IMPORTANCE OF FORMULATING MAIN IDEAS

When you formulate the main idea in your own words, you will understand the paragraph more clearly, and you will remember the content of the paragraph more easily. Another reason for formulating main ideas in your own words is that college instructors often base test questions on passages which have implied main ideas. Therefore, you cannot ignore the main ideas of paragraphs just because they are implied. You are responsible for the main ideas of paragraphs whether they are stated or not.

Your instructors assume that you understand passages with indirectly stated main ideas and that you have correctly formulated their main ideas. Since instructors may not always point out these implied main ideas in class lectures, it is especially important that you formulate them carefully as you read your textbooks. Of course, this will increase your understanding of the material you are reading.

THREE WAYS TO FORMULATE IMPLIED MAIN IDEAS

There are three ways you can formulate a main idea sentence:

1. The writer may present most of the main idea in one sentence, but the reader must add a word or phrase from another sentence to create a *complete* main idea. This can be represented by

    One sentence + a word or phrase = formulated
    　　　　　　　　from another　　　main idea sentence
    　　　　　　　　sentence (often
    　　　　　　　　the subject matter)

2. A writer may express a main idea indirectly by presenting *parts* of the main idea in two different sentences. These sentences may follow one another in the paragraph or they may be separated. The reader must combine these sentences. This can be represented by

    One sentence + another sentence = formulated
    　　　　　　　　　　　　　　main idea sentence

3. Finally, the writer may expect the reader to combine important ideas from several sentences in the paragraph. In this situation, readers must combine and interpret the author's ideas according to their own experience and knowledge. This means that you will have to use several of your own words to express the author's main idea. This can be represented by

    Important　+ important　+ important　= formulated
    information　information　information　main idea sentence

EXPLANATIONS AND EXAMPLES

You are about to read a psychology textbook passage whose main idea sentence can be formulated in this way:

---

1. One sentence + a word or a phrase = formulated
                from another   main idea sentence
                sentence (often
                the subject matter)

The subject matter of the paragraph, as you will discover in the first sentence, is *the content of our dreams,* or *the "stories" our dreams are made of.* In this paragraph there is no single sentence that expresses the main idea directly or completely, although the second sentence nearly does. Simply by adding the subject matter from the first sentence, you can easily formulate a complete main idea sentence.

When you read this paragraph, notice that the authors begin it with a question. The authors then answer the question for you in the second sentence. By combining information in the question and in the answer, you can formulate the main idea sentence.

Content of Dreams

~~Where do~~ *Most of* (the "stories" of our dreams) ~~come from? Most of them~~ (appear as a montage of the day's events in somewhat altered form.) Based on some 10,000 dreams reported by normal people, Calvin Hall (1966) found that most dreams are commonplace. They are most often played out in familiar settings, such as a house, although the house is usually not the dreamer's own home. The most popular room is the living room, followed by—in order—bedroom, kitchen, stairway, basement, bathroom, dining room, and hall. The room is often a composite of several rooms the dreamer has known. Women's dreams more commonly take place indoors, men's out-of-doors.

Psychology
by Diane Papalia and Sally Olds

---

montage (mŏn′ täzh) n. A rapid sequence of thematically related short scenes or images that exhibits different aspects of the same idea or situation.

composite (kəm pŏz′ ĭt) n. A structure made up of components or parts.

Who or what is the passage about? The subject matter is *the content of dreams.*

What is the main point the authors want you to understand about the content of dreams? The main idea is that *Most of the stories of our dreams appear as a montage of the day's events in somewhat altered form.*

Now look at a second example from a history textbook that also expresses the main idea indirectly. The subject matter, as you will discover, is *Reverend Cotton Mather's support of smallpox inoculations.*

Smallpox Inoculations

The key figure in the drama was the Reverend Cotton Mather, the Puritan clergyman, who was a member of England's Royal Society, an organization of the intellectual elite. In a Royal Society publication Mather read about the benefits of inoculation (deliberately infecting a person with a mild case of a disease) as a protection against the dreaded smallpox. In 1720 and 1721, when Boston suffered a major smallpox epidemic, Mather and a doctor ally urged people to be inoculated; there was fervent opposition, including that of Boston's leading physician. When the epidemic had ended, the statistics bore out Mather's opinion; of those inoculated, fewer than 3 percent died; of those who became ill without inoculation, nearly 15 percent perished. Though it was midcentury before inoculation was generally accepted as a preventive procedure, enlightened methods had provided colonial Americans with protection from the greatest killer disease of all, *smallpox.*

Reverend Cotton Mather's

A People and a Nation
by Mary Beth Norton et al.

ă pat ā pay â care ä father ĕ pet ē be ĭ pit ī tie î pier ŏ pot ō toe
ô paw oi noise o͞o took o͞o boot ou out th thin *th* this ŭ cut û urge
yo͞o abuse zh vision ə *a*bout, it*e*m, ed*i*ble, gall*o*p, circ*u*s

---

Puritan (pyoor′ ə tən) n. A member of a group of English Protestants who, in the sixteenth and seventeenth centuries, advocated strict religious discipline and simplification of the ceremonies and creeds of the church of England.

elite (ĭ lēt′) n. The best or most skilled members of a given social group.

inoculation (ĭ nŏk yə lā′ shən) n. Introducing the virus of a disease into the body in order to immunize or cure. (The authors define the term in parentheses.)

epidemic (ĕp ə dĕm′ ĭk) n. A contagious disease that spreads rapidly.

ally (ăl′ ī) n. One that is united with another in some formal or personal relationship.

fervent (fûr′ vənt) adj. Showing great emotion.

Who or what is the passage about? The subject matter is *Reverend Cotton Mather's support of smallpox inoculations.*

What is the main point the authors want you to understand about Mather's support of smallpox inoculations? The main idea is, *Though it was midcentury before inoculation was generally accepted as a preventive procedure,* **Reverend Cotton Mather's** *enlightened methods had provided colonial Americans with protection against the greatest killer disease of all,* **smallpox.**

As you can see, *smallpox inoculations* is part of the subject matter. It is mentioned in the heading and throughout the passage. But Cotton Mather's name also appears repeatedly throughout the passage. Therefore, the complete subject matter is *Reverend Cotton Mather's support of smallpox inoculations.* But what do the authors want you to *understand* about Cotton Mather's support of smallpox inoculations? The answer to this question is the main idea. This main idea sentence was formulated by adding other important information to the last sentence of the paragraph. Keep in mind that there are several correct ways to word the main idea for this paragraph.

ă pat ā pay â care ä father ĕ pet ē be ĭ pit ī tie î pier ŏ pot ō toe
ô paw oi noise oo took oo boot ou out th thin *th* this ŭ cut û urge
yoo abuse zh vision ə *a*bout, it*e*m, ed*i*ble, gall*o*p, circ*u*s

Now try this passage from an American history textbook. It is similar to the examples you have just seen. Read the paragraph.

Precisely at noon on May 16, 1868, the Chief Justice of the United States entered the Senate. Managers and counsel stood ready. Soon two senators who were seriously ill slowly made their way into the chamber, bringing the number of senators present to its full fifty-four. All principals in this solemn drama were present before the High Court of Impeachment except the accused: Andrew Johnson, President of the United States. Johnson, who never appeared to defend himself in person, waited anxiously at the White House as Chief Justice Salmon Chase ordered the calling of the roll. To each senator he put the questions, "How say you? Is the respondent, Andrew Johnson, President of the United States, guilty or not guilty of a high misdemeanor, as charged in this article?" Thirty-five senators answered, "Guilty," nineteen, "Not guilty." The total was one short of a two-thirds majority. The nation had come within one vote of removing its president from office.

A People and a Nation
by Mary Beth Norton et al.

---

counsel (koun′ səl) n. Lawyers or others giving legal advice.

chamber (chām′ bər) n. A hall for the meeting of an assembly, especially a legislative assembly.

principal (prĭn′ sə pəl) n. A main participant in a given situation.

solemn (sŏl′ əm) adj. Serious; grave; performed with full ceremony.

impeachment (ĭm pēch′ mənt) n. The charge before a court of justice of misconduct or wrongdoing in office. (Notice that this word does not mean the person was *removed* from office.)

respondent (rĭ spŏn′ dənt) n. The defendant or person who must respond to a legal charge.

misdemeanor (mĭs dĭ mē′ nər) n. An offense less serious than a felony, the punishment for which may be a fine or imprisonment in a local rather than a state institution.

ă pat ā pay â care ä father ĕ pet ē be ĭ pit ī tie î pier ŏ pot ō toe
ô paw oi noise o͞o took o͞o boot ou out th thin th this ŭ cut û urge
yo͞o abuse zh vision ə about, item, edible, gallop, circus

- Who or what is the passage about? On the line below, write a word or phrase that tells the subject matter:

_____

- What is the most important point the authors wants you to *understand* about the subject matter? Formulate a main idea *sentence* that answers this question and write the sentence here:

_____

_____

_____

The subject matter is *Andrew Johnson's impeachment.* The last sentence nearly states the main idea, but it leaves out one essential piece of information: the name of the president. To formulate the main idea, you could have chosen the last sentence and added Johnson's name. One correct formulation of the main idea would be as follows: ***In 1868,*** *the nation had come within one vote of removing its president,* ***Andrew Johnson,*** *from office.*

Let's now consider another way to formulate main ideas. This type of main idea may be formulated by combining two sentences that each contain part of the main idea. The paragraph below has a main idea that can be formulated this way.

2. One sentence + another sentence = formulated   main idea sentence

This government textbook passage has its main idea expressed indirectly. In order to formulate the main idea for this passage, you must combine two of the sentences. Now read this passage. The subject matter is indicated in the heading.

Chief Scapegoat: Evaluating Presidents

"Before you get to be President you think you can do anything," Lyndon Johnson told Richard Nixon, as he left the White House, "but when you get in that tall chair, as you're gonna find out,

Mr. President, you can't count on people. You'll find your hands tied and people cussin' you. The office is kinda like the little country boy found the hoochie-koochie show at the carnival, once he'd paid his dime and got inside the tent: It ain't exactly as it was advertised." Johnson's disappointment in the office matches the disappointment that the American people often have in those who occupy it: Presidents are the chief scapegoats in American politics, *because* Their performance almost always falls short of our expectations.

American Politics and Government
by Richard Pious

---

chief (chēf) adj. Highest in rank, authority, or office; principal or most important.

scapegoat (skāp′ gōt) n. A person or group who bears the blame for others.

Who or what is this passage about? The subject matter is *presidents as scapegoats.*

What is the main point the author wants you to understand about presidents as scapegoats? To answer this question, you must combine the last two sentences: *Presidents are chief scapegoats in American politics* **because** *their performance almost always falls short of our expectations.* Notice that you did not need to use *all* of the next-to-the-last sentence. The most important part of that sentence (which could stand alone as a sentence) is, "Presidents are the chief scapegoats in American politics." This sentence combined with the last sentence in the paragraph expresses the main idea of the passage. Notice how simple it was to do this by using the word *because.* You will often have to add a connecting word (such as *and, however,* and *because*) to show the relationship between the ideas in the two sentences.

ă pat ā pay â care ä father ĕ pet ē be ĭ pit ī tie î pier ŏ pot ō toe
ô paw oi noise o͞o took o͞o boot ou out th thin *th* this ŭ cut û urge
yo͞o abuse zh vision ə *a*bout, it*e*m, ed*i*ble, gall*o*p, circ*u*s

The main idea in the philosophy passage below is also implied. The passage is a challenging one since most students have less experience in reading philosophy than in reading other subjects.

Socrates disagreed with the Sophists. *because* He was convinced that there could be a solid basis for truth and that there are some moral principles to guide human beings when they ask "What should I do?" He rejected the Sophists' skepticism regarding knowledge and their relativism concerning morality. Regarding our knowledge, Socrates was fascinated by the fact, for example, that we can say about something that it is beautiful or about a human action that it is good. How is it that we can recognize something as beautiful or an action as good? No particular thing, he said, is perfectly beautiful, but insofar as it is beautiful, it is because it partakes of Beauty. . . .

Elements of Philosophy
by Samuel Stumpf

Socrates (sŏk′ rə tēz) n. 470?–399 B.C. Greek philosopher and teacher.

Sophist (sŏf′ ĭst) n. Any of a class of later Greek teachers of philosophy who came to be belittled and discredited for their oversubtle, self-serving reasoning.

principle (prĭn′ sə pəl) n. A basic truth, law, or assumption; a rule or standard, especially of good behavior; moral or ethical standards.

skepticism (skĕp′ tə sĭz əm) n. A doubting or questioning attitude or state of mind.

relativism (rĕl′ ə tĭv ĭz əm) n. The theory that all truth is relative to the individual and to the time or place in which he or she acts.

morality (mə răl′ ĭ tē) n. A set of ideas of right and wrong.

partake (pär tāk′) v. To take part or have a share; to have some quality or characteristic; show evidence.

ă pat   ā pay   â care   ä father   ĕ pet   ē be   ĭ pit   ī tie   î pier   ŏ pot   ō toe
ô paw   oi noise   o͞o took   o͞o boot   ou out   th thin   *th* this   ŭ cut   û urge
yo͞o abuse   zh vision   ə *a*bout, it*e*m, ed*i*ble, gall*o*p, circ*u*s

The subject matter of the passage is *Socrates' disagreement with the Sophists* (or, in other words, beliefs Socrates held that were different from what the Sophists believed). The first sentence of the paragraph tells you that Socrates disagreed with the Sophists. The second sentence explains *how* Socrates' beliefs differed from the Sophists' beliefs. By combining the first two sentences of the paragraph, you have formulated its main idea: *Socrates disagreed with the Sophists* **because** *he was convinced that there could be a solid basis for truth and that there are some moral principles to guide human beings when they ask, "What should I do?"*

Now you try this passage from a psychology textbook. Read the paragraph, determine its subject matter, and then formulate its main idea by combining the first two sentences.

What happens when animals and people are not allowed to sleep at all for various periods of time? Relatively little of a physiological nature. Human beings often develop hand tremors, double vision, droopy eyelids, and a lower pain threshold after five to ten sleepless days, and animals often lose a lot of weight, possibly because of the stress the animal is under to stay awake and the total disruption of the body's biorhythms (Webb, 1975).

Psychology
by Diane Papalia and Sally Olds

physiological (fĭz′ ē ə lŏj′ ĭ kəl) adj. Of or relating to the biological study of the functions of living organisms and their parts.

tremor (trĕm′ ər) n. A quick shaking movement; an involuntary trembling motion of the body.

threshold (thrĕsh′ ōld) n. The intensity below which a mental or physical stimulus cannot be perceived and can produce no response.

ă pat ā pay â care ä father ĕ pet ē be ĭ pit ī tie î pier ŏ pot ō toe
ô paw oi noise o͞o took   o͞o boot ou out th thin *th* this ŭ cut û urge
yo͞o abuse zh vision ə *a*bout, it*e*m, ed*i*ble, gall*o*p, circ*u*s

- Who or what is the passage about? On the line below, write a word or phrase that tells the subject matter:

_____

The subject matter is *sleep deprivation,* or *what happens when people and animals are not allowed to sleep for various periods of time.*

- What is the most important point the authors want you to *understand* about the subject matter? Formulate a main idea *sentence* that answers this question and write the sentence here:

_____

_____

_____

_____

Notice that the first sentence in the paragraph is actually a question. Whenever authors ask a question, you can expect them to answer it. This is one way that authors draw the reader's attention to important ideas. So whenever an author asks a question, you should read carefully to find the answer. In this paragraph, the authors immediately answer their question in the second sentence. By combining the question and the answer, you can easily formulate the main idea. One correct formulation of the main idea would be as follows: *Relatively little of a physiological nature happens when animals and people are not allowed to sleep at all for various periods of time.*

Finally, it will often be necessary to formulate a main idea by combining and interpreting the author's *ideas* from more than one sentence. This means that you will have to use some of your own words along with the author's words in order to formulate the main idea. The paragraph below has a main idea that can be formulated this way:

---

3.   Important   + important   + important   = formulated
      information   information   information   main idea sentence

---

This sample passage is from a biology textbook. Read the passage, determine its subject matter, and think about the ideas presented in several sentences that can be combined to formulate a main idea sentence that takes into consideration all the information in the paragraph.

> The (digestive system) provides nutrients, and the (excretory system) rids the body of metabolic wastes. The (respiratory system) supplies oxygen but also eliminates carbon dioxide. The (circulatory system) carries nutrients and oxygen to and wastes from the cells so that tissue fluid composition remains constant. The (immune system) helps protect the body from disease. The (nervous and hormonal systems) control body functions. The (nervous system) directs body movements, allowing the organism to manipulate the external environment, an important life-sustaining function.
>
> *Inquiry into Life*
> by Sylvia Mader

---

excretory system (ĕk′ skrə tôr ē) n. The system that rids the body of metabolic wastes.

respiratory system (rĕs′ pər ə tôr ē) n. The system that supplies the body with oxygen and eliminates carbon dioxide (i.e., the breathing system).

circulatory system (sûr′ kyə lə tôr ē) n. The system of structures by which blood and lymph are circulated throughout the body.

immune system (ĭ myo͞on′) n. The system that helps protect the body from disease.

The subject matter is *systems of the body.* What is the main point the author wants you to understand about these systems of the body? The main idea of this paragraph could be expressed as: *Each system of the body has specialized functions.* Based on the examples she presents, this is the main idea the author expects you to understand.

You can easily see that there is no *one* sentence in the passage that directly states the main idea. Each sentence tells about one or more body systems, and no single sentence gives you an overall main idea. This means that the author is implying the main idea; therefore, it is up to *you*

ă pat   ā pay   â care   ä father   ĕ pet   ē be   ĭ pit   ī tie   î pier   ŏ pot   ō toe
ô paw   oi noise   o͞o took   o͞o boot   ou out   th thin   *th* this   ŭ cut   û urge
yo͞o abuse   zh vision   ə *a*bout, it*e*m, ed*i*ble, gall*o*p, circ*u*s

to formulate a main idea sentence. There is no single phrase in the passage that can be combined with another sentence to form the main idea. Nor can you combine just two of the sentences from the paragraph to form the main idea since each sentence of the paragraph describes the special functions of a body system. Notice that the writer presents several systems of the body and explains their functions. The author does this to illustrate her main point.

Now look at a second example of a passage for which you must formulate the main idea by combining several important ideas. Read this passage from an American history textbook.

The Americans [i.e., American Indians], though, took a revenge of sorts. They gave the Europeans a virulent form of syphilis. The first recorded case of the new disease in Europe occurred in Barcelona, Spain, in 1493, shortly after Columbus's return from the Caribbean. Although less deadly than smallpox, syphilis was extremely dangerous and debilitating. It *that* spread quickly through Europe and Asia, carried by soldiers, sailors, and prostitutes, even reaching China in 1505.

> *A People and a Nation*
> by Mary Beth Norton et al.

---

virulent (vîr′ yə lənt) adj. Highly infectious or capable of causing disease.

syphilis (sĭf′ ə lĭs) n. An infectious venereal disease.

debilitating (dĭ bĭl′ ə tāt ĭng) adj. Having the effect of making one weak, tired, or feeble.

The subject matter is *syphilis from the Americans* or *syphilis from the New World*. In this paragraph there is more than one important idea that the authors want you to understand. They expect you to understand:

The American Indians gave the Europeans a virulent form of syphilis.

and

This disease spread quickly through Europe and Asia.

ă pat ā pay â care ä father ĕ pet ē be ĭ pit ī tie î pier ŏ pot ō toe
ô paw oi noise ōō took ōō boot ou out th thin *th* this ŭ cut û urge
yōō abuse zh vision ə *a*bout, it*e*m, ed*i*ble, gall*o*p, circ*u*s

A formulation of the complete main idea would be as follows: *The American Indians gave the Europeans a virulent form of syphilis, and it spread quickly through Europe and Asia.*

Remember that there is more than one correct way to express the main idea. For example, the main idea could also be stated: *A virulent form of syphilis that was transmitted from American Indians in the New World to Europeans spread quickly through Europe and Asia.* The names of specific places, exact dates, and the types of people who spread the disease are details of the paragraph and do not need to be included with the more important ideas expressed in the main idea.

Now it's your turn to read a passage and formulate a main idea sentence. This paragraph from a psychology textbook has an implied main idea. Determine its subject matter, and then use your own judgment to combine the important ideas from several sentences in order to formulate a main idea sentence.

Is there any difference in personality traits or intelligence between short and long sleepers? Early studies reported a few such differences. For example, short sleepers were said to be generally more "energetic," while long sleepers were more prone to be "worriers." But these findings were not confirmed by later studies, and it now seems that there are few reliable differences.

Introduction to Psychology
by Ron Plotnik

- Who or what is the passage about? On the line below, write a word or phrase that tells the subject matter:

  _____

- What is the most important point the author wants you to *understand* about the subject matter? Formulate a main idea *sentence* that answers this question and write the sentence here:

  _____

  _____

  _____

  _____

The subject matter of this paragraph is *differences in personality traits and intelligence between short and long sleepers.* The paragraph begins with a question that the author expects you to answer. A formulated main idea sentence that answers this question would be: *While early studies reported a few differences in personality traits and intelligence between short and long sleepers, these findings were not confirmed by later studies.* In order to formulate the main idea, you must draw from the information contained in several parts of the paragraph.

Now read this sociology textbook passage that has an implied main idea. Read the paragraph, determine its subject matter, and then use your judgment to formulate the main idea. You will do this by combining several important ideas in the passage.

> Other statistics reveal a similar picture. In 1985 only 2 of the nation's 50 states had female governors. When the Reagan administration began its second term in January 1985, there were only two women in the cabinet. In October 1981, Judge Sandra Day O'Connor of the Arizona Court of Appeals was sworn in as the nation's first female Supreme Court justice. But no woman has ever served as president of the United States, vice president, speaker of the House of Representatives, or chief justice of the Supreme Court.
>
> *Sociology*
> by Richard Schaefer

cabinet (căb′ ə nĭt) n. The group of persons appointed by a chief of state or prime minister to head the executive departments of the government and to act as official advisers.

● Who or what is the passage about? On the line below, write a word or phrase that tells the subject matter:

_____

ă pat ā pay â care ä father ĕ pet ē be ĭ pit ī tie î pier ŏ pot ō toe
ô paw oi noise ŏŏ took ōō boot ou out th thin *th* this ŭ cut û urge
yōō abuse zh vision ə *a*bout, it*e*m, ed*i*ble, gall*o*p, circ*u*s

- What is the most important point the author wants you to *understand* about the subject matter? Formulate a main idea *sentence* that answers this question and write the sentence here:

_____

_____

_____

_____

The subject matter of this passage is *the lack of women in high government positions.* But what does the author want you to understand about the lack of women in high government positions? Throughout the paragraph, the author gives statistics and specific examples of the few women who have held high government positions. In the final sentence of the paragraph, the author lists high government positions which no woman has ever held. Using your reasoning to combine these ideas will lead you to the main ideas: *Throughout our history, there have been very few women in high government positions.*

The main idea sentence of this paragraph could also be expressed correctly several other ways. For example:

In general, women have not held high U.S. government positions.

or

Historically, it has been a rare exception to have women in high positions in the U.S. government.

Incidentally, in this passage, you can determine that the author is referring to women in high government positions in the United States. Several details in the paragraph indicate this, even though the United States is not mentioned in the paragraph. These details are "the nation's 50 states," "the Reagan administration," "Judge Sandra Day O'Connor of Arizona," etc.

FORMULATING IMPLIED MAIN IDEAS
Chapter Summary

An **implied main idea** is a main idea that the author does not state directly as a single sentence within the paragraph. Therefore, you must *formulate* a main idea sentence that expresses the author's most important point.

Whenever you read a paragraph that has an *implied* main idea, you should formulate the main idea by doing this:

- Ask yourself, "What is the subject matter?" ("Who or what is the passage about?")

- Ask yourself, "What is the most important point the author wants me to *understand* about the subject matter?" Since there will not be a sentence in the paragraph that states the main idea,

- Answer this question by *formulating* a main idea sentence. You can do this one of three ways:

1. See if you can formulate the main idea by combining one sentence with a word or phrase from another sentence (this word or phrase will often be the subject matter):

   One sentence + a word or phrase from = formulated
                         another sentence (often   main idea
                         the subject matter)   sentence

2. See if you can formulate the main idea by combining two sentences from the paragraph:

   One sentence + another sentence = formulated
                                     main idea sentence

> **3.** See if you can formulate the main idea by combining and inter-
> preting important ideas from several sentences:
>
> Important   + important   + important   = formulated
> information   information   information   main idea
>   sentence

Remember the main idea must be a sentence. Also, keep in mind that there are often several equally correct ways to express the same main idea.

CHAPTER
3

FORMULATING IMPLIED MAIN IDEAS
Practice Exercises

All the practice exercises in this section have main ideas that are *implied.* Your task is to formulate an appropriate main idea sentence for each paragraph.

You may find that these passages are challenging and require more thought. They may also require more effort and patience. This is because the process of inferring and formulating main ideas involves higher-level thinking skills. To be an effective reader, however, you must understand the author's main ideas, even when he or she does not state them directly.

Because implied main ideas can require more effort, you may sometimes become frustrated and be tempted to give up. This is a normal feeling, as you will recall from the section on "Maintaining a Positive Attitude" in the Introduction. Even the best readers sometimes experience this frustration and must reread and rethink a passage in order to formulate its main idea. It is only through practice that you will gain experience and proficiency in formulating implied main ideas.

ADVANTAGES OF KNOWING HOW TO FORMULATE MAIN IDEAS

Even though developing this skill may be challenging at first, there are several payoffs for you as a student:

1. Formulating main idea sentences will help you *understand* complex textbook paragraphs that do not have a stated main idea sentence.

2. Formulating main idea sentences will help you *remember* the passage's main idea better because you have taken the time and effort to write it in your own words.

3. Formulating main idea sentences can help you *score higher on tests* because you understand your textbook chapters better.

4. Formulating main idea sentences can help you *improve your writing.*

For the five passages of this section, you will have to use your judgment to combine ideas in order to formulate main idea sentences. This is what you will most often have to do with textbook paragraphs that have implied main ideas.

Read each paragraph, determine its subject matter, and then formulate a main idea sentence.

1. This passage comes from a sociology textbook.

Fashions

Why do fashions occur in the first place? (1) One reason is that in some cultures, like ours, values change: what is new is good. Thus in many modern societies clothing styles change yearly, while people in traditional societies may wear the same style of clothing for many generations. (2) Many industries promote quick changes in fashions to increase their sales. Fashions are stimulated, too, (3) by the quest for prestige and social mobility. Although a new style occasionally originates from lower-status groups, as blue jeans did, most fashions trickle down from the top. (4) Upper-class people adopt some style or artifact as a badge of their status, but they cannot monopolize most status symbols for long. The style or object is adopted by the middle-class, maybe copied and modified for use by lower-status groups, providing people with the prestige of possessing a high-status symbol. By trickling down, however, the symbol eventually loses its prestige. The upper-class adopts a new style, until it too "trickles down" and must be replaced by another (Turner and Killian, 1972).

Sociology: An Introduction
by Alex Thio

promote (prə mōt′) v. To attempt to sell by advertising.

social mobility (sō′ shəl mō bĭl′ ə tē) n. Movement of individuals or groups from one stratum (level) of society to another.

artifact (är′ tə făkt) n. An object produced by human workmanship.

monopolize (mə nŏp′ ə līz) v. To dominate by excluding others.

ă pat ā pay â care ä father ĕ pet ē be ĭ pit ī tie î pier ŏ pot ō toe
ô paw oi noise ŏŏ took ōō boot ou out th thin *th* this ŭ cut û urge
yōō abuse zh vision ə *a*bout, it*e*m, ed*i*ble, gall*o*p, circ*u*s

- Who or what is the passage about? On the line below, write a word or phrase that tells the subject matter:

  _____

- What is the most important point the author wants you to *understand* about the subject matter? Formulate a main idea *sentence* that answers this question and write the sentence here:

  _____

  _____

  _____

  _____

2. This paragraph is from a U.S. government textbook.

Maternity Policy

Until recently, many companies refused to hire women because they might become pregnant and quit their jobs. Some companies required women to remain single and fired them if they married. These policies have not been in effect since the 1950s, but vestiges of the attitudes behind them remain. Until recently, on some airlines female flight attendants who became pregnant lost their seniority or their jobs. The Supreme Court has ruled that discriminatory policies against women of childbearing age violate the Civil Rights Act of 1964 and has ordered reinstatement and back pay for these women.

American Politics and Government
by Richard Pious

maternity (mə tûr′ nə tē) adj. Associated with pregnancy or childbirth.

vestige (věs′ tĭj) n. A trace or evidence of some thing that no longer exists.

seniority (sēn yôr′ ə tē) n. Being higher in position than others of the same rank by reason of a longer span of service.

ă pat ā pay â care ä father ě pet ē be ĭ pit ī tie î pier ŏ pot ō toe
ô paw oi noise o͞o took o͞o boot ou out th thin *th* this ŭ cut û urge
yo͞o abuse zh vision ə *a*bout, it*e*m, ed*i*ble, gall*o*p, circ*u*s

discriminatory (dĭs krĭm′ ə nə tôr ē) adj. Marked by or showing prejudice; biased.

reinstatement (rē ĭn stāt′ mənt) n. Restoring to a previous condition or position.

- Who or what is the passage about? On the line below, write a word or phrase that tells the subject matter:

  _____

- What is the most important point the author wants you to *understand* about the subject matter? Formulate a main idea *sentence* that answers this question and write the sentence here:

  _____

  _____

  _____

  _____

3. This passage is from a biology textbook.

Asexual Reproduction

Asexual reproduction, also known as **vegetative propagation,** is common in plants. In vegetative propagation, a portion of one plant gives rise to a completely new plant. Both plants now have identical genes. As an example, some plants have above-ground horizontal stems, called *runners,* and others have underground stems, called *rhizomes,* that produce new plants. To take a concrete example, strawberry plants grow from the nodes of runners and violets grow from the nodes of rhizomes. White potatoes can be propagated in a similar manner. White potatoes are actually portions of underground stems, and each eye is a node that will produce a new potato plant. Sweet potatoes are modified roots and may be propagated by planting

ă pat ā pay â care ä father ĕ pet ē be ĭ pit ī tie î pier ŏ pot ō toe
ô paw oi noise o͞o took ō͞o boot ou out th thin *th* this ŭ cut û urge
yo͞o abuse zh vision ə *a*bout, it*e*m, ed*i*ble, gall*o*p, circ*u*s

sections of the root. You may have noticed that the roots of some fruit trees, such as cherry and apple trees, produce "suckers," small plants that can be used to grow new trees.

Inquiry into Life
by Sylvia Mader

---

asexual reproduction (ā sĕk′ shoō əl rē prə dŭk′ shən) n. Reproduction involving a single individual, and without male and female gametes, as in binary fission or budding.

vegetative propagation (vĕj′ ə tā tĭv prŏp ə gā′ shən) n. Another name for asexual reproduction. A portion of one plant gives rise to a new plant that has identical genes. (The author helps the reader by using the phrase "also known as.")

gene (jēn) n. A hereditary unit that determines one of the traits an offspring will have.

runner (rŭn′ ər) n. An above-ground horizontal stem that produces new plants. (Notice that the author defines the term and uses the word "called" to help you recognize that she is defining a term.)

rhizome (rhī′ zōm) n. An underground stem that produces new plants.

- Who or what is the passage about? On the line below, write a word or phrase that tells the subject matter:

- What is the most important point the author wants you to *understand* about the subject matter? Formulate a main idea *sentence* that answers this question and write the sentence here:

ă pat   ā pay   â care   ä father   ĕ pet   ē be   ĭ pit   ī tie   î pier   ŏ pot   ō toe
ô paw   oi noise   oō took   ōō boot   ou out   th thin   *th* this   ŭ cut   û urge
yōō abuse   zh vision   ə *a*bout, it*e*m, ed*i*ble, gall*o*p, circ*u*s

4.   This excerpt is from a business textbook.

> From the development of the first computers in the late 1940s until the middle of the 1950s, Univac Corporation dominated the computer industry. In the mid-1950s the boards of directors of Univac and IBM implemented distinctly different strategic policies. The board of directors of Univac, which held about 60 percent of the world computer market at the time, decided that the most important future market for computer systems would continue to be in scientific data processing and that business data processing, at that time an almost totally undeveloped field, would remain a minor market for computer systems. The board of directors of IBM, however, which held about 10 percent of the computer market but was an important force in the office products industry, reached the opposite conclusion, deciding that the future growth of the computer industry would be primarily in the area of business data processing.
>
> *Principles of Management Information Systems*
> by George M. Scott

---

dominate (dŏm′ ə nāt) v. To occupy the preeminent position in or over; to control or rule by superior authority or power.

implement (ĭm′ plə mənt) v. To provide a definite plan or procedure to ensure the fulfillment of.

minor (mī′ nər) adj. Lesser or smaller in importance.

- Who or what is the passage about? On the line below, write a word or phrase that tells the subject matter:

- What is the most important point the author wants you to *understand* about the subject matter? Formulate a main idea *sentence* that answers this question and write the sentence here:

ă pat ā pay â care ä father ĕ pet ē be ĭ pit ī tie î pier ŏ pot ō toe
ô paw oi noise o͞o took o͞o boot ou out th thin *th* this ŭ cut û urge
yo͞o abuse zh vision ə *a*bout, it*e*m, ed*i*ble, gall*o*p, circ*u*s

_____

_____

_____

_____

5. This paragraph is from a sociology textbook.

Creating Geniuses

Like Edith, many geniuses have been deliberately subjected to a very stimulating environment. A well-known example is Norbert Wiener, a prime mover in the development of computers and cybernetics. He entered college at 11 and received his Ph.D. from Harvard at 18. According to his father, he was "essentially an average boy who had the advantage of superlative training" (Wiener, 1953). Many musical prodigies of the past, including Mozart and Beethoven, were subjected to rigorous daily training by their parents. Since 1945 a large number of ordinary children have been brought to the famous Japanese music teacher Shinichi Suzuki and he has successfully "trained every one of them—without exception—to be an excellent string musician" (Hoult, 1979). Nature may draw the outline of our traits and potential abilities, but that outline is broad and vague. Nurture appears both to determine the actual boundaries and to fill in the details (Nisbet, 1982).

Sociology: An Introduction
by Alex Thio

---

subject (sŭb jĕkt′) v. Expose to; cause to experience or undergo.

stimulating (stĭm′ yə lāt ĭng) adj. Eliciting or accelerating physiological or psychological activity; causing a response, excitement, or heightened action.

cybernetics (sī bər nĕt′ ĭks) n. Plural in form; used with a singular verb. The theoretical study of control processes in electronic, mechanical, and biological systems, especially the mathematical analysis of the flow of information in such systems.

ă pat ā pay â care ä father ĕ pet ē be ĭ pit ī tie î pier ŏ pot ō toe
ô paw oi noise o͝o took o͞o boot ou out th thin *th* this ŭ cut û urge
yo͞o abuse zh vision ə *a*bout, it*e*m, ed*i*ble, gall*o*p, circ*u*s

Ph.D. (Doctor of Philosophy) n. A graduate degree (earned after the undergraduate and master's degree).

superlative (soo pŭr′ lə tĭv) adj. Of the highest order or quality; surpassing or superior to all others.

prodigy (prŏd′ ə jē) n. A young person with exceptional talents or powers.

rigorous (rĭg′ ər əs) adj. Characterized by or acting with rigor; trying; strict; precisely accurate.

trait (trāt) n. A distinguishing feature, as of the character.

potential (pə tĕn′ shəl) adj. Possible, but not yet realized; capable of being but not yet in existence; latent.

- Who or what is the passage about? On the line below, write a word or phrase that tells the subject matter:

- What is the most important point the author wants you to *understand* about the subject matter? Formulate a main idea *sentence* that answers this question and write the sentence here:

ă pat ā pay â care ä father ĕ pet ē be ĭ pit ī tie î pier ŏ pot ō toe
ô paw oi noise o͝o took o͞o boot ou out th thin *th* this ŭ cut û urge
yo͞o abuse zh vision ə *a*bout, it*e*m, ed*i*ble, gall*o*p, circ*u*s

FORMULATING IMPLIED MAIN IDEAS
Answer Key for Practice Exercises

Compare your responses to the practice exercises on pages 127–134 with the acceptable formulations of the subject matter and main idea sentences given below.

1. *Subject matter:*   why fashions occur

    (The heading, *Fashions,* is too general.)

    Main idea: Fashions occur for a variety of reasons.

or

                                  Fashions occur for several reasons.

or

                                    There are four reasons fashions occur.

    (Notice the author begins this passage with a question and then answers it.)

2. *Subject matter:*   unfair maternity policies

    Main idea: In recent years Supreme Court rulings and legislation have changed unfair maternity policies to prevent discrimination.

or

                                    Unfair maternity policies have been changed by recent Supreme Court rulings and legislation to prevent discrimination.

    (You must combine the subject matter given in the heading with several ideas in order to formulate the main idea.)

3. *Subject matter:*   asexual reproduction
                                                (*or* vegetative propagation)

    Main idea: Asexual reproduction, or vegetative
                                                propagation, results in a completely
                                                new plant that has genes identical to
                                                the original one.

                                                            or

                                                A completely new plant with genes
                                                identical to the original one can be
                                                formed by asexual reproduction or
                                                vegetative propagation.

(The main idea of this paragraph is derived from *combining* the information in the first three sentences.)

4. *Subject matter:*   the computer marketing decisions of
                                                Univac and IBM in the mid-1950s

                                                            or

                                                IBM's and Univac's computer market-
                                                ing decisions

    Main idea: Unlike Univac, IBM made the deci-
                                                sion that business data processing
                                                would be the most important future
                                                market for computer systems.

                                                            or

                                                IBM, unlike Univac, determined that
                                                business data processing would be-
                                                come the greatest market for the com-
                                                puter industry.

(Again, you must "add up" the information contained in several sentences in order to formulate the main idea sentence.)

5. *Subject matter:*   developing our potential abilities

                                                            or

                                                how nature and nurture affect the de-
                                                velopment of our potential abilities

(The heading, *Creating Geniuses,* is too narrow since the passage discusses developing *every* person's potential.)

Main idea: Although nature may draw the outline of our traits and potential abilities, nurture appears both to determine the actual boundaries and to fill in the details.

or

Although we are born with certain abilities, excellent training is necessary if we are to reach our potential.

(The ideas in the last two sentences are combined to formulate the main idea sentence.)

FORMULATING IMPLIED MAIN IDEAS
Review Test

Determine the subject matter, then formulate a main idea sentence for each of these paragraphs. For each one you will have to formulate the main idea by combining ideas from several sentences.

1. This passage comes from a business textbook.

> Electronic computer data processing began after World War II. A landmark in its development was the Eniac, a 20-ton vacuum tube computer completed in 1946 by Mauchley and Eckert, professors of electrical engineering at the University of Pennsylvania. The Eniac now reposes in the Smithsonian Institution. In 1981, a party was held to celebrate the thirty-fifth birthday of the Eniac and the computer age. The Eniac was dusted off, plugged in, and assigned a set of calculations to perform. The same request was made of a Radio Shack TRS-80 microcomputer. The 30-lb microcomputer completed the task about 5 times as fast as the 20-ton behemoth Eniac, a startling indication of the tremendous advances made in computing technology in just 35 years.
>
> *Principles of Management Information Systems*
> by George M. Scott

---

repose (rē pōz′) v. To rest or remain.

behemoth (bǐ hē′ məth) n. Something enormous in size.

ă pat ā pay â care ä father ĕ pet ē be ǐ pit ī tie î pier ŏ pot ō toe
ô paw oi noise o͞o took o͞o boot ou out th thin *th* this ŭ cut û urge
yo͞o abuse zh vision ə *a*bout, it*e*m, ed*i*ble, gall*o*p, circ*u*s

139

- Who or what is the passage about? On the line below, write a word or phrase that tells the subject matter:

  _____

- What is the most important point the author wants you to *understand* about the subject matter? Formulate a main idea *sentence* that answers this question and write the sentence here:

  _____

  _____

  _____

  _____

  _____

2. This paragraph is an excerpt from a sociology textbook.

> Mayo wanted to find out what kinds of incentives and work conditions would encourage workers to work harder. He first systematically changed the lighting, lunch hours, coffee breaks, methods of payment (salary versus piece rate), and the like. Then he was surprised to find that no matter what changes were made the workers increased their productivity. When the light was very bright, they worked harder than before; but when it was changed to very dim, they still worked harder. When they were given two or three coffee breaks, they increased their output; when they were not allowed any coffee break, they continued to increase their output. Mayo later discovered that the increased productivity was actually due to all the attention the workers were getting from the researcher. They felt that they were not mere cogs of a machine but instead respected for their work; hence they reciprocated by working harder. The impact of the researcher's presence on subjects' behavior is now known as the **Hawthorne effect.** Social scientists today strive to avoid it by becoming a member of the group being studied, by using hidden cameras and tape recorders, or by using any means that prevents subjects from knowing they are being observed.
>
> *Sociology: An Introduction*
> by Alex Thio

incentive (ĭn sĕn′ tĭv) n. Something inciting to action or effort, such as the fear of punishment or the expectation of reward.

systematically (sĭ stə măt′ ĭk ə lē) adv. Carried on in a step-by-step procedure; done methodically.

productivity (prə dŭk tĭv′ ə tē) n. Useful results or outcomes.

reciprocate (rĭ sĭp′ rə kāt) v. To give or take mutually; to show or feel in response or return.

Hawthorne effect (hô′ thôrn ĭ fĕkt′) n. The impact of the researcher's presence on the subject's behavior. (The author uses the phrase "is now known as" to alert you to the definition he is presenting.)

- Who or what is the passage about? On the line below, write a word or phrase that tells the subject matter:

- What is the most important point the author wants you to *understand* about the subject matter? Formulate a main idea *sentence* that answers this question and write the sentence here:

3. This passage comes from a U.S. government textbook.

Every recent president has had the public's confidence during the "honeymoon" period. When asked in polls whether they "approve or disapprove of how the president is doing his job," 60 to 75 percent of the public had expressed approval of the performance of recent presidents during their first months in office. All presidents have slipped

ă pat ā pay â care ä father ĕ pet ē be ĭ pit ī tie î pier ŏ pot ō toe
ô paw oi noise o͞o took o͞o boot ou out th thin *th* this ŭ cut û urge
yo͞o abuse zh vision ə *a*bout, it*e*m, ed*i*ble, gall*o*p, circ*u*s

from this high point, however, and only Eisenhower, Kennedy, and Reagan left office with an approval rating higher than 50 percent.

Nation of Nations
by James W. Davidson et al.

- Who or what is the passage about? On the line below, write a word or phrase that tells the subject matter:

_____

- What is the most important point the authors want you to *understand* about the subject matter? Formulate a main idea *sentence* that answers this question and write the sentence here:

_____

_____

_____

_____

4. This paragraph comes from a sociology textbook.

    People might halt this growth [in population] through what Malthus called "preventive checks," by which he meant late marriage and sexual restraint, which would reduce birth rates. But Malthus doubted that people, especially the lower classes, had the will to exercise this restraint. Instead, he argued, population growth would eventually be stopped by nature. Its tools would be what Malthus called "positive checks"—disease and famine:

    Premature death must in some shape or other visit the human race. The vices of mankind (such as war) are active and able ministers of depopulation. . . . But should they fail in this war of extermination, sickly seasons, epidemics, pestilence, and plague advance in terrific array. . . . Should success still be incomplete, gigantic inevitable famine stalks in the rear, and with one mighty blow, levels the population (Malthus, 1798).

    Sociology: An Introduction
    by Alex Thio

---

preventive checks n. Reduction of the birthrate by late marriage and sexual restraint. (The author tells you what Malthus meant by this phrase with the words "by which he meant.")

restraint (rĭ strānt′) n. The act of holding back, restraining, or controlling.

exercise (ĕks′ ər sīz) v. To use.

positive checks n. Nature's stopping of population growth by disease and famine. (The author uses the phrase "what Malthus called" to explain the meaning of "positive checks.")

vice (vīs) n. An evil, degrading, or immoral practice or habit.

depopulation (dē pŏp yə lā′ shən) n. A sharp reduction in the population.

pestilence (pĕs′ tə ləns) n. Any unusually fatal epidemic disease.

array (ə rā′) n. An orderly arrangement, especially of troops.

famine (făm′ ĭn) n. A drastic and far-reaching shortage of food.

stalk (stôk) v. To pursue by tracking.

- Who or what is the passage about? On the line below, write a word or phrase that tells the subject matter:

  _____

- What is the most important point the author wants you to *understand* about the subject matter? Formulate a main idea *sentence* that answers this question and write the sentence here:

  _____

  _____

  _____

  _____

5. This passage is taken from an economics textbook.

> There is no unique or universally accepted way to respond to the economizing problem. Various societies, having different cultural and

---

ă pat   ā pay   â care   ä father   ĕ pet   ē be   ĭ pit   ī tie   î pier   ŏ pot   ō toe
ô paw   oi noise   o͞o took   o͞o boot   ou out   th thin   *th* this   ŭ cut   û urge
yo͞o abuse   zh vision   ə *a*bout, it*e*m, ed*i*ble, gall*o*p, circ*u*s

historical backgrounds, different mores and customs, and contrasting ideological frameworks—not to mention resources which differ both quantitatively and qualitatively—use different institutions in dealing with the reality of relative scarcity. The Soviet Union, the United States, and Great Britain, for example, are all—in terms of their accepted goals, ideology, technologies, resources, and culture—attempting to achieve efficiency in the use of their respective resources. The best method for responding to the unlimited wants–scarce resources dilemma in one economy may be inappropriate for another economic system.

Economics: Principles, Problems and Policies
by Campbell McConnell and Stanley Brue

- Who or what is the passage about? On the line below, write a word or phrase that tells the subject matter:

- What is the most important point the authors want you to *understand* about the subject matter? Formulate a main idea *sentence* that answers this question and write the sentence here:

FORMULATING IMPLIED MAIN IDEAS
Supplemental Exercises

1. This selection is taken from a music appreciation textbook.

> Wolfgang Amadeus Mozart (1756-1791), one of the most amazing child prodigies in history, was born in Salzburg, Austria. By the age of six, he could play the harpsichord and violin, improvise fugues, write minuets, and read music perfectly at first sight. At age eight, he wrote a symphony; at eleven, an oratorio; at twelve, an opera.
>
> *Music Appreciation*
> by Roger Kamien

• Who or what is the passage about? On the line below, write a word or phrase that tells the subject matter:

_____

• What is the most important point the author wants you to *understand* about the subject matter? Formulate a main idea *sentence* that answers this question and write the sentence here:

_____

_____

_____

2. This selection is taken from an economics textbook.

> What is a **balance sheet?** It is merely a statement of assets and claims which portrays or summarizes the financial position of a firm—in this case a commercial bank—at some specific point in time. Every balance sheet has one overriding virtue: By definition, it

must balance. Why? Because each and every known *asset,* being something of economic value, will be claimed by someone. Can you think of an asset—something of monetary value—which no one claims? A balance sheet balances because the value of assets equals the amount of their owners' claims.

Economics: Principles, Problems and Policies
by Campbell McConnell and Stanley Brue

- Who or what is the passage about? On the line below, write a word or phrase that tells the subject matter:

_____

- What is the most important point the authors want you to *understand* about the subject matter? Formulate a main idea *sentence* that answers this question and write the sentence here:

_____

_____

_____

_____

3. Here is a selection from a psychology textbook.

Foot-in-the-Door Technique

A door-to-door salesperson soon learns that if she can get the customer to comply with her request to let her in the door, the customer is more likely to comply with a later request to buy the product. This technique is known as the **foot-in-the-door technique.** It refers to the increased probability of compliance to a second request if a person complies with a small, first request. . . . For example, Jim Jones used the foot-in-the-door technique with his followers. When he was still in the United States, he slowly made more and more demands on the members of his church, such as attending services, giving money, and donating time. After the members agreed, he made larger requests, such as signing over their Social Security checks and ownership of their homes. Next, he asked them to move to the jungles of Guyana. Finally, he asked them to take their lives.

Introduction to Psychology
by Ron Plotnik

- Who or what is the passage about? On the line below, write a word or phrase that tells the subject matter:

  _____

- What is the most important point the author wants you to *understand* about the subject matter? Formulate a main idea *sentence* that answers this question and write the sentence here:

  _____

  _____

  _____

  _____

4. This passage comes from a psychology textbook. Write a word or phrase that tells the subject matter for *each paragraph.* Next, formulate a main idea sentence for *each paragraph.*

Are artists more creative than other people? Maybe, maybe not. The profession of artist is not the only one that requires creativity. Scientists, mathematicians, writers, teachers, business executives, doctors, lawyers, librarians, computer programmers—people in every line of work, if they are any good, look for ways to be creative. The football coach who invents a new play is being creative, as is the plumber who devises an innovative way to keep the washing machine from leaking. Artists occupy a special place in that they have devoted their lives

Subject Matter

_____

Main Idea

_____

_____

_____

to opening the channels of *visual* creativity.

Can a person become more creative? Almost certainly, if one allows oneself to be. Being creative, as we said, means making something new. It means learning to trust one's own interests, experiences, and references, and to use them to enhance life and work. Above all, it means discarding rigid notions of what has been or should be in favor of what *could* be. For both the artist and the observer of art, creativity develops when the eyes and mind are wide open, when the brain is operating on all its channels.

Living with Art
by Rita Gilbert and William McCarter

Subject Matter

_____

Main Idea

_____

_____

_____

CHAPTER

4

IDENTIFYING SUPPORTING DETAILS

1

Determining Subject Matter

2

Locating Directly Stated Main Ideas

3

Formulating Implied Main Ideas

4

Identifying Supporting Details

5

Recognizing Authors' Writing Patterns

6

Applying Comprehension
Skills to Longer Passages

7

Remembering College Textbook
Material through Organizing

8

Thinking Critically as You Read

149

INTRODUCTION

Thus far in Chapters 1, 2, and 3, we have covered several essential areas of comprehension: determining the subject matter (Chapter 1), locating directly stated main ideas (Chapter 2), and formulating implied main ideas (Chapter 3). In those chapters, you learned that whenever you read, you should ask yourself the following questions:

First ask yourself: • Who or what is the passage about?	Your answer will be: • The subject matter
Then ask yourself: • What is the main point the author wants me to understand about the subject matter?	Your answer will be: • The main idea
Now ask yourself: • Is there a single sentence in the passage that *directly states* the main idea?	If your answer is: • *Yes,* you must *locate* the main idea sentence. It may be the first sentence or the last sentence or elsewhere in the paragraph. • *No,* the main idea of the passage is *expressed indirectly,* and you will need to *formulate* the main idea.

You learned that there are several ways to formulate main ideas when they are not directly stated by the author.

---

1. Ask yourself if you can formulate the main idea by combining one sentence with a word or phrase from another sentence (this is likely to be the subject matter):

   One sentence + a word or phrase = formulated
               from another   main idea sentence
               sentence (often
               the subject matter)

2. Ask yourself if you can formulate the main idea by combining two different sentences from the paragraph:

   One sentence + another sentence = formulated main idea
                                   sentence

3. Ask yourself if you can formulate the main idea by combining and interpreting important ideas from several sentences:

   Important + important + important = formulated
   information   information   information   main idea
                                         sentence

Asking yourself these questions as you read a passage will focus your attention, sharpen your concentration, and improve your comprehension.

THE IMPORTANCE OF UNDERSTANDING SUPPORTING DETAILS

Certainly, the subject matter and main idea are essential to a thorough understanding of your textbooks. However, a paragraph consists of more than a subject matter and a main idea. The other sentences of the paragraph contain **supporting details.** Supporting details relate to or illustrate the main idea so that you can understand the main idea fully. For example, supporting details may consist of dates, names, places, descriptions, statistics, or other important points of information that

> The **supporting details** of a paragraph consist of the important information that helps you understand *more* about the main idea.

support the main idea. Because the supporting details help you understand *more* about the main idea, they should not be overlooked.

There are several benefits of examining and understanding the details which support a paragraph's main idea. First, understanding the supporting details is a key to understanding the main idea more *completely*. Second, understanding supporting details makes it easier to *remember* significant information from the passage because material that you understand is easier to remember. Third, and also related to memory, is the fact that understanding supporting details helps you grasp the *organization* of the entire paragraph. This enables you to take notes from and mark your textbooks intelligently and effectively. Finally, professors often ask test questions that are based on supporting details. Test questions about names, dates, places, and so forth are examples of questions based on supporting details. If you are better able to understand and remember supporting details, you will learn more and will score higher on tests.

Mastering the skills of determining subject matter, main idea, and supporting details of a passage is the starting point for becoming a successful reader and learner.

EXPLANATION AND EXAMPLES

Understanding supporting details helps you understand the main idea more completely. In your day-to-day activities, you constantly seek details that help you understand situations and events more thoroughly. For example, if you walk up to friends who are talking and ask what they're talking about, their answer might be, "Last night." (This is the subject matter.) You would automatically ask them, "What *about* last night?" They might then reply, "We had a fantastic time at the concert last night." (This is the main idea.) You would probably then ask further questions, such as, "Which group did you see? What did they play? Where was the concert? Who did you go with?" The answers to these questions will be the supporting details that help you understand the main idea more completely. In other words, it will help you understand why they had a great time at the concert.

Good readers consistently ask themselves questions as they read in order to understand the passage fully. There is nothing magical about this process; effective readers simply do it on a regular basis, whereas ineffective readers ask themselves few questions as they read—or sometimes none at all. One bonus of asking yourself questions is that you may become more interested in the subject and that you enjoy it more.

To be effective, the reading process must be an *interactive* one. This means that as you are reading, you mentally pose questions for the writer. Then you read to see if they are answered. Authors usually try to anticipate questions that the reader will ask and to provide the answers. But you may have some basic or specific questions (about a term, name, etc.) that you are not able to answer. First, go back and reread portions of your assignment. Unfortunately, the writer cannot anticipate every question that every reader will ask, and you may find that you will have to seek information on your own from other sources such as the textbook glossary, a dictionary, or another textbook on the same subject. Answering *your* specific questions about the passage will provide you with a deeper understanding of the main idea and key details.

What questions should you ask yourself as you read? Your questions should be based on the paragraph's main idea. You can turn a main idea sentence into a question by using words such as *who, what, where, when, why,* and *how.* Let's look at the sample paragraph from a psychology textbook that was used in Chapter 2. The subject matter is *the brain stem.* The main idea is that *the brain stem is responsible for many basic functions.* For this main idea, efficient readers would ask themselves, "*What* are the basic functions that the brain stem is responsible for?" This question will lead the reader to the supporting details that can help her or him understand the main idea more completely. Now reread the paragraph, and look for the answer to this question: "What are the basic functions that the brain stem is responsible for?"

The brain stem is responsible for many basic functions. It takes in information from several senses through sensory regions for vision, hearing, taste, balance, and touch in the facial area. It controls involuntary activity of the tongue, the larynx, the eyes, and the facial muscles through specific motor neurons for these areas. It controls levels of sleep and arousal through the reticular formation, nestled within its central core, and it coordinates the motor neurons in the spinal cord that control such activities as walking, breathing, and the beating of our hearts.

Psychology
by Diane Papalia and Sally Olds

Subject matter: brain stem

Main idea sentence: The brain stem is responsible for many basic functions.

What *additional* information do the authors want you to have so that you can understand more about the main idea? They want you to know the answer to this question: "*What* are the basic functions that the brain stem is responsible for?"

This answer will be the supporting details. The supporting details for this paragraph about the functions of the brain stem are listed here:

- it takes in information from several senses

- it controls certain involuntary activity

- it controls levels of sleep and arousal

- it coordinates motor neurons in spinal cord

Although every detail in the passage pertains to the main idea, not every detail is listed above because some are more important than others. How can you tell which supporting details are most important? The most important supporting details are the ones that are *essential* to your complete understanding of the main idea. Minor details may add interest, color, or clarification.

Here is a diagram of the main idea and essential supporting details in the passage on the brain stem.

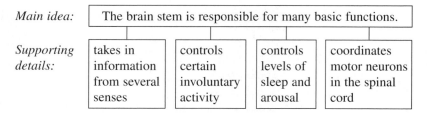

Now let's look at another example from a previous chapter. This passage comes from a business textbook. Read the passage again to recall its subject matter and main idea.

The electronic nature of computers gives them several important attributes. First, computers are extremely fast at processing instructions, that is, at performing calculations and at making logical comparisons. Second, computers are extremely accurate in their processing; rarely does a computer make an electronic mistake that it does not catch itself and signal to the computer operator. Almost all errors in computer data processing are caused by faulty programs prepared by humans. Third, computers are extremely reliable; being primarily electronic and without moving parts, they seldom have failures.

Principles of Management Information Systems
by George M. Scott

Subject matter: the electronic nature of the computer

Main idea sentence: The electronic nature of computers gives them several important attributes.

Now consider this: "What *additional* information does the author want me to know so that I can understand the main idea fully?" Create a question that will lead you to this additional information (the supporting details) and write your supporting detail question here:

_____

_____

_____

Did you ask a question such as this: "*What* are the important attributes of electronic computers?"

What information in the paragraph answers this question? List the three supporting details for the main idea here:

- _____

- _____

- _____

Your answer should have included these important supporting details: computers are extremely fast; computers are extremely accurate; and computers are extremely reliable. You can see that the author has used the words *first, second,* and *third* to direct your attention to these important supporting details.

This paragraph comes from a marketing textbook. Read the paragraph carefully.

> In the 1980s retailing management faced challenges perhaps unequaled since the Depression of the 1930s. Population increases and economic growth slowed down considerably since the 1960s. The costs of capital and energy soared, and unemployment and inflation were at uncomfortably high levels. Consumerism and government restrictions affecting retailing were likely to increase. The demographic and psychographic aspects of the consumer market were changing, and at a greater pace than in the past. These forces underlay several broad, significant trends in retailing.
>
> *Fundamentals of Marketing*
> by William Stanton

Subject matter: retailing management challenges

Main idea sentence: In the 1980s retailing management faced challenges perhaps unequaled since the Depression of the 1930s.

Ask yourself: "What *additional* information does the author want me to know so that I can understand the main idea fully?" Create a question that will lead you to this additional information (the supporting details). Write your supporting detail question here:

_____

_____

_____

_____

Did you ask a question similar to this: "*What* were the unusual challenges faced by retailing managers in the 1980s?"

What information in the paragraph answers this question? List the five supporting details for this main idea here:

- _____

- _____

- _____
- _____
- _____

Your answer should have included these important supporting details: population increases and economic growth slowed down; the costs of capital and energy soared; unemployment and inflation were high; restrictions affecting retailing increased; certain aspects of consumer markets changed rapidly.

CREATING SUPPORTING DETAIL QUESTIONS

As you have just seen, the question that you should ask in order to understand the important supporting details is *based on the main idea.* This question will lead you to the *additional* information the author wants you to have so that you can understand more about the main idea. To review the examples used earlier in this chapter:

Example 1

Main idea: The brain stem is responsible for many basic functions.

Supporting detail question: What are the basic functions that the brain stem is responsible for?

Example 2

Main idea: The electronic nature of computers gives them several important attributes.

Supporting detail question: What are the important attributes of electronic computers?

Example 3

> *Main idea:* In the 1980s, retailing management faced challenges perhaps unequaled since the Depression of the 1930s.
>
> *Supporting detail question:* What were the unusual challenges faced by retailing managers in the 1980s?

The supporting detail question is often an obvious and logical extension of the main idea. In many cases, you can create a supporting detail question simply by changing the main idea sentence into one or more questions. The supporting detail questions lead you to details that further explain the main idea.

There will be times when you must ask *more than one* question about the main idea. For example, consider a paragraph that has this main idea:

Example 4

> *Main idea:* Tempera is an opaque, watercolor medium whose use spans recorded history.
>
> An effective reader would probably create *two* important questions about this main idea:
>
> *Supporting detail question 1:* What exactly is tempera?
>
> *and*
>
> *Supporting detail question 2:* What about its use throughout recorded history?

These two questions are directly indicated by the main idea sentence. The main idea leads you to ask these two questions. The answers to these questions are the supporting details that the author wants you to know so that you can understand more about the main idea.

Now read the complete paragraph about tempera and look for the answers to both the supporting detail questions above.

Tempera is an opaque, watercolor medium whose use spans recorded history. It was employed by the ancient Egyptians, and is still used today by such familiar painters as Andrew Wyeth. Tempera refers to ground pigments and their color binders such as gum or glue, but is best known in its egg tempera form. It is a fast-drying medium that virtually eliminates brush strokes and gives extremely sharp and precise detail. Colors in tempera paintings appear almost gemlike in their clarity and brilliance.

Perceiving the Arts
by Dennis Sporre

tempera (tĕm′ pər ə) n. An opaque watercolor medium.

opaque (ō pāk′) adj. Not reflecting light; without luster; dull.

medium (mē′ dē əm) n. A type of artistic technique.

pigment (pĭg′ mənt) n. Dry coloring matter, usually a powder, to be mixed with water, oil, or another base to produce paint.

binder (bīn′ dər) n. A material used to ensure uniform consistency or adhesion to a surface.

virtually (vûr′ chōō ə lē) adv. Essentially; practically; in fact; to all purposes.

Subject matter: tempera

Main idea sentence: Tempera is an opaque, watercolor medium whose use spans recorded history.

To identify the supporting details you should ask yourself: "What *additional* information does the author want me to know so that I can understand the main idea fully?"

ă pat ā pay â care ä father ĕ pet ē be ĭ pit ī tie î pier ŏ pot ō toe
ô paw oi noise ŏŏ took ōō boot ou out th thin *th* this ŭ cut û urge
yōō abuse zh vision ə *a*bout, it*e*m, ed*i*ble, gall*o*p, circ*u*s

The two supporting detail questions and their answers are:

What exactly is tempera?

- It is made from ground pigments and color binders such as gum, glue, or egg.

- It is fast-drying.

- It leaves no brush strokes.

- It gives sharp, precise detail, and results in clear, brilliant color.

What about its use throughout recorded history?

- Tempera was employed by the ancient Egyptians.

- Tempera is still in use today by painters such as Andrew Wyeth.

There will be times when you will have several more questions to ask about a passage. For example, you might need to look up a word or term (such as *opaque, pigments,* or *binders*) or you may need to find out more information about a person, place, or event that is mentioned (for example, the painter Andrew Wyeth).

IDENTIFYING SUPPORTING DETAILS
Chapter Summary

The **supporting details** of a paragraph consist of the important information that helps you understand *more* about the main idea.

Once you have read a textbook paragraph and have identified its subject matter and main idea, you should look for and understand the supporting details. Supporting details relate to or illustrate the main idea so that you can understand the main idea fully.

Asking the following question will lead you to the supporting details:

"What *additional* information does the author want me to know so that I can understand the main idea fully?"

Remember that the supporting detail question is generally an obvious and logical extension of the main idea. In many cases, you simply change the main idea into one or more questions using words such as *who, what, where, when, why,* or *how.*

The answer to your question will be the supporting details. Supporting details consist of such things as:

- dates
- names
- places
- descriptions
- examples
- statistics
- other important points of information that support the main idea.

Because college textbook passages are often packed with information, it is not unusual for a reader to create several supporting detail questions. This is because several types of information are frequently needed in order to understand the main idea fully.

CHAPTER 4

IDENTIFYING SUPPORTING DETAILS
Practice Exercises

In the sample textbook passages below, you will be given the subject matter and main idea, although you should read each paragraph carefully and try to determine these yourself. You will know that you are comprehending accurately if you are able to do this.

You will need to create a supporting detail question for the main idea of each paragraph. Once you have written that question, write your answer to it in the spaces provided. To create a supporting detail question, ask yourself, "What additional information does the author want me to have so that I can understand the main idea fully?" Once you have created your question, its answer will be the supporting details. List each supporting detail on a separate line.

1. This passage comes from a computer science textbook.

> All information systems involve three activities. They receive data as input; they process data by performing calculations, combining data elements, updating accounts, and so on; and they provide information as output. This is true of manual, electromechanical, and computerized information systems.
>
> *Principles of Management Information Systems*
> by George M. Scott

---

input (ĭn′ pŏͦot) n. Something put into a system to achieve a result or output.

output (out′ pŏͦot) n. The amount of something produced or manufactured during a given span of time.

ă pat ā pay â care ä father ĕ pet ē be ĭ pit ī tie î pier ŏ pot ō toe
ô paw oi noise ŏͦo took ōͦo boot ou out th thin *th* this ŭ cut û urge
yŏͦo abuse zh vision ə *a*bout, it*e*m, ed*i*ble, gall*o*p, circ*u*s

Subject matter: activities of information systems

Main idea: All information systems involve three primary activities.

- What *additional* information does the author want you to know so that you can understand the main idea fully? Create a supporting detail question and write it here:

_____

_____

_____

_____

_____

- Now answer your question by *listing* the supporting details here:

_____

_____

_____

_____

2. This paragraph is from a psychology textbook.

    A number of theories for why we forget have been suggested. According to the theory of *motivated forgetting,* we forget material we need to forget; in other words, *we repress* certain uncomfortable memories. *Decay theory* holds that certain memories decay or fade with the passage of time if we do not use the information. *Interference theory* holds that we forget information because other information interferes with or confounds our memory. *Proactive interference* describes a situation where the material we learned first interferes with the ability to remember new material. *Retroactive interference* refers to a situation where information learned later interferes with our remembering previously learned material.

    Psychology
    by Diane Papalia and Sally Olds

repress (rĭ prĕs′) v. To hold back; restrain.

decay theory (dĭ kā′ thē′ ə rē) n. (The words "holds that" tell you that the authors are explaining the term in the passage.)

interference theory (ĭn tər fîr′ əns) n. (The words "holds that" tell you that the authors are explaining the term in the passage.)

proactive interference (prō ăk′ tĭv) n. (The words "describes a" tell you that the authors are explaining the term in the passage.)

retroactive interference (rĕt rō ăk′ tĭv) n. (The words "refers to" tell you that the authors are explaining the term in the passage.)

Subject matter: theories of forgetting

Main idea: A number of theories for why we forget have been suggested.

- What *additional* information do the authors want you to know so that you can understand the main idea fully? Create a supporting detail question and write it here:

_____

_____

_____

_____

_____

_____

- Now answer your question by *listing* the supporting details here:

_____

_____

_____

_____

_____

_____

ă pat ā pay â care ä father ĕ pet ē be ĭ pit ī tie î pier ŏ pot ō toe
ô paw oi noise o͞o took o͞o boot ou out th thin *th* this ŭ cut û urge
y͞o͞o abuse zh vision ə *a*bout, it*e*m, ed*i*ble, gall*o*p, circ*u*s

3. This paragraph is excerpted from a textbook on managing organizational behavior.

> Both as a principal party and as a third party, the manager must be a skilled participant in the dynamics of interpersonal conflict. He or she must be able to recognize situations that have the potential for conflict. Then the manager should be capable of diagnosing the situation and taking action through communications to ensure that the goals of the organization are best served.
>
> *Managing Organizational Behavior*
> by John R. Schermerhorn, Jr., et al.

---

dynamics (dī năm′ ĭks) n. The physical and intellectual forces that produce change in a given area.

potential (pə tĕn′ shəl) n. The inherent ability or capacity for growth.

Subject matter: managers dealing with interpersonal conflict

Main idea: A manager must be a skilled participant in the dynamics of interpersonal conflict.

● What *additional* information do the authors want you to know so that you can understand the main idea fully? Create a supporting detail question and write it here:

_____

_____

_____

_____

● Now answer your question by *listing* the supporting details here:

_____

_____

_____

ă pat ā pay â care ä father ĕ pet ē be ĭ pit ī tie î pier ŏ pot ō toe
ô paw oi noise o͝o took o͞o boot ou out th thin *th* this ŭ cut û urge
yo͞o abuse zh vision ə *a*bout, it*e*m, ed*i*ble, gall*o*p, circ*u*s

4.   An American history textbook is the source of this passage.

Washington was no fiery radical, nor was he a reflective political thinker. He had not played a prominent role in the prerevolutionary agitation, but his devotion to the American cause was unquestioned. He was dignified, conservative, respectable, and a man of unimpeachable integrity. The younger son of a Virginia planter, Washington had not expected to inherit substantial property and had planned to make his living as a surveyor. But the early death of an older brother and his marriage to the wealthy widow Martha Custis had made him a rich man. Though unmistakably an aristocrat, Washington was unswervingly committed to representative government. And he had other desirable traits as well. His stamina was remarkable; in more than eight years of war Washington never had a serious illness and took only one brief leave of absence. Moreover, he both looked and acted like a leader. Six feet tall in an era when most men were five inches shorter, his presence was stately and commanding.

A People and a Nation
by Mary Beth Norton et al.

fiery (fīr′ ē) adj. Easily excited or emotionally volatile.

radical (răd′ ĭ kəl) n. One who advocates political and social revolution.

agitation (ăj ĭ tā′ shən) n. The state of being agitated; disturbance; commotion.

unimpeachable (ūn ĭm pē′ chə bəl) adj. Beyond doubt or reproach; unquestionable.

substantial (səb stăn′ shəl) adj. Considerable in value or amount.

aristocrat (ə rĭs′ tə krăt) n. A person having the tastes, opinions, manners, and other characteristics of the upper class.

ă pat   ā pay   â care   ä father   ĕ pet   ē be   ĭ pit   ī tie   î pier   ŏ pot   ō toe
ô paw   oi noise   o͞o took   o͞o boot   ou out   th thin   *th* this   ŭ cut   û urge
yo͞o abuse   zh vision   ə *a*bout, it*e*m, ed*i*ble, gall*o*p, circ*u*s

Subject matter: George Washington

Main idea: George Washington was an unusual and distinguished man.

● What *additional* information do the authors want you to know so that
   you can understand the main idea fully? Create a supporting detail
   question and write it here:

_____

_____

_____

_____

● Now answer your question by *listing* the supporting details here:

_____

_____

_____

_____

_____

_____

5. This selection is from a humanities textbook.

The Declaration of Independence

   The Declaration, written largely by Jefferson and approved by
the Continental Congress on July 4, 1776, is a statement of political
philosophy as well as an act of rebellion. It is in fact typical of the
American Enlightenment that theory and its practical application are
combined in the same document. The Declaration may be divided
into two distinct parts: the first sets forth principles of democratic
government and proves, in the abstract, philosophical terms of the
Enlightenment, the right of the colonies to rebel. The second part
is a specific list of grievances against the king of Great Britain,
George III.

The Humanities
by M. A. Witt et al.

Enlightenment (ĕn lĭt' n mənt) n. A philosophical movement of the eighteenth century, concerned with the critical examination of previously accepted doctrines and institutions from the point of view of rationalism.

abstract (ăb' străkt) adj. Theoretical; not applied or practical.

grievance (grē' vəns) n. A complaint or protest based on certain circumstances.

Subject matter: the Declaration of Independence

Main idea: The Declaration of Independence is a statement of political philosophy as well as an act of rebellion.

Note: The main idea sentence can be made into two supporting detail questions. Try to create two questions and answer them both.

Supporting detail question 1:

- What *additional* information do the authors want you to know so that you can understand the main idea fully? Create a supporting detail question and write it here:

_____

_____

_____

_____

- Now answer your question by *listing* the supporting details here:

_____

_____

_____

_____

ă pat ā pay â care ä father ĕ pet ē be ĭ pit ī tie î pier ŏ pot ō toe
ô paw oi noise o͞o took o͞o boot ou out th thin *th* this ŭ cut û urge
y͞o͞o abuse zh vision ə *a*bout, it*e*m, ed*i*ble, gall*o*p, circ*u*s

Supporting detail question 2:

- What *additional* information do the authors want you to know so that you can understand the main idea fully? Create a second supporting detail question and write it here:

_____

_____

_____

_____

_____

- Now answer your question by *listing* the supporting details here:

_____

_____

_____

_____

_____

6. The same humanities textbook is also the source of this passage.

Absolutism as a form of government (manifested as absolute monarchy) began to take shape under Louis' predecessors, Henry IV and Louis XIII, but Louis XIV made it an unchangeable fact. He managed to transform France's traditionally restless, independent nobles into fawning courtiers eager to catch the smile of their king. As a child, Louis had witnessed the evils that seditious upper classes could inflict on society; now the central aim of his life was to transform these elements into loyal servants of the crown. A master showman, he created around him such an aura of grandeur that he became known as the Great Monarch. The upper nobility were expected to live at court, rather than in their own castles on their own lands. Louis moved his court from the palace of the Louvre in Paris to Versailles, twelve miles outside. There he built up a somewhat insulated world where he could entertain the nobles and keep an eye on them. The bourgeois, eager to buy their way into the nobility and to be presented at court, were not likely to cause any trouble; and the peasants and lower classes were so heavily taxed that they remained in an almost feudal stage of dependence. Louis saw to it that the monarchy became the primary source of privilege and honor in the society so that men would look to him as to the light. The "Sun King" was extolled as the center and source of all power, just as the sun was the center of the universe.

The Humanities
by M. A. Witt et al.

---

absolutism (ăb′ sə lo͞o tĭz əm) n. A form of government in which all power is vested in the monarch and his or her advisers.

predecessor (prĕd′ ĭ sĕs ər) n. An ancestor.

fawning (fôn′ ĭng) adj. Seeking favor or attention by flattery and obsequious behavior.

seditious (sĭ dĭsh′ əs) adj. Engaged in rebellion against the state.

transform (trăns fôrm′) v. To change markedly the form or appearance of.

nobility (nō bĭl′ ĭ tē) n. A class of persons distinguished by high birth or rank; aristocracy.

insulated (ĭn′ sə lā təd) adj. Detached; protected from; isolated.

bourgeois (bo͞or zhwä′) n. pl. The middle class.

feudal (fyo͞od′ l) adj. Characteristic of feudalism, wherein the peasants gave homage and service to the nobility.

extol (ĭk stōl′) v. To praise lavishly.

Subject matter: absolutism under Louis XIV

Main idea: Louis XIV made absolutism (absolute monarchy) as a form of government an unchangeable fact.

Note: This main idea sentence suggests *two* supporting detail questions. Try to create two questions and answer them both.

ă pat ā pay â care ä father ĕ pet ē be ĭ pit ī tie î pier ŏ pot ō toe
ô paw oi noise o͞o took o͞o boot ou out th thin *th* this ŭ cut û urge
yo͞o abuse zh vision ə *a*bout, it*e*m, ed*i*ble, gall*o*p, circ*u*s

Supporting detail question 1:

- What *additional* information do the authors want you to know so that you can understand the main idea fully? Create a supporting detail question and write it here:

_____

_____

_____

_____

- Now answer your question by *listing* the supporting details here:

_____

_____

_____

_____

Supporting detail question 2:

- What *additional* information do the authors want you to know so that you can understand the main idea fully? Create a second supporting detail question and write it here:

_____

_____

_____

_____

- Now answer your question by *listing* the supporting details here:

_____

_____

_____

_____

IDENTIFYING SUPPORTING DETAILS
Answer Key for Practice Exercises

Compare your responses for the practice exercises on pages 163–172 with these formulations of the supporting detail question and its answer.

1. *Supporting detail question:* What are the three primary activities of all information processing systems?

   Supporting details: All information processing systems:

   - receive data as input
   - process data
   - provide information as output

2. *Supporting detail question:* What are the theories of why we forget?

   Supporting details: Theories of why we forget are:

   - motivated forgetting theory
   - decay theory
   - interference theory—proactive interference and retroactive interference

   The authors present *three* theories of forgetting. Proactive and retroactive interference are a part of the interference theory. You may have assumed that they were two additional theories of forgetting since they were italicized. Careful readers would recognize that "proactive interference" and "retroactive interference" are parts of interference theory.

3. *Supporting detail question:* How can a manager be a skilled participant in dealing with interpersonal conflicts?

   Supporting details: The manager:

   - must recognize a situation that has the potential for conflict
   - must diagnose the situation
   - must take action through communication

4. *Supporting detail question:* In what ways was George Washington an unusual and distinguished man?

    Supporting details: George Washington:

    - was not a fiery radical
    - was devoted to the American cause
    - had unimpeachable integrity
    - an aristocrat, he had become wealthy
    - had remarkable stamina
    - looked and acted like a leader

5. *Supporting detail question 1:* How is the Declaration of Independence a "statement of political philosophy"?

    Supporting details: The Declaration of Independence is a statement of political philosophy because it:

    - sets forth principles of democratic government
    - proves the right of the colonies to rebel

    Supporting detail question 2: How is the Declaration of Independence an "act of rebellion"?

    Supporting detail: The Declaration of Independence is an act of rebellion because it:

    - contains a specific list of grievances against the king of England, George III

6. *Supporting detail question 1: Why* did Louis XIV want absolutism (absolute monarchy)?

    Supporting details: Louis XIV wanted an absolute monarchy because:

    - as a child he witnessed the evils of sedition (rebellion, revolt) by the upper class
    - he wished to make the upper class more loyal to him when he became the ruler

    Supporting detail question 2: How did Louis XIV make absolutism an "unchangeable fact"?

    Supporting details: To create an absolute monarchy, Louis XIV:

    - transformed independent nobles into servants of the crown

- moved all the nobility to the court, where they were expected to live

- allowed the bourgeois to buy their way into nobility

- taxed peasants and lower classes heavily

IDENTIFYING SUPPORTING DETAILS
Review Test

Read each of the following paragraphs carefully. Determine the subject matter. Locate or formulate the main idea for each paragraph. Then formulate your supporting detail question (or questions, if there is more than one), and write the answers. List each supporting detail on a separate line.

1.   This selection is taken from a psychology textbook.

> How much do you remember of what you learned over the past academic year? How many of your high school classmates could you call by name right now? How many times a week do you forget appointments, chores, and other details of everyday life? Before you groan in self-disgust, take heart at how normal you are. We all forget all kinds of things all the time.
>
> *Psychology*
> by Diane Papalia and Sally Olds

●   Who or what is the passage about? On the line below, write a word or phrase that tells the subject matter:

_____

●   What is the most important point the authors want you to understand about the subject matter? Locate or formulate a main idea sentence that answers this question and write the sentence here:

_____

_____

_____

_____

- What *additional* information do the authors want you to know so that you can understand the main idea fully? Create a supporting detail question and write it here:

  _____

  _____

  _____

  _____

- Now answer your question by *listing* the supporting details here:

  _____

  _____

  _____

  _____

2. This passage is an excerpt from a sociology textbook.

Why do fashions occur in the first place? (1) One reason is that in some cultures, like ours, values change: what is new is good. Thus in many modern societies clothing styles change yearly, while people in traditional societies may wear the same style of clothing for many generations. (2) Many industries promote quick changes in fashions to increase their sales. Fashions are stimulated, too, (3) by a quest for prestige and social mobility. Although a new style occasionally originates from lower-status groups, as blue jeans did, most fashions trickle down from the top. (4) Upper-class people adopt some style or artifact as a badge of their status, but they cannot monopolize most status symbols for long. The style or object is adopted by the middle-class, maybe copied and modified for use by lower-status groups, providing people with the prestige of possessing a high-status symbol. By trickling down, however, the symbol eventually loses its prestige. The upper-class adopts a new style, until it too "trickles down" and must be replaced by another (Turner and Killian, 1972).

Sociology: An Introduction
by Alex Thio

- Who or what is the passage about? On the line below, write a word or phrase that tells the subject matter:

  _____

- What is the most important point the author wants you to understand about the subject matter? Locate or formulate a main idea sentence that answers this question and write the sentence here:

  _____

  _____

  _____

  _____

- What *additional* information do the authors want you to know so that you can understand the main idea fully? Create a supporting detail question and write it here:

  _____

  _____

  _____

  _____

- Now answer your question by listing the supporting details here:

  _____

  _____

  _____

  _____

3. This paragraph is from a management textbook.

   One of the most successful industrialists of the early nineteenth century, Robert Owen was an outstanding pioneer of management. During the period 1800 to 1828, Owen carried out what was then regarded as an unprecedented experiment in the group of textile mills he managed in Scotland. It is not without good reason that he has been referred to as "the father of modern personnel management."

Management
by Harold Koontz et al.

- Who or what is the passage about? On the line below, write a word or phrase that tells the subject matter:

_____

- What is the most important point the authors want you to understand about the subject matter? Locate or formulate a main idea sentence that answers this question and write the sentence here:

_____
_____
_____
_____

- What *additional* information do the authors want you to know so that you can understand the main idea fully? Create a supporting detail question and write it here:

_____
_____
_____
_____
_____

- Now answer your question by *listing* the supporting detail here:

_____
_____
_____
_____
_____

4.   A biology textbook is the source of this passage.

> The digestive system provides nutrients, and the excretory system rids the body of metabolic wastes. The respiratory system supplies oxygen but also eliminates carbon dioxide. The circulatory system carries nutrients and oxygen to and wastes from the cells so that tissue fluid composition remains constant. The immune system helps protect the body from disease. The nervous and hormonal systems control body functions. The nervous system directs body movements, allowing the organism to manipulate the external environment, an important life-sustaining function.
>
> *Inquiry into Life*
> by Sylvia Mader

- Who or what is the passage about? On the line below, write a word or phrase that tells the subject matter:

  _____

- What is the most important point the author wants you to understand about the subject matter? Locate or formulate a main idea sentence that answers this question and write the sentence here:

  _____

  _____

  _____

  _____

- What *additional* information does the author want you to know so that you can understand the main idea fully? Create a supporting detail question and write it here:

  _____

  _____

  _____

  _____

- Now answer your question by *listing* the supporting details here:

_____

_____

_____

_____

5. This passage comes from a business textbook.

> Electronic computer data processing began after World War II. A landmark in its development was the Eniac, a 20-ton vacuum tube computer completed in 1946 by Mauchley and Eckert, professors of electrical engineering at the University of Pennsylvania. The Eniac now reposes in the Smithsonian Institution. In 1981, a party was held to celebrate the thirty-fifth birthday of the Eniac and the computer age. The Eniac was dusted off, plugged in, and assigned a set of calculations to perform. The same request was made of a Radio Shack TRS-80 microcomputer. The 30-lb microcomputer completed the task about 5 times as fast as the 20-ton behemoth Eniac, a startling indication of the tremendous advances made in computing technology in just 35 years.
>
> *Principles of Management Information Systems*
> by George M. Scott

- Who or what is the passage about? On the line below, write a word or phrase that tells the subject matter:

_____

- What is the most important point the author wants you to understand about the subject matter? Locate or formulate a main idea sentence that answers this question and write the sentence here:

_____

_____

_____

_____

- What *additional* information does the author want you to know so that you can understand the main idea fully? Create a supporting detail question and write it here:

  _____

  _____

  _____

  _____

  _____

- Now answer your question by *listing* the supporting details here:

  _____

  _____

  _____

  _____

6. This paragraph is from a psychology textbook.

> There are two branches of statistics: descriptive and inferential. Descriptive statistics provide a way to summarize data gathered from research. For example, you could determine the grade-point averages and study schedules of students in your psychology class and use descriptive statistics to summarize your findings. Inferential statistics use data from a sample to generalize and predict results in a larger population. You would need inferential statistics to predict the intelligence and study schedules of future psychology classes composed of students similar to those in your own class. Both descriptive statistics and inferential statistics are needed in psychological research.
>
> *Psychology*
> by Diane Papalia and Sally Olds

- Who or what is the passage about? On the line below, write a word or phrase that tells the subject matter:

  _____

- What is the most important point the authors want you to understand about the subject matter? Locate or formulate a main idea sentence that answers this question and write the sentence here:

  _____

  _____

  _____

  _____

- What *additional* information do the authors want you to know so that you can understand the main idea fully? Create a supporting detail question and write it on the lines here.

  _____

  _____

  _____

  _____

- Now answer your question by *listing* the supporting details here:

  _____

  _____

  _____

  _____

7. This selection is excerpted from a sociology textbook.

Mayo wanted to find out what kinds of incentives and work conditions would encourage workers to work harder. He first systematically changed the lighting, lunch hours, coffee breaks, methods of payment (salary versus piece rate), and the like. Then he was surprised to find that no matter what changes were made the workers increased their productivity. When the light was very bright, they worked harder than before; but when it was changed to very dim, they still worked harder. When they were given two or three coffee breaks, they increased their output; when they were not allowed any coffee break, they continued to increase their output. Mayo later discovered that the increased productivity was actually due to all the attention the workers were getting from the researcher. They felt that they were not mere cogs of a machine but instead respected for their work; hence they reciprocated by working harder. The impact of the researcher's presence on subjects' behavior is now known as the **Hawthorne effect.** Social scientists today strive to avoid it by becoming a member of the group being studied, by using hidden cameras and tape recorders, or by using any means that prevents subjects from knowing they are being observed.

Sociology: An Introduction
by Alex Thio

- Who or what is the passage about? On the line below, write a word or phrase that tells the subject matter:

_____

- What is the most important point the author wants you to understand about the subject matter? Locate or formulate a main idea sentence that answers this question and write the sentence here:

_____

_____

_____

_____

- What *additional* information does the author want you to know so that you can understand the main idea fully? Create a supporting detail question and write it here:

_____

_____

_____

_____

- Now answer your question by *listing* the supporting details here:

_____

_____

8. This passage comes from a U.S. history textbook.

> By the 1980s Asians had surpassed Hispanics in numbers of legal immigrants. By eliminating the national origins quota system, the Immigration Act of 1965 opened the door on a first-come, first-qualified basis, making possible the influx of people from China and Taiwan, Korea, Japan, the Philippines, Vietnam, Cambodia, Laos, Thailand, and India. As of 1990 about 6.5 million Asian-Americans lived in the United States. Like earlier immigrants from Europe, those from the Pacific rim came in waves. Some, like the Vietnamese "boat people" of the late 1970s, were driven from their homes by economic or political turmoil; others were drawn to reunite families or realize greater opportunities in the Western Hemisphere. Professional and educated Asian Indians emigrated in search of better jobs in the United States. Doctors and nurses constituted a large percentage of the early Korean immigrants. But letters home to relatives and other nationals soon attracted a more diverse population, which concentrated in small businesses.
>
> *Nation of Nations*
> by James W. Davidson et al.

- Who or what is the passage about? On the line below, write a word or phrase that tells the subject matter:

_____

- What is the most important point the authors want you to understand about the subject matter? Locate or formulate a main idea sentence that answers this question and write the sentence here:

_____

_____

_____

_____

- What *additional* information do the authors want you to know so that you can understand the main idea fully? Create a supporting detail question and write it here:

_____

_____

_____

_____

- Now answer your question by *listing* the supporting detail here:

_____

_____

_____

_____

IDENTIFYING SUPPORTING DETAILS
Supplemental Exercises

1. This passage comes from an art appreciation textbook.

> If we try to envision the environmental design of the future, we will be in precisely the position of Pierre L'Enfant, who laid out the city of Washington without knowing about the automobile. We don't know what lies ahead. We don't know what factors will influence human life fifty or a hundred years hence. Yes, certain things probably can be taken for granted. Population will increase, and there will be a greater need for housing. Industrial pollution must be eliminated or counteracted. But how will the dominance of the computer affect life and the environment? How will space travel influence future generations? Must we plan now for the colonization of the moon or of distant planets? Should the L'Enfant of our day set out to plan a capital city in the "swampland" of our galaxy? Environmental design is among the most dynamic and most perplexing of all the arts, because the environment keeps changing before our very eyes.
>
> *Living with Art*
> by Rita Gilbert and William McCarter

- Who or what is the passage about? On the line below, write a word or phrase that tells the subject matter:

  _____

- What is the most important point the authors want you to understand about the subject matter? Locate or formulate a main idea sentence that answers this question and write the sentence here:

  _____

  _____

189

- What *additional* information do the authors want you to know so that you can understand the main idea fully? Create a supporting detail question and write it here:

_____

_____

_____

_____

- Now answer your question by *listing* the supporting details here:

_____

_____

_____

_____

2. This passage comes from a U.S. history textbook. Write the subject matter and main idea for *each paragraph*. Next, create a supporting detail question and list the supporting details for *each paragraph*.

Second terms have been hard on many popular presidents, especially those re-elected by wide margins. For George Washington it was factionalism that marred his second term; for Thomas Jefferson, the embargo; for Franklin Roosevelt, the Court-packing plan; for Lyndon Johnson, the Vietnam War; and for Richard Nixon, Watergate. So too Ronald Reagan suffered a precipitous drop in his political fortunes as scandals racked his administration.

Subject Matter

_____

Main Idea

_____

_____

Supporting Detail Question

_____

_____

_____

A good deal of the problem could be traced to the president's hands-off approach to governing. In March 1987, at the administration's low point, former Senator Howard Baker of Tennessee was brought in as chief-of-staff to reorganize the White House. One of Baker's aides was shocked to discover how far matters had slipped: "There was no pattern of analysis, no coming together. Individual cabinet members were just doing what they wanted to do—the ones that were smart had realized that the White House really didn't matter. . . . [Aides] felt free to sign [the president's] initials on documents without noting that they were acting for him. When I asked a group of them, who among them thought they had authority to sign in the president's name, there was a long, uncomfortable silence. Then one answered, 'Well—everybody, and nobody.'"

Nation of Nations
by James W. Davidson et al.

Supporting Details

_____

_____

_____

_____

_____

_____

_____

Subject Matter

_____

_____

_____

Main Idea

_____

_____

Supporting Detail Question

_____

_____

_____

Supporting Details

_____

_____

_____

_____

_____

_____

3. This passage comes from a music appreciation textbook. Write the subject matter and main idea for *each paragraph.* Next, create a supporting detail question and list the supporting details for *each paragraph.*

Music in the Middle Ages (450–1450)

A thousand years of European history are spanned by the phrase *Middle Ages.* The "dark ages"—a time of migration, upheavals, and wars—began about 450 with the disintegration of the Roman Empire. But the later Middle Ages (until about 1450) were a period of cultural growth: romanesque churches and monasteries (1000–1150) and gothic cathedrals (1150–1450) were constructed, towns grew, and universities were founded.

During the Middle Ages a very sharp division existed among three main social classes: nobility, peasantry, and clergy. The nobles were sheltered within fortified castles; but the peasants lived miserably, and many were bound to the soil and subject to feudal overloads. This was an age of faith: all segments of society felt the powerful influence of the Roman Catholic church. Monks in monasteries held a virtual monopoly on learning; most people, including the nobility, were illiterate. Just as the cathedral dominated the medieval landscape and the medieval mind, so was it the center of musical life. Most important musicians were priests and worked for the church. Boys received music education in church schools, and an important occupation in monasteries was liturgical singing. Women were not allowed to sing in church but did make music in convents and some—like Hildegard of Bingen (1098–1179), abbess of Rupertsberg—wrote music for their choirs.

Subject Matter

_____

Main Idea

_____

_____

Supporting Detail Question

_____

_____

Supporting Details

_____

_____

_____

_____

Subject Matter

_____

Main Idea

_____

_____

Supporting Detail Question

_____

_____

Although most medieval music was vocal—the church frowned upon instruments because of their earlier role in pagan rites—instruments did serve as accompaniment and after about 1100 were used increasingly in church. (The organ was most prominent.) In the later Middle Ages, instruments were a source of controversy between composers, who wanted to create elaborate compositions, and the church, which wanted music only as a discreet accompaniment to the religious service.

Music: An Appreciation
by Roger Kamien

Supporting Details

_____

_____

_____

_____

Subject Matter

_____

Main Idea

_____

_____

Supporting Detail Question

_____

_____

Supporting Details

_____

_____

_____

_____

CHAPTER 5

RECOGNIZING AUTHORS' WRITING PATTERNS

1
Determining Subject Matter

2
Locating Directly Stated Main Ideas

3
Formulating Implied Main Ideas

4
Identifying Supporting Details

5
Recognizing Authors' Writing Patterns

6
Applying Comprehension
Skills to Longer Passages

7
Remembering College Textbook
Material through Organizing

8
Thinking Critically as You Read

195

Man's mind stretched to a new idea never goes back to its original dimensions.

Oliver Wendell Holmes (1841–1935),
Supreme Court Associate Justice

INTRODUCTION

The first four chapters of this book were devoted to acquainting you with the basic elements of the "art" of reading college textbooks: You learned to identify the subject matter, main idea, and supporting details of a passage.

With the help of the first four chapters in this book, you now bring four specific comprehension skills to your reading. You bring a greater depth of understanding about the structure of textbook passages that you read because you now know how to:

- determine the subject matter

- locate directly stated main ideas

- formulate implied main ideas

- identify supporting details

Here is a brief summary of the four reading comprehension skills you have learned so far.

Subject Matter: *Who* or *What* Is the Passage About?

First, you are aware that in college textbook passages the subject matter can be expressed by a word, name, or phrase. You are now able to read a passage and determine the subject matter by observing if the author:

- has identified the subject matter in a heading

or

- has identified the subject matter in bold print within a passage

or

- has used a word, name, or phrase more than once in a passage

or

- has stated the subject matter once in the passage and then referred to it throughout the passage with a pronoun (he, she, it, or they)

or

- does not mention the subject matter specifically, but has written the passage in such a manner that all the sentences refer to the subject matter

Locating Directly Stated Main Ideas: What Is the Main Point the Author Wants You to *Understand* about the Subject Matter?

Second, you are aware that in college textbook passages there is often a sentence that states the main idea directly. You know that very often this is the first sentence of the passage. The main idea can also be the last sentence, or it can be found elsewhere in the passage. Your task is to *locate* such a sentence if one appears in the paragraph.

Formulating Implied Main Ideas: What Is the Main Point the Author Wants You to *Infer* and *Understand* about the Subject Matter?

Third, you understand that there are paragraphs which do not contain a directly stated main idea. Instead, these paragraphs consist of facts, examples, descriptions, or explanations that *add up to,* or *suggest,* the main idea. When this is the case, you understand that, as a reader, *you* must formulate (that is, *think out* or *create*) main idea sentences for these paragraphs. By doing one of the following, you can formulate a main idea sentence. To formulate a main idea sentence, you can combine:

- one sentence plus the subject matter

    or

- one sentence plus another sentence

    or

- important information from two or more sentences

Identifying Supporting Details: What *Additional* Information Does the Author Want You to Know So That You Can Understand More about the Main Idea?

Fourth, you now read a passage looking for the important details that support the main idea. You have learned to ask yourself, "What additional information does the author want me to know so that I can understand more about the main idea?" You seek to locate and examine this information, the supporting details, and to understand how they relate to the author's main idea.

With these four specific reading comprehension skills, you should have a greater feeling of competency regarding college textbook reading.

Now, in this chapter you will be adding another element to the art of reading college textbooks: recognizing *authors' writing patterns.* You will become further acquainted with some of the basics of the "art of thinking," and you will see how authors translate their thinking into patterns of organization that they use in their writing. You will be introduced to five major writing patterns authors use when they write college textbook material.

You may be pleasantly surprised to learn that you are already acquainted with these five writing patterns. You use them constantly in your everyday life because they reflect *your* thinking patterns, just as they reflect an author's thinking patterns. For example:

A **writing pattern** is the way an author organizes and presents information and ideas to the reader.

You may think to yourself, "At the grocery store, I need to buy tomato sauce, mozzarella cheese, pepperoni, sausage, anchovies, olives, yeast, and flour." (This is an example of what is called the ***listing pattern.***)

or

You may think to yourself as you prepare to buy a birthday gift, "I'll go shopping for the present this afternoon. I'll wrap it and put it in the mail first thing tomorrow morning so that it will arrive by Saturday." (This is an example of the ***sequence pattern.***)

or

You may think, "Oh, *that's* what they mean when they say, 'wind chill factor'—how much colder the temperature actually *feels* because of the wind." (This is an example of the ***definition pattern.***)

or

You may think, "Should I go to the beach during spring break or should I go camping? What are the advantages of each? The disadvantages?" (This is a ***comparison-contrast pattern.***)

or

You may think, as your car comes slowly to a halt, "*Why* didn't I stop for gas this morning?" (This is an example of the ***cause-effect pattern.***)

These thinking patterns become writing patterns when we put our thoughts in written form. Isn't it interesting (and reassuring) to think that college textbook writers use these same patterns in their writing? This is because these patterns are convenient ways of organizing our thinking and our writing.

THE IMPORTANCE OF RECOGNIZING AUTHORS' WRITING PATTERNS

Writers use patterns to structure and organize the material they are writing about. They present information in a way that makes sense to them. Because textbook authors *want* readers to understand what they have written and to be able to follow their train of thought, they use *thinking* patterns that people are familiar with. Writers will use a particular pattern because it makes the material easier to comprehend. (By the way, instructors also use these patterns when presenting a lecture.)

One advantage of recognizing these patterns is that it allows the reader to *anticipate* the kind of information the author is likely to present next. Effective readers *predict* what is likely to come next in a textbook passage. This is a helpful reading strategy because the reader is actively involved in thinking about the passage. Effective readers also monitor their comprehension by noting whether their predictions were correct.

Although we commonly use these thinking patterns in our daily life, many students fail to recognize them when they encounter them in their textbooks. It is important for you, as a reader, to understand that the thinking patterns you use are the same ones that authors use. Recognizing these patterns in writing enables you to comprehend more clearly and to follow the writer's ideas.

Organized information is easier to remember. Understanding how the ideas and information in a passage are organized makes it easier for the reader to remember the information. If you can grasp the author's organization (pattern), you will comprehend and remember more of the material. As a bonus, in becoming aware of these patterns, you may discover that you can *write* more organized and clearer paragraphs. For example, answers that you write on essay tests will be better organized and more exact when you use an appropriate pattern to organize your own writing.

EXPLANATIONS AND EXAMPLES

You may have already noticed some of these writing patterns as they appeared in sample passages used in previous chapters of this book. Again, the five patterns that are emphasized in this chapter are the (1) listing pattern, (2) sequence pattern, (3) definition pattern, (4) comparison-contrast pattern, and (5) cause-effect pattern. Although these patterns are frequently used in textbook passages, not all passages in textbooks fall neatly into one of these categories. In fact, it is not unusual to see two or more patterns mixed in a single passage. In this chapter, however, most of the passages you read have only one pattern.

Below are sample paragraphs for each pattern. The passages are ones that have appeared earlier in this book.

1. Listing Pattern

The following passage on the attributes of electronic computers illustrates the listing pattern. The passage is from a business textbook. Read the paragraph to see *what* is being listed.

> The **listing pattern** presents a list of items. The author may present the items in *any order.*

> The electronic nature of computers gives them several important attributes. First, computers are extremely fast at processing instructions, that is, at performing calculations and at making logical comparisons. Second, computers are extremely accurate in their processing; rarely does a computer make an electronic mistake that it does not catch itself and signal to the computer operator. Almost all errors in computer data processing are caused by faulty programs prepared by humans. Third, computers are extremely reliable; being primarily electronic and without moving parts, they seldom have failures.
>
> *Principles of Management Information Systems*
> by George M. Scott

You can see, of course, that the author simply *lists* the three attributes of electronic computers: their speed, accuracy, and reliability. These attributes could have been listed in any order. The listing pattern is used to present a number of items when the order is not particularly important.

2. Sequence Pattern

In this paragraph on memory, the authors use the sequence pattern to show the *order* in which certain events occur. Although a sequence is a type of list, the order is important. Read this psychology textbook passage, and notice the steps and the order in which they are given.

> The **sequence pattern** presents a list of items in a *specific order.*

> Your memory works through four basic steps: First you have to perceive something—to see it, hear it, or become aware of it through some other sense. Second, you have to get it into your memory. Third, you put it away. And finally, you have to be able to find it so you can take it out.
>
> *Psychology*
> by Diane Papalia and Sally Olds

The authors present the four basic steps of memory in the order in which they *must* occur: perceiving something, getting it into memory, putting it away, and being able to find it.

3. Definition Pattern

The author of this government textbook paragraph defines a term for you. Read to see what is being defined.

> The **definition pattern** presents the *meaning* of an important concept or term that is then discussed throughout the passage.

What Is Government?

A Definition

Politics takes place everywhere, but the focus of this text is on politics in government. We have so many governments in our own country—thousands of municipal and county governments—that the Census Bureau had to come up with a definition when counting them so that it would know what to include and what to leave out. Its definition: If an organization can make law or collect a tax, it is a government.

American Politics and Government
by Richard Pious

Clearly, the author wants the reader to understand the definition of government: "an organization that can make law or collect a tax."

4. Comparison-Contrast Pattern

Writers often wish to emphasize similarities and differences between things. A *comparison* shows how two or more things are similar (or alike). A *contrast* points out the differences between two or more things. In the following paragraph, the author discusses two groups of people. Read the paragraph to determine what he says about them.

> The **comparison-contrast pattern** presents *similarities* (a comparison), *differences* (a contrast), or both.

Is there any difference in personality traits or intelligence between short and long sleepers? Early studies reported a few such differences. For example, short sleepers were said to be generally more "energetic," while long sleepers were more prone to be "worriers." But these findings were not confirmed by later studies, and it now seems that there are few reliable differences.

Introduction to Psychology
by Ron Plotnik

The author is discussing research findings on personality traits and intelligence of short and long sleepers. He explains that although early studies suggested some differences between long and short sleepers, later studies suggested that there were very few differences.

5. Cause-Effect Pattern

Textbook material that describes the reasons things happen (their *causes*) and describes their results or outcomes (their *effects*) can be expressed in a cause-effect pattern. In the following United States history textbook paragraph on smallpox inoculations in colonial days, the authors describe an important cause and an important effect. Read the passage to identify each of them:

> The **cause-effect pattern** presents *reasons* things happen (causes) and their *results* (effects).

The key figure in the drama was the Reverend Cotton Mather, the Puritan clergyman, who was a member of England's Royal Society, an organization of the intellectual elite. In a Royal Society publication Mather read about the benefits of inoculation (deliberately infecting a person with a mild case of a disease) as a protection against the dreaded smallpox. In 1720 and 1721, when Boston suffered a major smallpox epidemic, Mather and a doctor ally urged people to be inoculated; there was fervent opposition, including that of Boston's leading physician. When the epidemic had ended, the statistics bore out Mather's opinion: of those inoculated, fewer than 3 percent died; of those who became ill without inoculation, nearly 15 percent perished. Though it was midcentury before inoculation was generally accepted as a preventive procedure, enlightened methods had provided colonial Americans with protection from the greatest killer disease of all.

A People and a Nation
by Mary Beth Norton et al.

It is clear that because of inoculations (cause) there were fewer deaths from smallpox (effect).

You may not have been completely aware of these patterns when you read these passages in earlier chapters. With practice, you will be able to recognize the pattern the writer is using. This will speed your comprehension, help you predict what type of information is coming next in the passage, and improve your recall of the supporting details.

ADDITIONAL EXPLANATIONS AND EXAMPLES OF THE FIVE WRITING PATTERNS

Now let's look more closely at each of the five patterns. You will first read about the pattern; then you will examine and work with several passages that use the pattern. As you read these examples, concentrate on understanding how the information and ideas in them are organized. Ask yourself, "How do the ideas and information relate to each other and to the main idea?"

1. Listing Pattern
(Explanation and Additional Examples)

The listing pattern appears frequently in college textbooks because authors find it a clear, convenient way to convey information. In a listing pattern, the author lists a series of items. The order in which she or he arranges them is not especially important. In other words, the author could have listed any item first, and it probably would not have mattered.

Your task as a reader is to locate each of the items the author presents and to understand how the items are related to each other. For example, an author could list and describe the id, the ego, and the super-ego, Sigmund Freud's three components of the mind.

Here is a paragraph from an English composition textbook. Its subject matter is the use of metaphor. (*Metaphor* is a figure of speech in which a word is used in place of another word to show a likeness between them. For example, in "The winter of his life," *winter* means the last or final part, just as winter is the final season of the year.) In the paragraph below, the author's main idea is stated in the first sentence: *The varieties of metaphor serve several rhetorical purposes.* In the supporting details, the author lists ways in which metaphor can serve rhetorical purposes (to help people write more effectively) and she then presents an example of a vivid, powerful metaphor.

Read the passage to locate the two purposes of metaphor.

The Purposes of Metaphor

The varieties of metaphor serve several rhetorical purposes. First, they give color and vigor to writing, bring it to life, make it move. That result alone helps to win your audience. Second, using metaphor is one way to make the abstract concrete. Philosophers and psychologists frequently employ metaphor to help their readers grasp difficult concepts. In one of the most dramatic passages in philosophy, Plato illustrates the function of the soul by saying that it is like a team of two horses with its charioteer; the charioteer is the guiding force for the horses, one of which represents good instincts and the other, bad instincts.

Contemporary Composition
by Maxine Hairston

---

metaphor (mĕt′ ə fôr) n. An implied comparison between two things.

rhetorical (rĭ tôr′ ĭ kəl) adj. Concerned primarily with style or effect in writing or speech.

abstract (ăb′ străkt) n. Something theoretical.

concrete (kŏn krēt′) adj. Relating to an actual, specific thing or instance.

charioteer (chăr ē ə tîr′) n. A person who drives a chariot (an ancient horse-drawn, two-wheeled vehicle, used in war, races, and processions).

In this paragraph, the author *lists* two ways in which the use of metaphor can improve one's writing. They are (1) to give color and vigor to writing, to bring it to life, make it move, and (2) to make the abstract concrete.

ă pat　ā pay　â care　ä father　ĕ pet　ē be　ĭ pit　ī tie　î pier　ŏ pot　ō toe
ô paw　oi noise　o͞o took　o͞o boot　ou out　th thin　*th* this　ŭ cut　û urge
yo͞o abuse　zh vision　ə *a*bout, it*e*m, ed*i*ble, gall*o*p, circ*u*s

As you probably observed, the heading of this passage (the subject matter), "The Purposes of Metaphor," lets you predict what was likely to be listed. Also, the words *first* and *second* signal the reader that the author is presenting a series of items in this paragraph.

Now let's look at another passage that is organized according to the listing pattern. The subject matter of this business textbook passage is entrepreneurial ability (or enterprise), as you might predict from the heading and the italicized words. You can see that the author makes it clear that he is giving a list of items; he has even numbered them. His main idea is that *There are four related functions of entrepreneurs.* Notice that he could have presented the items in any order.

Now read the passage to identify these functions, which are given as important supporting details.

Entrepreneurial Ability

Finally, what can be said about this special human resource which we label *entrepreneurial ability,* or, more simply, *enterprise?* We shall give the terms a specific meaning by assigning four related functions to the entrepreneur.

1. The entrepreneur takes the initiative in combining the resources of land, capital, and labor in the production of a good or service. Both a sparkplug and a catalyst, the entrepreneur is at once the driving force behind production and the agent who combines the other resources in what is hoped will be a profitable venture.
2. The entrepreneur undertakes the chore of making basic business-policy decisions, that is, those nonroutine decisions which set the course of a business enterprise.
3. The entrepreneur is an innovator—the person who attempts to introduce on a commercial basis new products, new productive techniques, or even new forms of business organization.
4. The entrepreneur is obviously a risk bearer. This is apparent from a close examination of the other three entrepreneurial functions. The entrepreneur in a capitalistic system has no guarantee of profit. The reward for his or her time, efforts, and abilities may

> be attractive profits or losses and eventual bankruptcy. In short, the entrepreneur risks not only time, effort, and business reputation, but his or her invested funds and those of associates or stockholders.
>
> *Economics*
> by Campbell McConnell

---

entrepreneur (än trə prə nûr′) n. A person who manages and assumes the risk for business ventures.

catalyst (kăt′ l ĭst) n. One who precipitates (causes) a process or event, especially without being involved in or changed by the consequences. (The author defines it more specifically as "the agent who combines the other resources in what is hoped will be a profitable venture.")

innovator (ĭn′ ə vā tər) n. One who begins or introduces something new.

As you can see, the author has included a great deal of information about each of the four points. Since this passage is representative of the kind of material you would encounter in a college textbook, you would need to isolate and learn the important points. You would want to write them down or put them in your notes because you would need to learn them when studying for a test.

Here is one way you could condense the information the author lists as the four functions of entrepreneurs:

The entrepreneur:

1. takes the initiative (seeks to combine resources, land, capital, labor)

2. makes basic business-policy decisions

3. is an innovator (attempts new things)

4. is a risk taker (risks reputation and funds)

Your list should have four points, just as the author's did. The author of this passage chose to use numbers (*1, 2, 3, 4*) to emphasize each point

---

ă pat ā pay â care ä father ĕ pet ē be ĭ pit ī tie î pier ŏ pot ō toe
ô paw oi noise o͞o took o͞o boot ou out th thin *th* this ŭ cut û urge
y͞oo abuse zh vision ə *a*bout, it*e*m, ed*i*ble, gall*o*p, circ*u*s

rather than using signal words such as *first, second, third,* and *fourth,* (or *finally*). Sometimes authors will use letters (*a, b, c, d*) to make items in a list stand out clearly from each other.

It can be helpful to your comprehension and your recall to write down information about each point. However, you must be selective and write down only the most important information. This will prevent you from taking too much time and merely rewriting everything the author says.

In the following example of a passage that uses a listing pattern, you will be reading to locate each of the items the authors present and to understand how the items are related to each other. Reading this management textbook passage will confirm a prediction you might make about the subject matter because of the heading: the subject matter is *characteristics of groups* (in organizations). The main idea of the paragraph is that *Groups in organizations share four basic characteristics.* Now read the paragraph, being alert for signal words that the authors use to help you locate the four important supporting details that they list. As you write down each point, you will need to condense the information.

Characteristics of Groups

Groups—and the focus is on groups in the organization—have a number of characteristics. First, group members share one or more common goals, such as the goals of a product group to develop, manufacture, and market a new product. A second characteristic of groups is that they normally require interaction and communication among members. It is impossible to coordinate the efforts of group members without communication. Third, members within a group assume roles. In a product group, for example, individuals are responsible for designing, producing, selling, or distributing a product. Naturally, the roles are in some kind of relationship to each other to achieve the group task. Fourth, groups usually are a part of a larger group. The product group may belong to a product division which produces many products of a similar nature. Large groups may also consist of subgroups. Thus, within the product group may be a subgroup specializing exclusively in the selling of the product. Also, groups interface with other groups. Thus, product group A may cooperate with product group B in the distribution of their products. It is evident, then, that the systems point of view, which focuses on the interrelatedness of parts, is appropriate in understanding the functioning of groups.

Management
by Harold Koontz et al.

interaction (ĭn tər ăk′ shən) n. Action between two or more things.
interface (ĭn′ tər fās) v. To interact; to have dealings in common with.

Subject matter: characteristics of groups in organizations

Main idea sentence: Groups in organizations have four characteristics.

- *Supporting details:* _____

_____

_____

_____

_____

_____

_____

_____

_____

_____

_____

_____

- *Pattern:* _____

ă pat ā pay â care ä father ĕ pet ē be ĭ pit ī tie î pier ŏ pot ō toe
ô paw oi noise o͝o took o͞o boot ou out th thin *th* this ŭ cut û urge
yo͞o abuse zh vision ə *a*bout, it*e*m, ed*i*ble, gall*o*p, circ*u*s

Did you remember to condense each point as you wrote it? Here is one way you could have condensed the information.

Supporting details: The four characteristics are:

1. Group members share one or more common goals.

2. Groups require interaction and communication among members.

3. Members within a group assume roles.

4. Groups are usually a part of a larger group.

Again, you probably noticed the signal words the authors used to help the reader. The words *first, second, third,* and *fourth* announce each point in the list. (Sometimes authors use other signal words, such as *and, also,* and *another* to show that they are adding an item to a list.)

2. Sequence Pattern
(Explanations and Additional Examples)

In a sequence pattern, the author wants to show the *order* in which certain things or events occur. In a general way, a sequence is a type of list. However, in the sequence pattern, the items are given in a specific order. The order is important.

Authors use the sequence pattern for a variety of purposes. First, they may use it to present steps in a process (for example, steps in a science experiment or how a Congressional bill becomes a law). Second, authors use the sequence pattern to show time order, or the order in which events occurred. Usually they present the events from the earliest event to the last event (for example, stages in children's language development, events in a famous person's life, or geologic time periods of the earth). Sequence is also called *chronological order* or *time order.* Finally, authors may use the sequence pattern to present items according to their degree of importance; often they arrange them in order of greatest importance to least importance (for example, the symptoms of an illness, the levels of management in a corporation, or the major products that the United States exports to other countries).

In the sequence pattern, each item or event is related in some way to the item or event that comes before it and to the one that comes after it. Your responsibility as an active reader is to locate each of the events or items in the sequence and to understand how they are arranged.

Here is a paragraph from a marketing textbook whose subject matter is *marketing research*. Its main idea is that *Marketing research is used in a very wide variety of situations*. As you read this passage, look for the important supporting details, and notice how they relate to each other.

> Marketing research is a major component or subsystem within a marketing information system. It is used in a very wide variety of marketing situations. Typically, in a marketing research study, the problem to be solved is first identified. Then a researcher normally conducts a situation analysis and an informal investigation. If a formal investigation is needed, the researcher decides whether to use secondary or primary sources of information. To gather primary data, the researcher may use the survey, observation, or experimental method. Normally, primary data are gathered by sampling. Then the data are analyzed, and a written report is prepared.
>
> *Fundamentals of Marketing*
> by William Stanton

secondary (sĕk′ ən dĕr ē) adj. One step removed from the first; derived from what is primary or original.

primary (prī′ mĕr ē) adj. Occurring first in time or sequence; original.

In this passage, the author identifies the process of marketing research and then presents the steps in which marketing research is done. The steps are: identifying the problem to be solved; conducting a situation analysis; conducting an informal investigation, or a formal one if it is needed; deciding whether to use secondary or primary sources; analyzing the data; and preparing a written report. You can see that these items are presented in the order in which they must be done.

The author uses certain signal words to point out each successive step in the process. He calls the reader's attention to each step of the marketing research process by using the words *first, then,* and *then.*

ă pat ā pay â care ä father ĕ pet ē be ĭ pit ī tie î pier ŏ pot ō toe
ô paw oi noise o͝o took o͞o boot ou out th thin *th* this ŭ cut û urge
yo͞o abuse zh vision ə *a*bout, it*e*m, ed*i*ble, gall*o*p, circ*u*s

The following paragraphs on early record-keeping devices present the information in chronological order. The indirectly expressed main idea of this computer science textbook passage is that *Record-keeping devices have developed and improved throughout history.* As you read each paragraph, notice the supporting details in which the author refers to dates and periods of time.

The First Record Keepers and Their Tools

People lived on earth for eons without keeping records, but as tribes grew into nations, trade and commerce developed. By 3500 B.C. Babylonian merchants were keeping records on clay tablets. An early manual calculating device was the abacus. Although over 3,000 years old, it's still used today in some parts of the world.

Record-keeping techniques continued to develop through the centuries, with such innovations as record audits (the Greeks) and budgets (the Romans). In 1642 the first mechanical calculating machine was developed by Blaise Pascal, a brilliant young Frenchman. (A modern programming language has been named in his honor.) About 30 years later, Gottfried von Leibniz, a German mathematician, improved on Pascal's invention by producing a machine which could add, subtract, multiply, divide, and extract roots.

Computer Concepts and Applications with BASIC
by Donald H. Sanders

---

eon (ē′ ŏn) n. An indefinitely long period of time; an age; eternity.

abacus (ăb′ ə kəs) n. A manual computing device consisting of a frame holding parallel rods strung with movable counters.

audit (ô′ dĭt) n. An examination of records or accounts to check their accuracy; an adjustment or correction of accounts.

As an active reader, you should have observed that the author has traced the following developments: the Babylonian merchants' use of

---

ă pat ā pay â care ä father ĕ pet ē be ĭ pit ī tie î pier ŏ pot ō toe
ô paw oi noise   o͞o took o͞o boot ou out th thin *th* this ŭ cut û urge
yo͞o abuse zh vision ə *a*bout, it*e*m, ed*i*ble, gall*o*p, circ*u*s

clay tablets (3500 B.C.); abacus, a manual calculating device (3000 years old); Greeks being the first to use record audits; Romans being the first to use budgets; Blaise Pascal's first mechanical calculating machine (1642); and Gottfried von Leibniz's improvements of Pascal's machine (approximately 1670). The dates and time periods in this passage are the signals that guide you through this paragraph.

When you see several dates in a paragraph, you should predict that the author is utilizing chronological order. Careful reading of the paragraph should tell you whether your prediction was correct. (By the way, do you realize that 3500 B.C. was approximately 5500 years ago?)

This selection from a management textbook concerns a famous theory of human needs. These needs are arranged in a hierarchy (*hierarchy* means things or people arranged in increasing order of importance). The main idea is that *There are five basic levels of human needs, according to Abraham Maslow's theory.* Be sure to notice the words "ascending order of importance" in the opening sentence of the paragraph. The authors mean that they are listing basic survival needs first (lowest level), and that as each successive basic need is satisfied, the person is able to move to the next higher need. Now read the paragraph to find the needs the authors present in the supporting details so that you can write them below in a concise (brief and clear) manner.

The Needs Hierarchy

The basic human needs identified by Abraham Maslow in an ascending order of importance are the following:

1. **Physiological Needs**   These are the basic needs for sustaining human life itself—food, water, clothing, shelter, sleep, and sexual satisfaction. Maslow took the position that until these needs are satisfied to the degree necessary to maintain life, other needs will not motivate people.
2. **Security, or Safety, Needs**   These are the needs to be free from physical danger and the fear of loss of a job, property, food, clothing, or shelter.
3. **Affiliation, or Acceptance, Needs**   Since people are social beings, they need to belong, to be accepted by others.

4. **Esteem Needs**   According to Maslow, once people begin to satisfy their need to belong, they tend to want to be held in esteem both by themselves and by others. This kind of need produces such satisfactions as power, prestige, status, and self-confidence.

5. **Need for Self-Actualization**   Maslow regarded this as the highest need in his hierarchy. It is the desire to become what one is capable of becoming—to maximize one's potential and to accomplish something.

Management
by Harold Koontz et al.

---

ascending (ə sĕn′ dĭng) adj. Going or moving upward.

hierarchy (hī′ ə rär kē) n. A body of entities arranged in a graded series.

physiological (fĭ sē ə lŏj′ ĭ kəl) adj. Characteristic of the normal functioning of a living organism.

security (sĭ kyōōr′ ə tē) n. Freedom from risk or danger; safety.

affiliation (ə fĭl ē ā′ shən) n. Association or connection with someone or something.

esteem (ĕ stēm′) n. Favorable regard; respect.

self-actualization (sĕlf ăk chōō əl ĭ zā′ shən) n. The desire to become what one is capable of becoming.

Subject matter: Maslow's hierarchy of needs theory

Main idea sentence: There are five levels of basic human needs according to Maslow's hierarchy of needs theory.

- *Supporting details:* _____

_____

_____

_____

ă pat ā pay â care ä father ĕ pet ē be ĭ pit ī tie î pier ŏ pot ō toe
ô paw oi noise ŏŏ took ōō boot ou out th thin *th* this ŭ cut û urge
yōō abuse zh vision ə *a*bout, it*e*m, ed*i*ble, gall*o*p, circ*u*s

_____

_____

_____

_____

_____

_____

_____

- *Pattern:* _____

Did you locate and condense the following supporting details in the hierarchy of needs sequence? They are:

1. physiological needs (food, water, clothing, etc.)

2. security or safety needs (free from fear of physical danger or loss of security)

3. affiliation or acceptance needs (need to belong; to be accepted)

4. esteem needs (need to feel valued by others and yourself)

5. need for self-actualization (desire to become what one is capable of becoming; to achieve one's potential)

In this paragraph, the authors use numbers and bold print to identify each level of needs. This is their way of telling you that they consider this to be important information that you should learn—and as an alert student, you would expect to see it asked on a test.

3. Definition Pattern
(Explanation and Additional Examples)

In the definition pattern, the author's purpose is to explain the meaning of an important term or concept he or she is introducing. The mere fact that an author takes an entire paragraph to explain a term's meaning tells you that it is an important word or concept. In every academic subject there will be certain key terms and concepts that you will be expected to know. In fact, you *must* know them if you want to understand a subject and do well in it.

Here is a short paragraph from a humanities textbook. The subject matter is the *meaning of humanities*. The main idea is stated directly in the last sentence. Read the paragraph to learn how the authors define humanities.

Today we think of the humanities as a loosely defined group of cultural subject areas rather than as scientific, technical, or even socially oriented subjects. Thus, by the term *humanities* we generally mean art, literature, music, and the theater—areas in which human values and individual expressiveness are celebrated.

The Humanities
by Louise Dudley et al.

humanities (hyo͞o măn′ ə tēz) n. pl. Those branches of knowledge concerned with mankind and culture. (The authors have defined the term the way they are using it in the textbook: art, literature, music, and the theater—areas in which human values and individual expressiveness are celebrated.)

When you read a definition paragraph, you should be sure that you understand all the words used in the definition itself. For example, you must know the word *expressiveness* in order to fully grasp the definition of the term *humanities* in the paragraph above. (*Expressiveness,* by the way, refers to the ways in which individual creativity is shown.) You must also take care to note every part of the definition. Make it a point to learn the special terms in each definition as you encounter them because they may be used throughout the rest of a course. Finally, it is very likely that you will be asked definitions on a test, so study them carefully and learn them thoroughly.

Authors often use clue words such as *means, is, is defined as, refers to,* and *the term* to indicate the definition pattern. For example, the authors of the humanities passage above used the phrase "by the ***term** hu-manities* we generally ***mean.*** . . ." Watch also for terms in bold print or italics since these words are often defined, as both the examples in this section illustrate.

ă pat ā pay â care ä father ĕ pet ē be ĭ pit ī tie î pier ŏ pot ō toe
ô paw oi noise o͝o took o͞o boot ou out th thin *th* this ŭ cut û urge
yo͞o abuse zh vision ə *a*bout, it*e*m, ed*i*ble, gall*o*p, circ*u*s

Here is a paragraph that is taken from a biology textbook and uses the definition pattern. The subject matter is *atoms*. The main idea is the sentence which states the definition of atoms. Read the paragraph to learn how the author defines atoms, then write this definition as a complete sentence in the appropriate space below. Remember, in this paragraph, the definition sentence *is* the main idea sentence.

Atoms

The matter that makes up the substance of living things is composed of chemicals, and chemicals are made of atoms. The word *atom* is a term meaning the smallest unit of matter, nondivisible by chemical means. While it is possible to split an atom by physical means, an atom is the smallest unit to enter into chemical reactions.

Inquiry into Life
by Sylvia Mader

atom (ăt′ əm) n. The smallest unit of matter, nondivisible by chemical means. (The author tells you she is defining the word when she says it is "a term meaning.")

nondivisible (nŏn dĭ vĭs′ ə bəl) adj. Incapable of being divided.

Subject matter: atoms

● *Main idea sentence (definition):* _____

_____

_____

_____

_____

_____

_____

ă pat   ā pay   â care   ä father   ĕ pet   ē be   ĭ pit   ī tie   î pier   ŏ pot   ō toe
ô paw   oi noise   o͞o took   o͞o boot   ou out   th thin   *th* this   ŭ cut   û urge
yo͞o abuse   zh vision   ə *a*bout, it*e*m, ed*i*ble, gall*o*p, circ*u*s

_____

_____

- *Pattern:* _____

The author wants you to understand that *The word* atom *is a term meaning the smallest unit of matter, nondivisible by chemical means.* This is the main idea of the paragraph. The author signals the reader that she is giving a definition by using the words "the **word** atom is a **term meaning.**"

4. Comparison-Contrast Pattern (Explanation and Additional Examples)

A paragraph that explains the *similarities* between two or more things is presenting a *comparison.* A paragraph that explains the *differences* between two or more things is presenting a *contrast.* A paragraph may contain comparisons, contrasts, or both.

You should watch for these clue words that signal a comparison: *similarly, likewise,* and *also.* Watch for these clue words that suggest a contrast: *however, in contrast, on the other hand,* and *nevertheless.*

Here is a humanities textbook paragraph about two famous composers: Handel and Bach. The main idea is expressed in the opening sentence: *The Baroque era was certainly an age of contrast, and the lives and music of Handel and Bach illustrate this principle vividly.* From the way the main idea sentence is worded, you should expect that the rest of the paragraph (the supporting details) will present differences between these two composers' lives. Read the passage to learn what these differences were.

Johann Sebastian Bach (1685–1750)

The Baroque era was certainly an age of contrast, and the lives and music of Handel and Bach illustrate this principle vividly. Bach led a relatively uneventful musical career that saw him employed as one of a number of musical functionaries who served at court and church in Protestant Germany. Virtually his entire life was spent within sixty miles of his birthplace. Handel, on the other hand, developed his profession in the company of the leading musical patrons of Germany, Italy, and England. His music was composed for the contemporary international taste, and the last years of his life were filled with great public acclaim and financial success.

The Humanities
by M. A. Witt

Baroque era (bə rōk′ îr′ ə) n. A time period from about 1550 to 1700 in Europe characterized by ornate and richly ornamented styles.

functionary (fŭngk′ shə nĕr ē) n. An official; a person who holds an office or trust.

patron (pā′ trən) n. Anyone who supports, protects, or champions; benefactor.

The differences presented are these: Bach led an uneventful life composing music for the church and at court within 60 miles of his birthplace, while Handel composed contemporary music for international patrons in Germany, Italy, and England. Handel enjoyed great public acclaim and financial success.

In addition to preparing the reader to expect contrasts by the way the main idea sentence is worded, the author helps the reader one other way. He uses the phrase "on the other hand" to signal the reader that the other composer's life (Handel's) is now being presented and that it differs from the first composer's life (Bach's).

The following passage from a sociology textbook is organized in an interesting way. The subject matter is *upper-class society.* In the first paragraph the author describes the differences between the two segments of people in the upper class (the *upper*-upper class and the *lower*-upper class).

ă pat ā pay â care ä father ĕ pet ē be ĭ pit ī tie î pier ŏ pot ō toe
ô paw oi noise   o͝o took o͞o boot ou out th thin *th* this ŭ cut û urge
yo͞o abuse zh vision ə *a*bout, it*e*m, ed*i*ble, gall*o*p, circ*u*s

The implied main idea of the first paragraph is that *There are many differences between these two segments of the upper class.* In the second paragraph, the author tells the ways in which the two divisions of the upper class are alike. The implied main idea of the second paragraph is that *Because both segments of the upper class are very, very rich, they have the money and the leisure time to acquire and do many things, and their power and actions influence the lives of millions.*

The first paragraph presents many differences between the two segments of the upper class, while the second paragraph presents several similarities. As you read the passage, pay attention to the contrasts and the comparisons.

The Upper Class

Though it is a mere 1 to 3 percent of the population, the upper class possesses at least 25 percent of the nation's wealth. This class has two segments: upper-upper and lower-upper. Basically, the upper-upper class is the "old rich"—families that have been wealthy for several generations—an aristocracy of birth and wealth. Their names are in the *Social Register,* a listing of acceptable members of high society. A few are known across the nation, such as the Rockefellers, Roosevelts, and Vanderbilts. Most are not visible to the general public. They live in grand seclusion, drawing their income from the investment of their inherited wealth. In contrast, the lower-upper class is the "new rich." Although they may be wealthier than some of the old rich, the new rich have hustled to make their money like everybody else beneath their class. Thus their prestige is generally lower than that of the old rich, who have not found it necessary to lift a finger to make their money, and who tend to thumb their noses at the new rich.

However its wealth is acquired, the upper class is very, very rich. They have enough money and leisure time to cultivate an interest in the arts and to collect rare books, paintings, and sculpture. They generally live in exclusive areas, belong to exclusive social clubs, rub elbows with each other, and marry their own kind—all of which keeps them so aloof from the masses that they have been called the *out-of-sight class* (Fussel, 1983). More than any other class, they tend to be conscious of being members of a class. They also command an enormous amount of power and influence here and abroad, as they hold many top government positions, run the Council on Foreign Relations, and control multinational corporations. Their actions affect the lives of millions.

Sociology: An Introduction
by Alex Thio

---

segment (sĕg′ mənt) n. Any of the parts into which something can be divided.

aristocracy (ăr ĭ stŏk′ rə sē) n. A hereditary, privileged ruling class or nobility.

seclusion (sĭ kloo̅′ zhən) n. The state of being removed or set apart from the others; solitude; privacy.

aloof (ə loo̅f′) adj. Distant, especially in one's relations with other people; indifferent.

abroad (ə brôd′) adv. In a foreign country; out of one's own country.

What are the differences the author notes between the two segments of the upper class in the first paragraph? The upper-upper class is called the "old rich" because they inherited their money; they are accepted in high society; most live in seclusion and live off the income from their inherited wealth. The lower-upper class is called the "new rich" because they have had to earn their own money; they have lower prestige than the old rich, who look down on them. In this paragraph the author uses the words "in contrast" to signal the difference between the old rich and the new rich.

In the second paragraph the author compares the old rich and the new rich. Both are extremely rich and have the money and the time to cultivate their interest in the arts; both live in exclusive areas and tend to socialize with and marry within their class; both remain aloof from the other classes; both are class-conscious; both have a great deal of power and influence here and abroad; the actions of both affect the lives of millions.

ă pat ā pay â care ä father ĕ pet ē be ĭ pit ī tie î pier ŏ pot ō toe
ô paw oi noise oo̅ took oo̅ boot ou out th thin *th* this ŭ cut û urge
yoo̅ abuse zh vision ə *a*bout, it*e*m, ed*i*ble, gall*o*p, circ*u*s

The paragraph below is taken from a psychology textbook. In it, the authors use the comparison-contrast pattern to present two basic kinds of memory loss. The main idea is that *There are two different kinds of memory loss, anterograde amnesia and retrograde amnesia.* The authors use the supporting details to define each type of amnesia in order to emphasize the important way in which they differ. Read the paragraph to learn how the two types of memory loss are different from each other; then write the supporting details that explain the differences.

There are two basic kinds of memory loss. In *anterograde amnesia,* the inability to create new permanent memories, patients typically cannot learn the names of their doctors, the hospitals they're in, or any other new information they're exposed to after the traumatic event or illness that caused the amnesia. In *retrograde amnesia,* the inability to recall information that had been learned before the onset of the amnesia, patients may not remember experiences in their earlier life or the name of the president of the United States.

Psychology
by Diane Papalia and Sally Olds

anterograde amnesia (ăn tîr′ ō grād ăm nē′ shə) n. (The authors explain this term in the passage.)

retrograde amnesia (rĕt′ rə grād ăm nē′ shə) n. (The authors explain this term in the passage.)

Anterograde amnesia means that a person cannot create new permanent memories. Retrograde amnesia means that a person cannot recall information that had been learned before the amnesia. These two types of amnesia differ in a significant way: in one type, new information cannot be remembered, while in the other type, previous information cannot be recalled.

Subject matter: two basic kinds of memory loss

ă pat ā pay â care ä father ĕ pet ē be ĭ pit ī tie î pier ŏ pot ō toe
ô paw oi noise o͞o took o͞o boot ou out th thin *th* this ŭ cut û urge
yo͞o abuse zh vision ə *a*bout, it*e*m, ed*i*ble, gall*o*p, circ*u*s

Main idea sentence: There are two different kinds of memory loss, anterograde amnesia and retrograde amnesia.

- *Supporting details:* _____

_____

_____

_____

_____

_____

_____

_____

- *Pattern:* _____

Although the authors do not use any special words to signal the contrast in this paragraph, they do put the two terms, *anterograde amnesia* and *retrograde amnesia,* in italics to draw attention to them. Careful reading reveals a major difference (or contrast) between the two types of amnesia. Also, notice that this paragraph contains not only the comparison-contrast pattern, but also the definition pattern because the two terms, anterograde amnesia and retrograde amnesia, are defined.

By the way, there is a difference between the word *con*trast (accent on first syllable) and con*trast* (accent on second syllable). *Con*trast is a noun; it means a difference or unlikeness between two or more things. (For example, the difference between Handel's and Bach's lives is an interesting *con*trast). The word con*trast* is a verb; it means to point out or show the differences between two or more things. (For example, "Handel's life con*trast*ed sharply with Bach's.")

5. Cause-Effect
(Explanation and Additional Examples)

Textbook authors often use the cause-effect pattern to describe the reasons things happen and their results. Something that produces a result or outcome is called a *cause.* The result or outcome itself is called an *effect.*

Watch for clue words that indicate a cause: information that comes before words such as *causes, produces, leads to, results in;* and information that follows words such as *because, is due to, resulted from, is caused by.* Watch for clue words that indicate an effect: information that comes before words such as *results from, was caused by, occurs because, is due to;* and information that follows words such as *resulted in, therefore, lead to, as a result of, the effect was.*

The following paragraph from a history textbook concerns U.S. society in 1860. The authors state the main idea in the first sentence: *The United States in 1860 was a far more diverse and complex society than it had been in 1800.* Diversity and complexity are the effects, and the authors present them before presenting the causes. Now read the paragraph to learn *why* U.S. society was more complex in 1860 than it was in 1800. The supporting details explain the causes that led to this change.

The United States in 1860 was a far more diverse and complex society than it had been in 1800. (1) Industrialization, specialization, urbanization, and immigration had altered the ways people lived and worked. (2) Economic growth not only created new jobs in towns and cities but also caused clearer distinctions in wealth and status. (3) Inequality increased everywhere, and competition and insecurity produced resentments and conflict. (4) Increasingly, cities housed ostentatious wealth and abject poverty, and violence and disorder became commonplace.

A People and a Nation
by Mary Beth Norton et al.

diverse (dī vûrs') adj. Distinct in kind; unlike; having variety in forms.

complex (kəm plĕks') adj. Involved or intricate. (Note that the accent is on the last syllable.)

industrialization (ĭn dŭs' trē əl ə zā' shən) n. The development of industry; to become industrialized.

ă pat ā pay â care ä father ĕ pet ē be ĭ pit ī tie î pier ŏ pot ō toe
ô paw oi noise o͞o took o͞o boot ou out th thin *th* this ŭ cut û urge
yo͞o abuse zh vision ə *a*bout, it*e*m, ed*i*ble, gall*o*p, circ*u*s

urbanization (ûr bə nə zā′ shən) n. To make urban (like a city) in character or nature.

ostentatious (ŏs tĕn tā′ shəs) adj. Characterized by or given to ostentation; showy; pretentious.

abject (ăb′ jĕkt) adj. Of the most miserable kind; wretched.

The authors list four causes of U.S. society's becoming more diverse and complex. To help the reader recognize that there was not one reason but *four* reasons this change occurred, the authors even use numbers to signal each cause. Each of the numbered sentences in the paragraph explains a cause.

As noted earlier, authors may use more than one pattern in a paragraph. The use of numbers in this paragraph may have made you think of the listing pattern. The two dates, 1800 and 1860, may have made you think of the comparison-contrast or sequence pattern. Although you may have thought of these patterns, the authors' *primary* (most important) purpose is to explain to the reader *why* there were certain changes that occurred in U.S. society during that time period. Therefore, the cause-effect pattern is the primary pattern.

Remember, when you are deciding which pattern an author has used, you must be guided by the main idea. Think about the *relationship* between the main idea and the supporting details. Then choose the pattern that shows the *most important* relationship between the main idea and the supporting details.

The next example comes from a sociology textbook. You may recall this passage about Malthus's theory that population growth would eventually be stopped by the "positive checks" of nature: disease and famine. The subject matter of this paragraph is *the failure of Malthus's theory*. A combination of the first and the next-to-the-last sentence states the main idea: *Because Malthus failed to foresee three revolutions that undermined his theory, the awful fate of overpopulation which he predicted has not yet come to pass.* In this paragraph, the author explains these three revolutions more fully.

ă pat ā pay â care ä father ĕ pet ē be ĭ pit ī tie î pier ŏ pot ō toe
ô paw oi noise o͞o took o͞o boot ou out th thin *th* this ŭ cut û urge
y͞o͞o abuse zh vision ə *a*bout, it*e*m, ed*i*ble, gall*o*p, circ*u*s

Read the passage and follow the author's cause-effect pattern.

Malthus failed to foresee three revolutions that undermined his theory: the revolutions in contraception, agricultural technology, and medicine. He did not anticipate the development of very effective and convenient contraceptives such as the pill and the IUD (intrauterine contraceptive device). He did not expect that birth control, which he condemned as a vice, would become widespread. Especially in the West, the use of contraceptives has helped bring birth rates down to a point lower than Malthus thought possible. Meanwhile, the technological revolution has allowed farmers to increase production by raising the yield of their land, not just by adding farmland. Finally, medical advances have given us an arsenal of effective weapons against the contagious diseases that Malthus expected would devastate overpopulated nations. As a result, instead of being reduced by disease, overpopulated nations continue to grow more crowded. Thus the awful fate Malthus predicted has not come to pass—or at least, not yet. His theory, however, has served as a warning to nations that populations cannot expand indefinitely, because natural resources are finite.

Sociology: An Introduction
by Alex Thio

contraception (kŏn trə sĕp′ shən) n. Prevention of pregnancy; a means or method of preventing pregnancy.

arsenal (är′ sə nəl) n. A source of supply; a stock of weapons.

finite (fī′ nĭt) adj. Having boundaries; limited.

The author uses the phrase "as a result" to introduce the effect (result) of *one* of the causes (improved medical technology). At the end of the paragraph, he uses the word *thus* to signal the reader that he is presenting the overall result.

In this final example from a psychology textbook, the authors describe possible causes for organic mental retardation. The first

ă pat ā pay â care ä father ĕ pet ē be ĭ pit ī tie î pier ŏ pot ō toe
ô paw oi noise ᴏᴏ took ᴏ̄ᴏ̄ boot ou out th thin *th* this ŭ cut û urge
yᴏ̄ᴏ̄ abuse zh vision ə *a*bout, it*e*m, ed*i*ble, gall*o*p, circ*u*s

sentence of the paragraph states the main idea: *Organic retardation may be due to a number of different physical reasons.* Organic retardation is the result that the authors are trying to explain. Read the paragraph to determine the supporting details in which the authors present the possible causes.

> **Organic retardation** may be due to a number of different physical reasons. It may stem from a chromosomal disorder like Down's syndrome, which also produces certain distinct physical characteristics. It may come from a disorder of metabolism, like phenylketonuria (PKU). Or it may result from problems during the prenatal period such as maternal illness, infection, or drug ingestion. Sometimes it accompanies a major physical birth defect like hydrocephaly, in which a baby is born with an abnormally large head. In this and other instances, the cause is unknown although it is clearly physical in origin. This type of defect can usually be detected before or shortly after birth. About one in four mentally retarded persons—some 2 million people—are in this class. Their IQs are usually below 50, and they are equally likely to come from the highest social classes as from the lowest (Zigler & Seitz, 1982).
>
> *Psychology*
> by Diane Papalia and Sally Olds

organic retardation (ôr găn′ ĭk rē tär dā′ shən) n. Permanently impaired mental functioning that is caused by damage or disease in an organ of the body.

chromosomal (krō mə sō′ məl) adj. Of or pertaining to chromosomes (genetic material).

metabolism (mə tăb′ ə lĭz əm) n. The physical and chemical processes involved in sustaining life.

prenatal (prē nāt′ l) adj. Occurring or existing before birth.

ingestion (ĭn jĕs′ chən) n. Taking into the body by mouth; swallowing something.

ă pat ā pay â care ä father ĕ pet ē be ĭ pit ī tie î pier ŏ pot ō toe
ô paw oi noise o͞o took o͞o boot ou out th thin *th* this ŭ cut û urge
y͞o͞o abuse zh vision ə *a*bout, it*e*m, ed*i*ble, gall*o*p, circ*u*s

hydrocephaly (hī drō sĕf′ ə lē) n. An excessive accumulation of fluid in the head causing it to be abnormally large.

Subject matter: possible causes of organic retardation

Main idea sentence: Organic retardation may be due to a number of different physical reasons.

- *Supporting detail causes:* _____

_____

_____

_____

_____

_____

_____

- *Pattern:* _____

For the possible causes, you should have listed chromosomal disorders (such as PKU); problems during the prenatal period (such as maternal illness, infection, or drug ingestion); that it may accompany a major physical defect (such as hydrocephaly); or be due to unknown causes that are clearly physical in origin. Sometimes an author will state that a cause is unknown. This does not mean that there is no cause—just that the cause is not known.

In each of the examples in this section, there were several causes, but only one effect. You may encounter a passage which discusses only one cause and only one effect (for example, a factory goes out of business, and its employees no longer have jobs). You will also see paragraphs in which there is one cause but many effects. (For example, when the Supreme Court makes a ruling on a case, there are many effects. These could include the creation of new laws throughout the country, changes in business or government policies, and changes in attitudes.) Your task as a reader is to identify *all* the causes and effects, and to see how each relates to the main idea.

ă pat ā pay â care ä father ĕ pet ē be ĭ pit ī tie î pier ŏ pot ō toe
ô paw oi noise ŏŏ took ōō boot ou out th thin *th* this ŭ cut û urge
yōō abuse zh vision ə *a*bout, it*e*m, ed*i*ble, gall*o*p, circ*u*s

A Word about Mixed Patterns

In this chapter, you read and worked with passages which contained only *one* writing pattern. Working with just one writing pattern at a time enabled you to understand each pattern clearly. You should realize, however, that authors sometimes combine two or more of these writing patterns in the same passage. This is called a ***mixed pattern.***

Even when authors combine writing patterns, one will usually be the more important pattern of organization for the passage. For example, in a passage in which the author has used the cause-effect pattern as the primary writing pattern, he or she may also use the listing pattern to list the causes or effects.

The passage below is a mixed pattern because it contains several sentences which indicate different writing patterns. The patterns are identified beside the passage.

Robotics.   With the age of the computer has arrived the age of the robot. These robots are information machines with the manual dexterity to perform tasks too unpleasant, too dangerous, or too critical to assign to human beings. Examples are pattern-cutting robots in garment businesses, which are able to get the most apparel out of bolts of cloth; robots used in defense to perform underwater military missions; robots used by fruit growers to pick fruit; and even robots that patrol jail corridors at night and report any persons encountered. Especially controversial are the robots that do tedious jobs better than human beings do—jobs such as welding or paint spraying in new-car plants. Clearly, these robots signal the end of jobs for many factory workers—a troublesome social problem.

definition: robot

list: examples of ways robots are used

cause: increased use of robots

effect: loss of jobs for factory workers

Tools for an Information Age
by H. L. Capron

RECOGNIZING AUTHORS'
WRITING PATTERNS
Chapter Summary

A **writing pattern** is the way an author organizes and presents information and ideas to the reader.

In this chapter, you learned five of the writing patterns textbook authors frequently use. When you are deciding which pattern an author has used, you must be guided by the main idea. Your task as a reader is to follow the authors' thinking to see how the authors have related the supporting details to the main idea. Textbook passages are often organized according to one of the five writing patterns:

1. LISTING PATTERN

The *listing pattern* presents a list of items. The author may present the items in *any order.*

- Your task as a reader is to identify *all* items listed.
- Clues to watch for: enumeration (*1, 2, 3, 4,* etc.) or letters (*a, b, c,* etc.); words such as *first, second,* and *also.*

2. SEQUENCE PATTERN

The *sequence pattern* presents a list of items in a *specific order.* The order is important.

- Your task as a reader is to identify *all* items in the series and to note their order.

231

- Clues to watch for: enumeration (*1, 2, 3, 4,* etc.) or letters (*a, b, c,* etc.); dates and words that suggest time (*first, second, then, next, finally, in the sixteenth century, in the 50s*).

3. DEFINITION PATTERN

The *definition pattern* presents an explanation of an important concept or term that is then discussed throughout the passage.

- Your task as a reader is to understand all parts of the definition.

- Clues to watch for: words such as *is, is defined as, this term means, is known as, refers to, the word.* Watch for terms in bold print or italics. Definitions may also appear in parentheses, be set off by commas or dashes, or follow a colon.

4. COMPARISON-CONTRAST PATTERN

The *comparison-contrast pattern* presents similarities (a comparison), differences (a contrast), or both.

- Your task as a reader is to recognize *all* the similarities or differences an author presents.

- Clues to watch for in a comparison: words such as *similarly, likewise, also.*

- Clues to watch for in a contrast: words such as *however, in contrast, on the other hand, nevertheless.*

5. CAUSE-EFFECT PATTERN

The *cause-effect pattern* presents reasons things happen (causes) and their results (effects).

- Your task as a reader is to differentiate between causes and effects—to identify *all* the causes and *all* the effects.

- Clues to watch for that indicate a cause: information that comes before words such as *causes, produces, leads to, results in;* information that follows words such as *because, is due to, resulted from, is caused by.*

- Clues to watch for that indicate an effect: information that comes before words such as *results from, was caused by, occurs because, is due to;* information that follows words such as *resulted in, therefore, lead to, as a result of, the effect was.*

A Reminder about Mixed Patterns

Although textbook authors often use just one writing pattern in a passage, it is not unusual for authors to combine two, or even three, patterns in a single passage. This is referred to as a mixed pattern. In this case, simply try to identify the most important writing pattern.

Being alert to organizational patterns will help you predict, comprehend, and recall important information in your college textbooks. Using what you know about an author's organizational patterns can make you a more competent and confident reader.

RECOGNIZING AUTHORS'
WRITING PATTERNS
Practice Exercises

In the textbook passages below, you will be given the subject matter and the main idea. Of course, you should still read the paragraphs carefully to be sure you have comprehended the subject matter and main idea accurately. Then determine how the supporting details are related to the main idea. For each paragraph, you are told which writing pattern the author has used to organize the supporting details. Write the information from the paragraph that is organized by the pattern. In other words, give the definition, list the items, show the sequence, note the causes and effects, or write the comparison-contrast. Finally, write any clues from the paragraph that indicate to you which writing pattern is being used. This could be a word in the title, a heading, or a word or phrase such as "first," "however," or "in contrast to."

1.   This passage comes from a psychology textbook.

Amnesia is the general term for a variety of memory disorders that arise from different causes and affect the memory in different ways. A number of neurologic conditions that cause damage to the brain produce memory deficits of one kind or another. They're probably the most frequent complaint of patients who have suffered strokes, infectious diseases of the brain, and traumatic injuries. In addition, memory disorders are often the earliest signs of a number of neurologic illnesses, including Alzheimer's disease, a progressive degenerative disease of the brain that usually occurs in old age.

Psychology
by Diane Papalia and Sally Olds

amnesia (ăm nē′ zhə) n. A general term for a variety of memory disorders that arise from different causes and affect the memory in different ways. (The authors have boldfaced this word; they use the words "is the general term" to alert readers that this word is being explained in the passage.)

neurologic (n$\overline{oo}$ rə lŏj′ ik) adj. Pertaining to the nervous system.

deficit (dĕf′ ə sĭt) n. A shortage.

traumatic (trô mă′ tĭk) adj. Pertaining to emotional shock that creates substantial and lasting damage to the psychological development of the individual.

Alzheimer's disease (ăls′ hī mərs dĭ zēz′) n. A progressive degenerative disease of the brain that usually occurs in old age (defined by the author).

degenerative (dĭ jĕn′ ər ə tĭv) adj. Irreversibly deteriorating; steadily worsening.

Subject matter: amnesia

Main idea sentence: Amnesia is the general term for a variety of memory disorders that arise from different causes and affect the memory in different ways.

- *Pattern:* definition

- *Question A:* What is defined here? Write the sentence that gives the definition.

- *Question B:* What clues in the paragraph suggest that the authors have used a definition pattern?

2. This passage comes from a human development textbook.

Stress plays an important part in heart disease. Psychologists have recognized a behavior pattern termed Type A that characterizes people having a higher incidence of cardiovascular problems. Type A's

ă pat ā pay â care ä father ĕ pet ē be ĭ pit ī tie î pier ŏ pot ō toe
ô paw oi noise $\overline{oo}$ took $\overline{oo}$ boot ou out th thin *th* this ŭ cut û urge
y$\overline{oo}$ abuse zh vision ə *a*bout, it*e*m, ed*i*ble, gall*o*p, circ*u*s

are described as hard-driving, competitive, and ambitious, preoccupied with a sense of time urgency, and impatient and easily angered when things go "wrong." . . . A noncoronary-prone pattern known as Type B is defined by the relative absence of these traits. Apparently Type A behavior poses as significant a risk for heart disease as do smoking, high cholesterol level, and high blood pressure. Type A people are about twice as likely to die of heart disease as are their Type B counterparts.

Human Development
by James Vander Zanden

cardiovascular (kär dē ō văs′ kyə lər) adj. Pertaining to or involving the heart or blood vessels.

noncoronary-prone (nŏn kôr′ ə nĕr ē prōn) adj. Not likely to have a coronary thrombosis (the formation of a blood clot that blocks a vessel or occurs in a heart cavity).

Subject matter: stress, heart disease, and behavior types

Main idea sentence: Type A people are about twice as likely to die of stress-related heart disease as are their type B counterparts.

- *Question A:* What is contrasted here? (In terms of stress-related heart disease, how do Type A people differ from Type B people?) List the differences.

ă pat ā pay â care ä father ĕ pet ē be ĭ pit ī tie î pier ŏ pot ō toe
ô paw oi noise ŏŏ took ōō boot ou out th thin *th* this ŭ cut û urge
yōō abuse zh vision ə *a*bout, it*e*m, ed*i*ble, gall*o*p, circ*u*s

- *Question B:* What clues in the paragraph suggest that the author has used a comparison-contrast pattern?

_____

_____

3. This passage is excerpted from a marketing textbook.

> The psychoanalytic school of thought, founded by Sigmund Freud and later modified by his followers and critics, has had a tremendous impact on the study of human personality and behavior. Freud contended that there are three parts to the mind—the id, the ego, and the superego. The id houses the basic instinctive drives, many of which are antisocial. The superego is the conscience, accepting moral standards and directing the instinctive drives into acceptable channels. The id and the superego are sometimes in conflict. The ego is the conscious, rational control center that maintains a balance between the uninhibited instincts of the id and the socially oriented, constraining superego.
>
> *Fundamentals of Marketing*
> by William Stanton

psychoanalytic (sī kō ăn ə lĭt′ ĭk) adj. Pertaining to psychoanalysis, a therapeutic approach developed by Freud that aims to eliminate anxiety by giving the patient insight into unconscious conflicts that affect behavior and emotions.

id (ĭd) n. The part of the mind that houses the basic instinctive drives, many of which are antisocial.

ego (ē′ gō) n. The conscious, rational control center that maintains a balance between the id and the superego.

superego (sū′ pər ē gō) n. The conscience.

antisocial (ăn tĭ sō′ shəl) adj. Pertaining to behavior that violates the rights of others.

rational (răsh′ ən əl) adj. Having or exercising the ability to reason; logical.

ă pat ā pay â care ä father ĕ pet ē be ĭ pit ī tie î pier ŏ pot ō toe
ô paw oi noise o͝o took o͞o boot ou out th thin th this ŭ cut û urge
yo͞o abuse zh vision ə about, item, edible, gallop, circus

Subject matter: the three parts to the mind

Main idea sentence: Freud contended that there are three parts to the mind—the id, the ego, and the superego.

Pattern: listing

- *Question A:* What is being listed in this paragraph? List the items.

- *Question B:* What clues in the paragraph suggest that the author has used a listing pattern?

4. A sociology textbook is the source of this paragraph.

The Results of Deprivation

Since the fourteenth century there have been more than 50 recorded cases of "feral children"—children supposedly raised by animals. One of the most famous is "the wild boy of Aveyron." In 1797 he was captured in the woods by hunters in southern France. He was about eleven years old and completely naked. The "wild boy" ran on all fours, had no speech, preferred uncooked food, and could not do most of the simple things done by younger children. A group of experts pronounced him hopelessly retarded. But Jean Itard, a physician, disagreed. He set out to train the boy, whom he later called Victor. After three months Victor seemed a little more human. He wore clothing. He got up at night to urinate in the toilet. He learned to sit at a table and eat with utensils. He started to show human emotions such as joy, gratitude, and remorse. But although he lived to be more than 40 years old, he never learned to speak nor ever became a normal person.

Sociology: An Introduction
by Alex Thio

deprivation (dĕp rə vā′ shən) n. The condition of being deprived; being without.

feral (fĕr′ əl) adj. Existing in a wild or untamed state.

remorse (rĭ môrs′) n. Bitter regret.

Subject matter: Victor, "the wild boy of Aveyron."

Main idea sentence: Although Victor, a feral child known as "the wild boy of Aveyron," received special training from about age 11, he never over-came the effects of his early deprivation.

Pattern: cause-effect

- *Question A:* What causes and effects are presented in the passage? List the specific causes and their effects.

Cause 1: _____

Effects: _____

_____

Cause 2: _____

Effects: _____

_____

- *Question B:* What clues in the paragraph suggest that the author has used a cause-effect pattern?

_____

_____

ă pat ā pay â care ä father ĕ pet ē be ĭ pit ī tie î pier ŏ pot ō toe
ô paw oi noise o͞o took o͞o boot ou out th thin *th* this ŭ cut û urge
yo͞o abuse zh vision ə *a*bout, it*e*m, ed*i*ble, gall*o*p, circ*u*s

5. This selection comes from a computer science textbook.

> The history of the punched card dates back to 1801, when a French weaver named Joseph Marie Jacquard invented them to control his mechanical looms. But it was the problem of completing the 1880 census count that led to the use of cards as a medium for data processing. The inventor of punched card techniques was Dr. Herman Hollerith, a statistician. The Census Bureau hired him to find a solution to the census problem. In 1887, Hollerith developed his machine-readable card concept and designed a device known as the "census machine." Tabulating with Hollerith's methods took only one-eighth of the time previously required, and so his techniques were adopted for use in the 1890 count. Although the population had increased from 50 to 63 million in the decade after 1880, the 1890 count was completed in less than 3 years. (Of course, this is intolerably slow by today's standards. The 1950 census, using punched card equipment, took about 2 years to produce; the computerized 1980 census yielded figures in a few months.)
>
> *Computer Concepts and Applications with BASIC* by Donald Sanders

---

census (sĕn′ səs) n. An official count of the population.

intolerably (ĭn tŏl′ ər ə blē) adv. Incapable of being tolerated; unbearably.

Subject matter: punched cards

Main idea sentence: The use of punched cards as a means of data processing dates back to 1801 and improved greatly by 1950.

Pattern: sequence

- *Question A:* What sequence is being presented? List the dates and the details that form the sequence.

ă pat ā pay â care ä father ĕ pet ē be ĭ pit ī tie î pier ŏ pot ō toe
ô paw oi noise o͞o took ō͞o boot ou out th thin *th* this ŭ cut û urge
yo͞o abuse zh vision ə *a*bout, it*e*m, ed*i*ble, gall*o*p, circ*u*s

_____

_____

_____

_____

_____

- *Question B:* What clues in the paragraph suggest that the author has used a sequence pattern?

_____

_____

RECOGNIZING AUTHORS' WRITING PATTERNS
Answer Key for Practice Exercises

Compare your responses to the practice exercises on pages 235–242 with the answers given below:

1. *Question A:* What term is being defined, and how do the authors define it?

   - Amnesia is the general term for a variety of memory disorders that arise from different causes and affect the memory in different ways.

   Question B: What clue words in the paragraph suggest that the authors have used a definition paragraph?

   - "Amnesia" is in bold print.

   - The words "is the general term for" are used.

   - Every supporting detail in the paragraph tells more about the meaning of amnesia.

2. *Question A:* What is being contrasted and what are the differences?

   - Type A people have a higher incidence of stress-related heart disease than do Type B people.

   Question B: What clue words in the paragraph suggest that the author has used a comparison-contrast pattern?

   - The author described two behavior types (A and B) for the purpose of *contrasting* them. Although he hasn't used words such as *in contrast* or *however,* he is nevertheless showing that these are opposite types.

   (In this passage, no comparison is being made; only a contrast is presented.)

3. *Question A:* What is being listed in this paragraph and what are the items?

   Three parts to the mind:

   - the id—instinctive drives, often antisocial

- the ego—conscious, rational control

- the superego—conscience

Question B: What clue words in the paragraph suggest that the author has used a listing pattern?

- the words "there are three parts"
  (The last four sentences describe the three parts.)

4. *Question A:* What causes and effects are presented in the passage?

- Cause 1: Growing up in the wild, the feral child Victor was deprived of a normal upbringing.

- Effects: Victor never learned to speak and never became a normal person.

- Cause 2: Victor was later trained by Jean Itard, a physician.

- Effects: Victor acquired more human behavior (wearing clothes, eating at a table, showing human emotions).

Question B: What clue words in the paragraph suggest that the author has used the cause-effect pattern?

- The heading uses the word *results* ("The Results of Deprivation").

5. *Question A:* What sequence is being presented in the paragraph and what are the items in it?

- Punched cards date back to 1801.

- The 1880 census led to the use of punched cards.

- In 1887 Hollerith developed a "census machine."

- In 1890 the "census machine" was used in the census.

- The 1950 census used punched card equipment (the census took 2 years).

- The 1980 census was computerized (census took a few months).

Question B: What clue words in the paragraph suggest that the author has used the sequence pattern?

- All the dates indicate a chronological order.

RECOGNIZING AUTHORS' WRITING PATTERNS
Review Test

Read each of the following paragraphs carefully. Determine the subject matter and main idea for each paragraph. Using a dictionary, define the words listed below each passage according to the way they are used *in the paragraph*. (Remember, you may not need to use a dictionary for a word if the author has defined it for you in the passage.)

Identify the subject matter, main idea, and major writing pattern that the author has used to organize the supporting details. There will be one exercise for each major pattern. Next, list the supporting details that are organized by the pattern. In other words, give the definition, list the items, show the sequence, note the causes and effects, or write the comparison-contrast. Then, just as you did in the Practice Exercises, write any clues from the paragraph that indicated to you which writing pattern was used. This could be a word in the title, a heading, or a word or phrase such as *first, however,* or *in contrast to.*

1. This passage comes from a psychology textbook.

> What do people want from their friends? According to a survey of 216 people at four stages of life—high school seniors, newlyweds, parents whose youngest child was about to leave home, and people getting ready to retire—five specific dimensions of friendship are important (Weiss & Lowenthal, 1975). We look for *similarity* (in personality, values, or attitudes, with an emphasis on shared activities or experiences); *reciprocity* (helping, understanding, and accepting each other, with an emphasis on mutual trust and ability to share confidences); *compatibility* (enjoyment in being together); *structure* (geographic closeness, convenience, or long duration of acquaintance); and *role modeling* (admiration and respect for the friend's good qualities).
>
> *Psychology*
> by Diane Papalia and Sally Olds

reciprocity: _____

compatibility: _____

- *Subject matter:* Who or what is the passage about?

_____

- *Main idea sentence:* What do the authors want you to understand about
  the subject matter?

_____

_____

_____

_____

- *Pattern:* Which writing pattern have the authors used to organize the
  supporting details?

_____

- What information from the paragraph is organized by the pattern? List
  the supporting details here:

_____

_____

_____

_____

_____

- What clues from the paragraph suggest that this pattern is being used?

_____

_____

2. This excerpt is taken from a marketing textbook.

   For a company to operate successfully today, management must
develop an orderly method for gathering and analyzing the mass of
information that is relevant to the organization. A marketing information system is such a method. It is a structure designed to generate

and process an information flow to aid managerial planning and decision making in a company's marketing program. A marketing information system is a future-oriented, continuously operating, computer-based process. It is designed to handle internal and external data and to prevent problems as well as to solve them.

Fundamentals of Marketing
by William J. Stanton

relevant: _____

generate: _____

- *Subject matter:* Who or what is the passage about?

  _____

- *Main idea sentence:* What does the author want you to understand about the subject matter?

  _____

  _____

  _____

  _____

- *Pattern:* Which writing pattern has the author used to organize the supporting details?

  _____

- What information from the paragraph is organized by the pattern? List the supporting details here:

  _____

  _____

  _____

  _____

  _____

- What clues from the paragraph suggest that this pattern is being used?

  _____

  _____

3. This selection is taken from a human development textbook.

> In contrast with polygyny, *polyandry* is rare among the world's societies. And in practice, polyandry has not usually allowed freedom of mate selection for women; it has often meant simply that younger brothers have sexual access to the wife of an older brother. Thus where a father is unable to afford wives for each of his sons, he may secure a wife for only his oldest son.
>
> *Human Development*
> by James Vander Zanden

polygyny: _____

polyandry: _____

secure: _____

- *Subject matter:* Who or what is the passage about?

  _____

- *Main idea sentence:* What does the author want you to understand about the subject matter?

  _____

  _____

  _____

  _____

- *Pattern:* Which writing pattern has the author used to organize the supporting details?

  _____

- What information from the paragraph is organized by the pattern? List the supporting details here:

  _____

  _____

  _____

  _____

_____

_____

- What clues from the paragraph suggest that this pattern is being used?

_____

_____

4. This excerpt comes from a human development textbook.

> One of the key concepts advanced by Maslow is the *hierarchy of needs*. . . . Maslow felt that human beings have certain basic needs that they must meet before they can go on to fulfill other needs. At the bottom of Maslow's pyramid are fundamental requirements to satisfy physiological needs (including food, water, and sex) and safety needs. Next Maslow identified a set of psychological needs centering on belongingness (love) needs and esteem needs. Finally, at the top of the pyramid, he placed the need to realize one's unique potential to the fullest, what he termed *self-actualization*.
>
>

Human Development
by James Vander Zanden

hierarchy: _____

physiological: _____

esteem: _____

self-actualization: _____

- *Subject matter:* Who or what is the passage about?

_____

- *Main idea sentence:* What does the author want you to understand about the subject matter?

_____

_____

_____

- *Pattern:* Which writing pattern has the author used to organize the supporting details?

_____

- What information from the paragraph is organized by the pattern? List the supporting details here:

_____

_____

_____

_____

_____

_____

- What clues from the paragraph suggest that this pattern is being used?

_____

_____

5. A U.S. history textbook is the source of this excerpt.

The Sources of the Cold War

Unsettled International Environment

After overseeing the defeat of Germany and Japan, President Truman participated in the rapid deterioration of Soviet-American relations—the Cold War. In this new conflict, competitive ideologies, propaganda, reconstruction programs, military alliances, atomic arms development, and spheres of influence condemned the world once again to instability and fear. Some conflict was inevitable after the Second World War, because the international environment was so unsettled. First, the world was in serious economic trouble. Across Europe and Asia, factories, bridges, transportation and communications systems, and houses had been reduced to rubble. Agricultural production was low, and displaced persons wandered around in search of food and family members. How would this devastated world be pieced back together? America and Russia each offered a different model. Second, the collapse of Germany and Japan created power vacuums that drew the two major powers into collision as they sought to claim influence in countries where the Axis had once held sway. Third, political turmoil within nations spurred Soviet-American competition. In Greece and China, for example, where civil wars were waged between leftists and conservative regimes, the two powers favored different sides. Fourth, empires were disintegrating. In this process of decolonization, the European imperial nations were forced to withdraw by nationalist rebels and by their own financial constraints. New nations were born in the Middle East and Asia, and America and Russia competed to win them as friends who might provide military bases, resources and markets. Finally, conflict seemed inevitable because of the shrinkage of the globe. That is, because of the triumph of the airplane and the advent of the "air age," the world became more compact. Nations were brought closer together by faster travel; at the same time, they became more vulnerable to surprise attack from the air. The Americans and Soviets once again collided as they strove to establish defensive positions, sometimes far from home.

A People and a Nation
by Mary Beth Norton et al.

deterioration: _____

ideology: _____

inevitable: _____

vacuum: _____

turmoil: _____

constraint: _____

imperial: _____

nationalist: _____

- *Subject matter:* Who or what is the passage about?

_____

- *Main idea sentence:* What do the authors want you to understand about the subject matter?

_____

_____

_____

_____

- *Pattern:* Which writing pattern have the authors used to organize the supporting details?

  _____

- What information from the paragraph is organized by the pattern? List the supporting details here:

  _____

  _____

  _____

  _____

  _____

- What clues from the paragraph suggest that this pattern is being used?

  _____

  _____

CHAPTER
5

**RECOGNIZING AUTHORS'
WRITING PATTERNS**
Supplemental Exercises

1. This passage comes from a sociology textbook.

> Although there are different styles for dying—just as there are different styles for living—Kübler-Ross (1969) finds that dying people typically pass through five stages in accommodating themselves to impending death: *denial* that they will die, *anger* that life will shortly end, *bargaining* with God or fate to arrange a temporary truce, *depression* or "preparatory grief," and *acceptance.* Not everyone passes through all the stages, and individuals slip back and forth between stages. And a great many other factors also influence the dying experience, including differences in gender, ethnic membership, personality, the death environment, and the nature of the disease itself. Death cannot be understood except in the total context of a person's previous life and current circumstances. In sum, over the past decade or so, public and professional awareness of the dying person's experience has increased dramatically and has given impetus to a more humane approach to death.
>
> *Sociology*
> by James Vander Zanden

- *Subject matter:* Who or what is the passage about?

  _____

- *Main idea sentence:* What does the author want you to understand about the subject matter?

  _____

  _____

  _____

  _____

253

- *Pattern:* Which writing pattern has the author used to organize the supporting details?

  _____

- What information from the paragraph is organized by the pattern? List the supporting details here:

  _____

  _____

  _____

  _____

  _____

  _____

- What clues from the paragraph suggest that this pattern is being used?

  _____

  _____

2.   This passage comes from an information systems textbook.

> A major incentive for office automation is improved productivity. Information-processing technology serves the cause of productivity in two ways. First, computers perform many of the routine tasks that people used to perform manually. This not only speeds up the work, but also reduces errors in the results. Second, information-processing equipment lets people produce output in greater quantities and of better quality.
>
> *Information Systems in Business: An Introduction*
> by James O. Hicks, Jr.

- *Subject matter:* Who or what is the passage about?

  _____

- *Main idea sentence:* What does the author want you to understand about the subject matter?

  _____

  _____

_____

_____

- *Pattern:* Which writing pattern has the author used to organize the supporting details?

_____

- What information from the paragraph is organized by the pattern? List the supporting details here:

_____

_____

_____

_____

_____

_____

_____

- What clues from the paragraph suggest that this pattern is being used?

_____

_____

3. This passage comes from a chemistry textbook.

> LASER is an acronym for Light Amplification by Stimulated Emission of Radiation. It is a special type of emission that involves either atoms or molecules. Since the discovery of laser in 1960, it has been used in numerous systems designed to operate in the gas, liquid, and solid states. These systems emit radiation with wavelengths ranging from infrared through visible UV [ultraviolet], to the X ray.
>
> *Chemistry*
> by Raymond Chang

- *Subject matter:* Who or what is the passage about?

_____

- *Main idea sentence:* What does the author want you to understand about the subject matter?

_____

_____

_____

_____

- *Pattern:* Which writing pattern has the author used to organize the supporting details?

_____

- What information from the paragraph is organized by the pattern? List the supporting details here:

_____

_____

_____

_____

_____

- What clues from the paragraph suggest that this pattern is being used?

_____

_____

4. This passage comes from a computer science textbook.

> In traditional economics courses, we learned that the cornerstones of an economy are land, labor, and capital. That tradition now is being challenged, and we speak of *four* key economic elements: land, labor, capital, and information. We are converting from an industrial society to an information society. We are moving from physical labor to mental labor, trading muscle power for brain power. Just as people moved from the farms to the factories when the Industrial Revolution began, so we must adjust to the information age.
>
> *Computers: Tools for an Information Age*
> by H. L. Capron

- *Subject matter:* Who or what is the passage about?

  _____

- *Main idea sentence:* What does the author want you to understand about the subject matter?

  _____

  _____

  _____

  _____

- *Pattern:* Which writing pattern has the author used to organize the supporting details?

  _____

- What information from the paragraph is organized by the pattern? List the supporting details here:

  _____

  _____

  _____

  _____

  _____

- What clues from the paragraph suggest that this pattern is being used?

  _____

  _____

5. This passage comes from a chemistry textbook.

   The applications of lasers are quite numerous. Their high intensity and ease of focus make them suitable for eye surgery, for drilling holes in metals and welding, and for nuclear fusion. The fact that they are highly directional and have precisely known wavelengths makes them very useful for telecommunications. Lasers are also used in isotope separation, holography (three-dimensional photography), compact disks, and even in supermarkets to read Universal Product Codes. Lasers have played an important role in the spectroscopic investigation of molecular properties and of many chemical and biological processes.

Chemistry
by Raymond Chang

- *Subject matter:* Who or what is the passage about?

_____

- *Main idea sentence:* What does the author want you to understand about the subject matter?

_____

_____

_____

_____

- *Pattern:* Which writing pattern has the author used to organize the supporting details?

_____

- What information from the paragraph is organized by the pattern? List the supporting details here:

_____

_____

_____

_____

_____

_____

_____

- What clues from the paragraph suggest that this pattern is being used?

_____

_____

6. This passage comes from a chemistry textbook. Write the subject matter, main idea, and pattern for *each paragraph.*

The Atomic Theory—From Early Ideas to John Dalton

In the fifth century B.C. the Greek philosopher Democritus expressed the belief that all matter is composed of very small, indivisible particles, which he named *atomos* (meaning uncuttable or indivisible). Although Democritus' idea was not accepted by many philosophers of his day (notably Plato and Aristotle), his suggestion persisted through the centuries. Experimental evidence from early scientific investigations provided support for the notion of "atomism" and gradually gave rise to our modern definitions of elements and compounds. However, it was not until 1808 that an English scientist and school teacher, John Dalton, formulated a precise definition of the indivisible building blocks of matter that we call atoms.

Dalton's atomic theory marks the beginning of the modern era of chemistry. The hypotheses about the nature of matter on which Dalton based his theory can be summarized as follows:

- Elements are composed of extremely small particles, called atoms. All atoms of a given element are identical, having the same size, mass, and chemical properties. The atoms of one element are different from the atoms of all other elements.

- Compounds are composed of atoms of more than one element. In any compound, the ratio of the numbers of atoms of any two of the elements present is either an integer or a simple fraction.

Subject Matter

_____

Main Idea

_____

_____

_____

Pattern

_____

Subject Matter

_____

Main Idea

_____

_____

_____

Pattern

_____

- A chemical reaction involves only the separation, combination, or rearrangement of atoms; it does not result in their creation or destruction.

As you can see, Dalton's concept of an atom was far more detailed and specific than the description of Democritus. The first hypothesis states that atoms are different for different elements. Dalton made no attempt to describe the structure or composition of atoms—he had no idea what an atom is really like. But he did realize that the different properties shown by elements such as hydrogen and oxygen, for example, can be explained by assuming that hydrogen atoms are not the same as oxygen atoms.

The second hypothesis suggests that, in order to form a certain compound, we need not only atoms of the right kinds of elements, but the correct numbers of these atoms as well. The last hypothesis is another way of stating the *law of conservation of mass,* which says that *matter can neither be created nor destroyed.* Since matter is made of atoms that are unchanged in a chemical reaction, it follows that mass must be conserved as well. Dalton's brilliant insight into the nature of matter was the main cause of the rapid progress of chemistry in the nineteenth century.

Chemistry
by Raymond Chang

Subject Matter

_____

Main Idea

_____

_____

_____

Pattern

_____

Subject Matter

_____

Main Idea

_____

_____

_____

Pattern

_____

CHAPTER

5

RECOGNIZING AUTHORS'
WRITING PATTERNS
Textbook Excerpt and Comprehension Quiz

"Communicating Interculturally" from *Business Communications Today,* 4th ed., by Courtland L. Bovée and John V. Thill, McGraw-Hill, Inc., 1995, pp. 59–68.

Prepare Yourself to Read

Before you read this selection, read and think about its title. Then, in one or two sentences, write a few of the things that you already know about intercultural communication.

_____

_____

_____

Complete your preview of this selection by reading

- the first paragraph

- the headings of each section

- any diagrams, illustrations, and photographs

- all of the last paragraph

Ask and answer questions as you read.

Use questions to guide your reading. Turn section headings into questions. If there are no headings, create questions based on what the paragraphs or sections seem to be about.

Read actively to find answers to your questions.

261

Copyright © 1996 by The McGraw-Hill Companies, Inc.

COMMUNICATING INTERCULTURALLY

RECOGNIZING CULTURAL DIFFERENCES

Cultural differences can affect your ability to send and to receive messages. When you write to or speak with someone in another culture, you encode your message using the assumptions of your own culture. However, the receiver decodes it according to the assumptions of the other culture, so your meaning may be misunderstood. The greater the difference between the sender's culture and the receiver's culture, the greater the chance for misunderstanding.[1]

Consider the U.S. computer sales representative who called on a client in China. Hoping to make a good impression, the salesperson brought an expensive grandfather clock as a gift. Unfortunately, the differences between the sender's culture and the receiver's culture interfered with the communication process. Instead of being pleased, the Chinese client was deeply offended, because in China receiving a clock as a gift is considered bad luck.[2]

Such problems arise when we assume, wrongly, that other people's attitudes and lives are like ours. As a graduate of one training program said: "I used to think it was enough to treat people the way I wanted to be treated. But [after taking the course] . . . I realized you have to treat people the way *they* want to be treated."[3] Acknowledging and exploring these differences is an important step toward understanding how culture affects the communication process. As you'll see in the following sections, cultural differences show up in social values, ideas of status, decision-making habits, attitudes toward time, use of space, cultural context, body language, manners, and legal and ethical behavior.

Social Values

Although the United States is home to millions of people having different religions and values, the major influence is the Puritan work ethic. The predominant U.S. view is that money solves many problems, that material comfort (earned by individual effort) is a sign of superiority, and that people who work hard are better than those who don't. By and large, people in the United States assume that people from other cultures also dislike poverty and value hard work. In fact, many societies condemn materialism, and some prize a more carefree lifestyle.

As a culture, people in the United States are goal-oriented. They want to get their work done efficiently, and they assume that everyone else does too. They think they're improving things if they can figure out a way for two people using modern methods to do the same work as four people using the "old way." In countries such as India and Pakistan, where unemployment is high, creating jobs is more important than working efficiently. Executives in these countries would rather employ four workers than two, and their values influence their actions as well as the way they encode and decode messages.

Roles and Status

Culture dictates the roles people play, including who communicates with whom, what they communicate, and in what way. For example, in many countries women still don't play a prominent role in business, so female executives who visit these countries may find that they're not taken seriously as businesspeople. Culture can define roles by the way people refer to each other. In the United States people show respect for superiors and top managers by addressing them as "Mr. Roberts" or "Mrs. Gutierrez." However, in China, it's customary to show respect for organizational rank by addressing businesspeople according to their official titles, such as "President" or "Manager."[4]

Concepts of status also differ. Most U.S. executives send status signals that reflect materialistic values. The big boss has a large corner office, deep carpets, an expensive desk, and handsome accessories. In other cultures status is communicated in other ways. The highest-ranking executives in France sit in the middle of an open area, surrounded by lower-level employees. In the Middle East fine possessions are reserved for the home, and business is conducted in cramped and modest quarters. An executive from another culture who assumes that such office arrangements indicate a lack of status would be making a big mistake.

Decision-Making Customs

In the United States and Canada, businesspeople try to reach decisions as quickly and efficiently as possible. The top people are concerned with reaching an agreement on the main points, and they leave the details to be worked out later by others. In Greece this approach would backfire. A Greek executive assumes that anyone who ignores the details is being evasive and untrustworthy. Spending time on each little point is considered a mark of good faith. Similarly, Latin Americans prefer to make their deals slowly, after much discussion.

Cultures also differ in terms of who makes the decisions. In the United States many organizations are dominated by a single figure who says yes or no to the major deals. It is the same in Pakistan, where you can get a decision quickly if you reach the highest-ranking executive.[5] In other cultures, decision making is shared. In Japan the negotiating team arrives at a consensus through an elaborate, time-consuming process. Agreement must be complete—there is no majority rule. And like businesses everywhere, Japanese firms expect their managers to follow the same decision-making process regardless of whether they're in Tokyo or in Toledo, Ohio.

Concepts of Time

Differing perceptions of time are another factor that can lead to misunderstandings. German and U.S. executives see time as a way to plan the business day efficiently, focusing on only one task during each scheduled period. Because time is so limited, German and U.S. executives try to get to the point quickly when communicating.

However, executives from Latin America and Asia see time as more flexible. In these cultures, building a foundation for the business relationship is more important than meeting a deadline for completing a task. Seen in this light, it's not surprising that people in such cultures do not observe strict schedules. Instead, they take whatever time is needed to get to know each other and explore the background issues.[6]

If a salesperson from Chicago called on a client in Mexico City and was kept waiting 30 minutes in the outer office, that salesperson would feel angry and insulted, assuming the client attaches a low priority to the visit. In fact, the Mexican client doesn't mean to imply anything at all by this delay. To the Mexican, a wait of 30 minutes is a matter of course; the workday isn't expected to follow a rigid, preset schedule.[7]

Concepts of Personal Space

Like time, space means different things in different cultures. The classic story of a conversation between a U.S. executive and a Latin American executive is that the interaction may begin at one end of a hallway and end up at the other, with neither party aware of having moved. During the conversation the Latin American executive instinc-

Before traveling to Saudi Arabia, U.S. executives Donald Rumson and John Anders studied the Saudi culture carefully. Thus, when it came time for them to meet their Arab associates at the Sheraton Hotel in Jedda, they tried to put their Arab associates at ease by standing closer than would normally be comfortable for most North Americans.

tively moves closer to the U.S. executive, who unconsciously steps back, resulting in an intercultural dance across the floor.

People in Canada and the United States usually stand about five feet apart during a business conversation. This distance is uncomfortably close for people from Germany or Japan. But to Arabs or Latin Americans, this distance is uncomfortably far. Because of these differing concepts of personal space, a Canadian manager may react negatively (without knowing exactly why) when a Latin American colleague moves closer during their conversation. And the Latin American colleague may react negatively (again, without knowing why) when the Canadian manager backs away.

Cultural Context

One of the ways we assign meaning to a message is according to its **cultural context,** the pattern of physical cues and implicit understanding that convey meaning between two members of the same culture. However, people convey contextual meaning differently from culture to culture. In a **high-context culture** such as South Korea or Taiwan, people rely less on verbal communication and more on the context of nonverbal actions and environmental setting to convey meaning. The rules of everyday life are rarely explicit in high-context cultures; as they grow up, people learn how to recognize situational cues (such as gestures and tone of voice) and how to respond as expected.[8]

In a **low-context culture** such as the United States or Germany, people rely more on verbal communication and less on circumstances and implied meaning to convey meaning. Expectations are usually spelled out in a low-context culture through explicit statements, such as "Please wait until I'm finished" or "You're welcome to browse." In this way, a businessperson in a low-context culture not only explains his or her own actions but also cues the other person about what to do or what to expect next.[9]

Imagine the confusion and frustration of someone from a low-context culture trying to sell products to a client from a high-context culture. If the client says nothing after the salesperson names a price, the salesperson may assume that the silence means rejection and may try to save the sale by naming a lower figure. However, in the high-context culture, silence means only that the client is considering the first offer. By misinterpreting this silence and lowering the price, the salesperson loses needed profits.

Body Language

Gestures help members of a culture clarify confusing messages, but differences in body language are a major source of misunderstanding during intercultural communication. Furthermore, don't make the mistake of assuming that someone from another country who speaks your language has mastered the body language of your culture. Instead, learn some of the basic differences in the way people supplement their words with body movement. Take the signal for *no.* People in the United States and Canada shake their heads back and forth; people in Bulgaria nod up and down; people in Japan move their right hands; people in Sicily raise their chins. Or take eye contact. Businesspeople in the United States assume that a person who won't meet their gaze is evasive and dishonest. In many parts of Latin America and Asia, however, keeping your eyes lowered is a sign of respect. Among many Native-American groups, it's a sign of disrespect for children to maintain eye contact with adults.[10] So when some teachers scold Native-American students by saying, "Look at me when I'm talking to you," they only create confusion.

Sometimes people from different cultures misread an intentional signal sent by body language; sometimes they overlook the signal entirely or assume that a meaningless gesture is significant. An Arab man indicates a romantic interest in a woman by running a hand backward across his hair; most Westerners would not understand the significance of this gesture.[11] On the other hand, an Egyptian might mistakenly assume that a Westerner who exposes the sole of his or her shoe is offering a grave insult.

Social Behavior and Manners

What is polite in one culture may be considered rude in another. In Arab countries it's impolite to take gifts to a man's wife but acceptable to take gifts to his children. In Germany giving a woman a red rose is considered a romantic invitation, inappropriate if you are trying to establish a business relationship with her. In India you might be invited to visit someone's home "any time." If you're not familiar with the culture, you may be reluctant to make an unexpected visit, and you might therefore wait for a definite invitation. But your failure to take the invitation literally is an insult, a sign that you do not care to develop the friendship.

In any culture, rules of etiquette may be formal or informal. Formal rules are the specifically taught "rights" and "wrongs" of how to behave in common social situations, such as table manners at meals. When formal rules are violated, members of a culture can explain why they feel upset. In contrast, informal social rules are more difficult to identify and are usually learned by watching how people behave and then imitating that behavior. Informal rules govern how males and females are supposed to behave, when it is appropriate to use a person's first name, and so on. When informal rules are violated, members of a culture are likely to feel uncomfortable, although they may not be able to say exactly why.[12]

Legal and Ethical Behavior

From culture to culture, what is considered legal and ethical behavior varies widely. In some countries companies are expected to pay government officials extra fees for approving government contracts. These payments aren't illegal or unethical, merely routine. However, the same payments are seen as bribes in the United States, Sweden, and many other countries, where they are both illegal and unethical. In fact, U.S.-based companies are generally not allowed to bribe officials anywhere in the world. (The U.S. Foreign Corrupt Practices Act, which governs company payments to foreign officials, allows a few exceptions, such as small payments that speed but don't actually influence government actions.)[13]

When you conduct business around the world, you may also find that other legal systems differ from what you're accustomed to. In the United Kingdom and the United States, someone is innocent until proven guilty, a principle that is rooted in English common law. In Mexico and Turkey, someone is presumed guilty until proven innocent, a principle that is rooted in the Napoleonic code.[14] These distinctions can be particularly important if your firm must communicate about a legal dispute in another country.

DEALING WITH LANGUAGE BARRIERS

Although three out of four companies polled in a recent survey said that cultural differences frequently complicate their international business relationships, only one in three complained of significant language problems. Nevertheless, U.S. businesspeople may underestimate linguistic barriers because the burden of adjustment generally rests with "the other side." Most multinational business is conducted in English, which is the official language in more than 40 countries and the most commonly studied second language in countries considered to be major trading partners of the United States.[15]

Still, language differences can trip you up even if you're a U.S. executive doing business in an English-speaking country. A U.S. paper products manufacturer learned this the hard way while trying to crack the English market for paper napkins by using its usual advertising slogan: "There is no finer paper napkin for the dinner table." Unfortunately for the U.S. company, *napkin* is the British term for *diaper.*[16]

Misunderstandings involving vocabulary, pronunciation, or usage are also likely when U.S. businesspeople deal with people who use English as a second language (and some 650 million people fall into this category). Some of these millions are extremely fluent; others have only an elementary command of English. Although you may miss a few subtleties when dealing with those less fluent in your own language, you'll still be able to communicate. However, don't assume that the other person understands everything you say. Your message can be mangled by slang, idioms, and local accents. One group of English-speaking Japanese employees who transferred to Toyota's U.S. office had to enroll in a special course to learn that "Jeat yet?" means "Did you eat yet?" and that "Cannahepya?" means "Can I help you?"

When you deal with people who don't speak your language at all, you have three options: You can learn their language, use an intermediary or a translator, or teach them your language. Becoming fluent in a new language requires a major commitment. At the U.S. State Department, foreign service officers take six months of language training and then continue their studies at their foreign posts. Even the Berlitz method, famous for the speed of its results, requires a month of intensive effort. Language courses can be quite expensive as well. So unless you're planning to spend several years abroad or to make frequent trips over an extended period, learning another language may take more time and more money than you can afford.

A more practical approach is to use an intermediary or a translator. An experienced translator can analyze a message, understand its meaning in the cultural context, consider how to convey the meaning in another language, and then use verbal and nonverbal signals to encode or decode the message for someone from another culture. If your company has an overseas subsidiary, you may want to seek help from local employees who are bilingual. You can also hire bilingual professionals such as advertising consultants and lawyers.

The option of teaching other people to speak your language doesn't appear to be very practical at first glance. However, many multinational companies do, in fact, offer language-training programs for employees. The program Michael Copeland devised for the managers of P&G's Brazilian subsidiary is a case in point. Learning English represented a good compromise for the Portuguese- and Spanish-speaking employees, and it reinforced their relationship with P&G headquarters.

Tenneco is another U.S.-based company that instituted an English-language training program—in this case, for its Spanish-speaking employees in a New Jersey plant. The training concentrated on practical English for use on the job, and thanks to the classes, both accidents and grievances declined, and productivity improved.[17] Nevertheless, requiring employees to use a specific language when they're on the job can create communication problems. In general, the magnitude of the language barrier depends on whether you are writing or speaking. Written communication is generally easier to handle.

Barriers to Written Communication

Because so many international business letters are written in English, U.S. firms don't always worry about translating their correspondence. One survey of 100 companies engaged in international business revealed that between 95 and 99 percent of their business letters to other countries are written in English. Moreover, 59 percent of the companies reported that the letters they receive from people in other countries are usually written in English, although they also receive letters written in Spanish and French.[18]

Regardless of where they're located, some multinational companies ask all their employees to use English when writing to employees in other lands. For example, Nissan employees use English for internal memos to colleagues in other countries, even though the corporation is based in Japan. Similarly, English is the official business language of Philips, the global electronics giant based in the Netherlands.[19]

However, many other forms of written communication have to be translated. Advertisements are almost always translated into the language of the culture in which the products are being sold. Warranties, repair and maintenance manuals, and product labels require translation, as well. In addition, many multinational companies translate policy and procedure manuals for use in overseas offices. Reports from foreign branches to the home office may be written in one language and then translated into another. One multinational company, E. I. Du Pont de Nemours & Company, translates roughly 70,000 pages of documents per year.[20]

When documents are translated literally, communication can break down. For example, the advertising slogan "Come alive with Pepsi" was once mistranslated for German audiences as "Come out of the grave" and for Thai audiences as "Bring your ancestors back from the dead."[21] Part of the message is almost inevitably lost during any translation process. So it's critical for you to consider the meaning of the message and the way it will appear to the receiver when translating from one language into another.

Barriers to Oral Communication

Oral communication usually presents more problems than written communication. If you've ever studied another language, you know it's easier to write in that language than to conduct a conversation. Even if the other person speaks your language, you may have a hard time understanding the pronunciation if the person isn't proficient. For example, many nonnative English speakers can't distinguish between the English sounds *v* and *w*, so they say "wery" for "very." At the same time, many people from the United States cannot pronounce the French *r* or the German *ch*.

Also, people use their voices in different ways, which can lead listeners to misunderstand their intentions. Russian speakers, for instance, speak in flat, level tones in their native tongue. When they speak English, they maintain this pattern, and non-Russian listeners may assume that the speakers are bored or rude. Middle Easterners tend to speak more loudly than Westerners and may therefore mistakenly be considered more emotional. On the other hand, the Japanese are soft-spoken, a characteristic that implies politeness or humility to Western listeners.

Idiomatic expressions are another source of confusion. If a U.S. executive tells an Egyptian executive that a certain product "doesn't cut the mustard," chances are communication will fail. Even when the words make sense, their meanings may differ according to the situation. For example, suppose you are dining with a German woman who speaks English quite well. You inquire, "More bread?" She says, "Thank you," so you pass the bread. She looks confused; then she takes the breadbasket and sets it down without taking any. In German, *thank you (danke)* can also be used as a polite refusal. If the woman had wanted more bread, she would have used the word *please* (*bitte* in German).

When speaking in English to people who speak English as a second language, you may find these guidelines helpful:

- *Try to eliminate noise.* Pronounce words clearly, stop at distinct punctuation points, and make one point at a time.

- *Look for feedback.* Be alert to signs of confusion in your listener. Realize that nods and smiles don't necessarily mean understanding.

- *Rephrase your sentence when necessary.* If someone doesn't seem to understand you, choose simpler words; don't just repeat the sentence in a louder voice.

- *Don't talk down to the other person.* Try not to overenunciate, and don't "blame" the listener for not understanding. Use phrases such as "Am I going too fast?" rather than "Is this too difficult for you?"

- *Use objective, accurate language.* Avoid throwing around adjectives such as *fantastic* and *fabulous,* which people from other cultures might consider unreal and overly dramatic.

- *Let other people finish what they have to say.* If you interrupt, you may miss something important. You'll also show a lack of respect.

DEALING WITH ETHNOCENTRIC REACTIONS

Although language and cultural differences are significant barriers to communication, these problems can be overcome by maintaining an open mind. Unfortunately, many of us lapse into **ethnocentricism,** the tendency to judge all other groups according to our own group's standards, behaviors, and customs. When we make such comparisons, we too often decide that our group is superior.[22]

By reacting ethnocentrically, you ignore the distinctions between your own culture and another person's culture. You assume that others will act the same way you do, that they will operate from the same assumptions, and that they will use language and symbols the same way you do. If they do not, you may mistakenly believe that they are in error, that their way is invalid, or that it's inferior to your own. An ethnocentric reaction makes you lose sight of the possibility that your words and actions will be misunderstood. It also makes you more likely to misinterpret or belittle the behavior of others.

Ethnocentric people are often prone to **stereotyping,** attempting to predict individuals' behavior or character on the basis of their membership in a particular group or class. When someone first starts to investigate the culture of another group, he or she may stereotype characteristics as a way of understanding the common tendencies of that group's members, but the next step is to move beyond the stereotypes to relationships with real people. Unfortunately, when ethnocentric people stereotype an entire group of people, they do so on the basis of limited, general, or inaccurate evidence, and they frequently develop biased attitudes toward the group.[23] They fail to communicate with individuals as they really are. Instead of talking with Abdul Karhum, unique human being, ethnocentric people think only about talking to an Arab. Although they've never met an Arab, they may already believe that all Arabs are, say, hagglers. Abdul Karhum's personal qualities become insignificant in the face of such preconceptions. Everything he says and does will be forced to fit the preconceived image, even if it's wrong.

Often both parties in an intercultural exchange are guilty of ethnocentrism, stereotyping, and prejudice. Little wonder, then, that misunderstandings arise. Fortunately, a healthy dose of open-mindedness can prevent a lot of problems.

REFERENCES

1. Larry A. Samovar and Richard E. Porter, "Basic Principles of Intercultural Communication," in *Intercultural Communication: A Reader,* 6th ed., edited by Larry A. Samovar and Richard E. Porter (Belmont, Calif.: Wadsworth, 1991), 12.

2. Kathleen K. Reardon, "It's the Thought that Counts," *Harvard Business Review,* September–October 1984, 141.

3. Otto Kreisher, "Annapolis Has a New Attitude Toward Sexual Harassment," *San Diego Union,* 30 July 1990, A-6.

4. Robert O. Joy, "Cultural and Procedural Differences that Influence Business Strategies and Operations in the People's Republic of China," *SAM Advanced Management Journal,* Summer 1989, 29–33.

5. "Pakistan: A Congenial Business Climate," *Nation's Business,* July 1986, 50.

6. David A. Victor, *International Business Communication* (New York: Harper-Collins, 1992), 234–239; Mohan R. Limaye and David A. Victor, "Cross Cultural Business Communications Research: State of the Art and Hypotheses for the 1990s," *Journal of Business Communication* 28, no. 3 (Summer 1991): 277–299.

7. Carley H. Dodd, *Dynamics of Intercultural Communication,* 3rd ed. (Dubuque, Iowa: Brown, 1991), 215.

8. Edward T. Hall, "Context and Meaning," in *Intercultural Communication: A Reader,* 6th ed., edited by Larry A. Samovar and Richard E. Porter (Belmont, Calif.: Wadsworth, 1991), 46–55.

9. Dodd, *Dynamics of Intercultural Communication,* 69–70.

10. Richard E. Porter and Larry A. Samovar, "Basic Principles of Intercultural Communication," in *Intercultural Communication: A Reader,* 6th ed., edited by Larry A. Samovar and Richard E. Porter (Belmont, Calif.: Wadsworth, 1991), 5–22; David A. Victor, personal communication, 1993.

11. Laray M. Barna, "Stumbling Blocks in Intercultural Communication," in *Intercultural Communication: A Reader,* 6th ed., edited by Larry A. Samovar and Richard E. Porter (Belmont, Calif.: Wadsworth, 1991), 345–352.

12. Sharon Ruhly, *Intercultural Communication,* 2d ed., MODCOM (Modules in Speech Communication) (Chicago: Science Research Associates, 1982), 14.

13. Karen P. H. Lane, "Greasing the Bureaucratic Wheel," *North American International Business,* August 1990, 35–37; Arthur Aronoff, "Complying with the Foreign Corrupt Practices Act," *Business America,* 11 February 1991, 10–11; Bill Shaw, "Foreign Corrupt Practices Act: A Legal and Moral Analysis," *Journal of Business Ethics* 7 (1988): 789–795.

14. Philip R. Harris and Robert T. Moran, *Managing Cultural Differences,* 3d ed. (Houston: Gulf, 1991), 260.

15. Judy F. West and Judy C. Nixon, "International Business Communication Opportunities: A Key to Success," *1989 Proceedings of the Sixteenth International Convention of the Association for Business Communication,* 232; Marguerite P. Shane Joyce, "Intercultural Business Communication: Prescription for Success," speech before the Tenth Annual Conference on Languages and Communication for World Business and the Professions, Eastern Michigan University (Ypsilanti, Mich.), 3 April 1991, 9; Stephen Karel, "On Language," *American Demographics,* May 1989, 54.

16. David A. Ricks, "International Business Blunders: An Update," *B&E Review,* January–March 1988, 12.

17. Vern Terpstra, *The Cultural Environment of International Business* (Cincinnati: South-Western, 1979), 19.

18. Retha H. Kilpatrick, "International Business Communication Practices," *Journal of Business Communication* 21 (Fall 1984): 36.

19. Victor, *International Business Communication,* 36.

20. Doreen Mangan, "What's New in Language Translation: A Tool for Examining Foreign Patents and Research," *New York Times,* 19 November 1989, sec. 3, 15.

21. Victor, *International Business Communication,* 39; Harris and Moran, *Managing Cultural Differences,* 64.

22. Geert Hofstede, *Cultures and Organizations* (London: McGraw-Hill, 1991), 211.

23. Richard W. Brislin, "Prejudice in Intercultural Communication," in *Intercultural Communication: A Reader,* 6th ed., edited by Larry A. Samovar and Richard E. Porter (Belmont, Calif.: Wadsworth, 1991), 366–370.

"Communicating Interculturally" from *Business Communications Today,* 4th ed., by Courtland L. Bovée and John V. Thill, McGraw-Hill, Inc., 1995, pp. 59–68.

COMPREHENSION QUIZ

True or False

Directions: In the blank provided, indicate whether each statement is true or false.

_____ 1. Your ability to send and receive messages can be affected by cultural differences.

_____ 2. Although the United States and Canada can be viewed as a melting pot of people with different religions and values, the major influence in the United States is the Puritan work ethic: if you work hard and achieve success, you will find favor in the eyes of God.

_____ 3. People from different cultures share similar concepts of status.

_____ 4. Executives from Latin America and Asia view time as more flexible than do German and U.S. executives.

_____ 5. The rules of polite behavior differ from culture to culture and country to country.

_____ 6. English is the most prevalent spoken and written language used in international business.

_____ 7. Warranties, repair and maintenance manuals, and product labels require translation into the language of the country in which the products are sold.

_____ 8. Oral communication usually presents fewer problems than written communication.

Multiple Choice

Directions: For each item, select the best answer.

_____ 9. People from other cultures may have different
   a. manners
   b. decision-making habits
   c. attitudes toward time
   d. all of the above

_____10. As a culture, people in the United States
   a. prize a care-free lifestyle
   b. believe creating jobs is more important than getting work
      done efficiently
   c. are goal-oriented
   d. all of the above

_____11. Decision making is a shared responsibility in
   a. Pakistan
   b. Japan
   c. the United States and Canada
   d. Greece

_____12. An "intercultural dance" can occur during conversations
   between
   a. executives from the United States and Canada
   b. male and female executives
   c. executives from the Middle East
   d. executives from cultures that have different concepts of
      personal space

_____13. In many parts of Latin America and Asia, keeping your eyes
   lowered is a sign of
   a. respect
   b. evasiveness
   c. dishonesty
   d. disrespect

_____14. The more practical approach to use when dealing with people
   who do not speak your language at all is to
   a. become fluent in their language
   b. use an intermediary or a translator
   c. use only written communication with them
   d. all of the above

_____15. An example of an idiomatic expression is
    a. "Thank you very much."
    b. "Do you understand?"
    c. "This doesn't cut the mustard."
    d. "What time is it?"

_____16. Which of the following can be a barrier to oral communication when speaking to foreigners?
    a. pronunciation
    b. idiomatic expressions
    c. differences in loudness and tone of voice
    d. all of the above

_____17. When speaking in English to those for whom English is a second language, it is a good idea to
    a. repeat a sentence in a louder voice when they do not understand
    b. ask "Is this too difficult for you?" when they do not understand
    c. pronounce words clearly and stop at distinct punctuation points
    d. use idiomatic expressions

_____18. An *ethnocentric reaction* is
    a. communicating across cultural barriers
    b. judging all other groups according to our own group's standards, behaviors, and customs
    c. making attempts to communicate clearly
    d. recognizing and adjusting for cultural differences

_____19. When we react ethnocentrically, we
    a. assume that others act the same way we do
    b. ignore the distinctions between our own culture and another person's culture
    c. assume that others use language and symbols the same way we do
    d. all of the above

_____20. People who are ethnocentric tend to
    a. stereotype others
    b. investigate the culture of another group
    c. move beyond stereotypes to relationships with real people
    d. communicate with individuals as they really are

CHAPTER

6

APPLYING COMPREHENSION SKILLS TO LONGER PASSAGES

1
Determining Subject Matter

2
Locating Directly Stated Main Ideas

3
Formulating Implied Main Ideas

4
Identifying Supporting Details

5
Recognizing Authors' Writing Patterns

6
Applying Comprehension
Skills to Longer Passages

7
Remembering College Textbook
Material through Organizing

8
Thinking Critically as You Read

279

He who adds not to his learning diminishes it.

The Talmud

INTRODUCTION

In this chapter, you will be reading longer passages because college reading isn't limited to single paragraphs. Fortunately, one of the hallmarks of a mature reader is the ability to deal with increasingly longer, more complex textbook passages. For example, a reader moves from comprehending a sentence to comprehending a paragraph. The reader then connects the information in a paragraph with the information in the next paragraph, and the next (all the while following the writer's main ideas). Soon the reader has followed the writer's thoughts throughout the chapter and subsequently throughout all the chapters of the book.

In one sense, reading longer passages is easier. You can see the *overall subject matter* and the *overall main idea* instead of just smaller parts. Seeing the overall organization of a longer section of a textbook chapter (or even the entire chapter) promotes comprehension and recall.

In this chapter you will learn how to determine the overall subject matter and the overall main idea for a longer passage. You will also learn how to write a summary of a longer textbook selection. But first, you will find out how to read and study a textbook assignment in an organized, intelligent manner.

READING A TEXTBOOK ASSIGNMENT

It is important to apply systematically the reading skills you have learned in this book so that you can locate and comprehend the significant information in college textbook passages. It is equally important for you to have a systematic way to approach reading longer assignments or even entire chapters in a college textbook. Many students simply open the book to the first page of the assignment and begin reading. Later, they complain that they had trouble getting interested in what they were reading, that their mind wandered, that it took them longer than necessary to read the assignment, that they were not sure what they were supposed to learn and remember from the chapter they were reading, and that they became discouraged and quit reading. Even those who finish reading their assignments sometimes complain they cannot remember what they read even though they understood the important information.

What can you do to understand and remember as much as possible of what you read in your textbooks? There are several popular "study formulas," and all of them have certain procedures in common:

- getting ready to read

- reading to understand each passage

- following up

Let's look at each of these.

Getting Ready to Read

You need to take a few minutes to prepare to read effectively and efficiently. This means that you will want to get a general idea of what the assignment will be about before you actually begin reading. In other words, you want an overview so that you can see the "big picture" and how the "parts" fit together. This not only aids your comprehension, but it can also increase your concentration, motivation, and interest in what you are about to read. It also allows you to assess your background knowledge, that is, what you already know about the topic.

To survey a chapter, read the *chapter title;* this should tell you what the overall subject matter is. Next, read the *chapter introduction* if there is one; this will give you background information that you need, or it may present some of the important points made in the chapter. Read the *headings;* these tell the reader what topics the author has divided the overall subject matter into and how he has organized them. Look at any *pictures, charts, diagrams, or other graphic material* in the chapter; these will be helpful to your understanding. Finally, skip to the *chapter summary* if there is one; it usually contains many of the most important ideas in the chapter in brief form.

At this point, you will also be able to decide whether you can read the entire assignment all at once or whether you need to divide it into smaller parts. A thirty-page chapter may be too much for you to read and study comfortably all at one time. Divide it into smaller portions that you can concentrate on effectively and successfully.

Get Ready to Read

Overview the chapter by reading the

- title
- introduction
- pictures, charts, and diagrams
- summary

If the assignment or chapter is long, divide it into smaller parts.

Reading to Understand Each Passage

The second step is to read and understand each passage in an assignment. To effectively comprehend a longer passage, you must read with a specific purpose. In other words, you must determine what you want to learn from each passage of the textbook assignment. Reading for a specific purpose also enables you to monitor your comprehension, and it increases your interest and concentration.

Perhaps the best way to determine what you need to learn from the text assignment is to *take the headings and turn them into questions.* As noted in Chapter 1, headings often indicate the subject matter of a paragraph. Answering the questions you create from the heading (the subject matter) can lead you to the important main ideas and supporting details in the passage. For example, if the heading in an economics textbook is

"Full Production," you should ask yourself, "What is full production?" Often you will find that you can create several questions from a heading. If the heading in a history textbook says, "The War Begins," you would want to know: "What war? When did it begin? Why did it begin? Who was involved? Where did it begin?" You should then read the passage, seeking the main ideas and details that answer your questions. The questions you create will guide your reading of each section as you selectively seek the answers to your questions. When creating questions from the headings, you are actually predicting many of the questions your instructor may ask you on a test.

In addition to turning headings into questions, you may find that the textbook author has included *chapter questions*. These usually appear at the end of the chapter, although they sometimes appear at the begininng of the chapter or are distributed throughout the chapter. If a textbook contains chapter questions, read them before you read the chapter. Keep them in mind as you read. You should be able to answer these questions when you have finished reading the chapter. After all, you may be asked some of those questions on a test. The chapter questions also enable you to monitor or check your comprehension. That is their primary purpose.

Your professor may also give you questions to keep in mind as you read a chapter, or you may have *questions in a study guide* that accompanies your textbook. Creating questions from headings and using questions provided by the textbook author or your professor can improve your comprehension and recall if you actively search for answers to the questions as you read.

Read to Understand Each Passage

Determine what you want to understand by

- turning headings into questions
- reading the chapter questions
- using questions given to you by your instructor
- using questions that appear in a study guide

Read by actively searching for main ideas and supporting details that answer the questions.

Reading for a specific purpose—that is, to answer questions—can help you score higher on tests. Many of the questions you create and seek to answer as you read will be the very same ones that appear on tests.

Following Up

Students who are new to college often close their textbook as soon as they have read the last paragraph in a chapter. More experienced students know that if they want to *remember* the material, they need to take some additional steps. They also know that it is important that they take those steps immediately after reading, while the material is still "fresh in their minds" (that is, while the material is still in their short-term memories). Good readers know that forgetting occurs very rapidly and that they need to rehearse the material in order to learn it (transfer it from their short-term memory into their long-term or permanent memory). The fact is, unless you take some special steps beyond simply reading the textbook assignment, you will have forgotten half of what you have read by the time you finish reading the chapter.

A very effective way both to monitor your comprehension and to transfer material into long-term memory is to *say the answers out loud to the questions you created from the chapter headings or to the questions printed in your textbook or given by your instructor.* Remember, *if*

Follow Up

After you read, organize and rehearse the material to transfer it into long-term memory by using these techniques:

- answering out loud the questions you created or used to guide your reading

- underlining and annotating the textbook selection

- writing a summary based on the main ideas of the selection

- writing the overall main idea

- outlining or mapping

- making study cards

---

you can't say it, you don't know it. The time to check your comprehension and recall is right after you finish reading—not while you are taking a test on the material in class! Try to answer the questions created from headings as you finish reading each section. If you cannot answer a question out loud, go back and find the answer, and then say it out loud. If there are chapter questions, study guide questions, or questions from your professor, you can answer them after you finish reading the chapter. The key to success is to go back and find the answer to any questions you are unsure about, and then to say the correct answer aloud.

Many students find it extremely helpful to organize the material by writing down the important main ideas and details presented in a chapter. The strategies discussed in this chapter *(determining the overall subject matter, determining the overall main idea, and summarizing)* and in the next chapter *(underlining and annotating textbook passages, outlining and mapping, and making study cards)* are effective ways to organize, rehearse, and learn the material through writing. In any case, you should always use the technique by answering study questions out loud, and you should reinforce your learning by using whichever writing strategies seem most appropriate to help you answer the particular textbook material you are studying.

In Chapter 7, you will learn how to organize material by underlining and annotating a textbook selection, by outlining or mapping, and by making study cards.

EXPLANATION AND EXAMPLES OF OVERALL SUBJECT MATTER AND OVERALL MAIN IDEA

As the title of this chapter suggests, you will now be applying every skill you have learned—identifying subject matter, main idea, supporting details, and author's writing pattern—to longer textbook selections. Some of the passages will be more challenging than others. This will depend on how much background knowledge you have of the passage's subject matter and on how many new ideas and terms are presented in the selection.

In addition to determining the subject matter and main idea for each paragraph, you will be determining the subject matter and main idea for the *entire* passage, or, in other words, the **overall subject** *matter* and *overall main idea.* The examples in this section demonstrate how you can apply to entire selections the skills you have already learned.

OVERALL SUBJECT MATTER

Just as the subject matter of a single paragraph must be general enough to include all the information contained in the paragraph, so must the overall subject matter of a textbook section be broad enough to include all the subject matters of the individual paragraphs that make up that section.

The subject matter of the first paragraph below is *characteristics of the middle class.* The subject matter of the second paragraph is the *two strata of the middle class.* The subject matter of both paragraphs, the **overall subject matter,** could be expressed simply as *the middle class.* Authors frequently give the overall subject matter of a section in a heading, just as the author does here.

> The **overall subject matter** is the topic that all of the paragraphs of a longer passage have in common.

OVERALL MAIN IDEA

Just as the overall subject matter must include the subject matters of the separate paragraphs in a selection, so must the **overall main idea** include the main ideas of the separate paragraphs that make up the entire passage. In the passage below, the main idea of the first paragraph is stated in the second sentence: *Middle-class people are distinguished from those above them primarily by their lesser wealth and power, and from those below them by their white-collar, non-manual jobs.* The main idea of the second paragraph is implied: *The middle class can be differentiated into two strata, upper-middle class and lower-middle class, by occupational prestige, income, and education.* One way of expressing the overall main idea would be as follows: *Middle-class people are different from both the upper class and the lower class, and the middle class can be differentiated into two subgroups, the upper-middle class and the lower-middle class.* This statement combines the main ideas of each of the individual paragraphs. Just as the main ideas of paragraphs must always be sentences, the overall main idea must also be expressed as a sentence.

> The **overall main idea** is a sentence that summarizes the main ideas of the paragraphs of a longer passage.

The Middle Class

The middle class is not as tightly knit as the upper class. Middle-class people are distinguished from those above them primarily by their lesser wealth and power, and from those below them by their white-collar, non-manual jobs.

This class can be differentiated into two strata by occupational prestige, income, and education. The *upper-middle class* consists mostly of professional and business people with high income and education, such as doctors, lawyers, and corporate executives. The *lower-middle class* is far larger in size and much more diverse in occupation. It is made up of people in relatively low-level but still white-collar occupations, such as small-business owners, store and traveling salespersons, managers, technicians, teachers, and secretaries. Though they have less income and education than the upper-middle class, the lower-middle class has achieved (at least until very recently) the middle-class dream of owning a suburban home and living a comfortable life.

Sociology: An Introduction
by Alex Thio

Subject Matter

characteristics of the middle class

Main Idea

Middle-class people are distinguished from those above them primarily by their lesser wealth and power and from those below them by their white-collar, non-manual jobs.

Subject Matter

the two strata of the middle class

Main Idea

The middle class can be differentiated into two strata, upper-middle class and lower-middle class, by occupational prestige, income, and education.

---

non-manual (nŏn măn′ yōō əl) adj. Not performed by physical labor; not done by hand.

strata (strāt′ ə, stră′ tə) n. pl. Levels of society. A stratum (sing.) is composed of people with similar social, cultural, or economic status.

ă pat ā pay â care ä father ĕ pet ē be ĭ pit ī tie î pier ŏ pot ō toe
ô paw oi noise ōō took ōō boot ou out th thin *th* this ŭ cut û urge
yōō abuse zh vision ə *a*bout, it*e*m, ed*i*ble, gall*o*p, circ*u*s

prestige (prĕ stēzh′) n. Prominence or influential status achieved through success, renown, or wealth.

suburban (sə bûr′ bən) adj. Of or pertaining to a suburb (a residential area or community outlying a city).

The subject matter and main idea for each of the paragraphs are given above. When you study longer passages, you need to understand how the subject matters of the individual paragraphs fit together. You can do this by identifying an *overall subject matter* that ties together the subject matters of the paragraphs.

Overall subject matter: *the middle class*

Overall main idea: *The middle class is different from the upper class and the lower class, and the middle class can be differentiated into two subgroups, the upper-middle class and the lower-middle class.*

Here is another example of a longer passage. It is taken from the same sociology textbook. Begin by turning the heading into the question and asking yourself, "Who or what is the lower class?" Then read the passage to answer your question. Together, the subject matter and main ideas of the individual paragraphs should provide the answer to your question. Finally, write the overall subject matter and overall main idea in the spaces provided.

The Lower Class

The lower class consists primarily of those who have very little education and whose jobs, if they have them, are manual and carry very little prestige.

There are two strata within the lower class. The working class consists of skilled and unskilled manual laborers. Some working-class people, such as construction

Subject Matter
characteristics of the lower class

Main Idea
The lower class consists primarily of those who have very little education and whose jobs, if they have them, are manual and carry very little prestige.

ă pat ā pay â care ä father ĕ pet ē be ĭ pit ī tie î pier ŏ pot ō toe
ô paw oi noise ŏŏ took ōō boot ou out th thin *th* this ŭ cut û urge
yōō abuse zh vision ə *a*bout, it*e*m, ed*i*ble, gall*o*p, circ*u*s

workers, carpenters, and plumbers, are skilled workers and may make more money than those in the lower reaches of the middle class, such as secretaries and teachers. But their jobs are more physically demanding and, especially in the case of factory workers, more dangerous. Other working-class people are unskilled, such as migrant workers, janitors, and dishwashers. There are also many women in this class working as domestics, cleaning ladies, and waitresses, and they are the sole breadwinners in their households. Since they are generally underpaid, they have been called the working poor (Gilbert and Kahl, 1982).

The lower-lower class, or simply "lower class," is characterized by joblessness and poverty. It includes the chronically unemployed, the welfare recipients, and the impoverished aged. These people live in run-down houses, wear old clothes, eat cheap food, and lack proper medical care. Very few have finished high school. They may have started out in their youth with poorly paying jobs that required little or no skill, but their earning power began to drop when they reached their late twenties. A new underclass has emerged in recent years: skilled workers in mechanized industry who have become unskilled workers in electronically run factories.

Sociology: An Introduction
by Alex Thio

Subject Matter

the working class

Main Idea

The working class is made up of skilled and unskilled manual laborers.

Subject Matter

characteristics of the lower-lower class

Main Idea

The lower-lower class is characterized by joblessness and poverty.

chronically (krŏn′ ĭk lē) adv. Of long duration; continuing.

recipient (rĭ sĭp′ ē ənt) n. One who receives.

impoverish (ĭm pŏv′ ər ĭsh) v. To make poor.

Overall subject matter: _____

_____

Overall main idea: _____

_____

_____

_____

You can combine the three subject matters of these paragraphs into one overall subject matter, *the lower class*. Again, notice that the author uses the heading to indicate the overall subject matter of the passage. One way of stating the overall subject matter and the overall main idea of these three paragraphs is:

Overall subject matter: *the lower class*

Overall main idea: *The lower class consists of the working class and the lower-lower class, and is made up of those who have very little education and whose jobs, if they have them, are manual jobs that carry very little prestige.*

Here is another example of a longer passage. It is taken from a different sociology textbook. Begin by turning the headings into questions and asking yourself, "What is social stratification?" and "What are open and closed systems?" Then read the passage to answer your questions. The subject matter and main idea of the individual paragraphs should provide the answers. Finally, write the overall subject matter and overall main idea in the spaces provided.

ă pat ā pay â care ä father ĕ pet ē be ĭ pit ī tie î pier ŏ pot ō toe
ô paw oi noise o͝o took o͞o boot ou out th thin *th* this ŭ cut û urge
yo͞o abuse zh vision ə *a*bout, it*e*m, ed*i*ble, gall*o*p, circ*u*s

Patterns of Social Stratification

Open and Closed Systems

Stratification systems differ in the ease with which they permit people to move in or out of particular strata. As we will see later in the chapter when we discuss social mobility, people often move vertically up or down in rank or horizontally to another status of roughly similar rank. Where people can change their status with relative ease, we refer to the arrangement as an **open system.** In contrast, where people have great difficulty in changing their status, we call the arrangement a **closed system.** A somewhat similar distinction is conveyed by the concepts *achieved status* and *ascribed status.* Achieved statuses are open to people on the basis of individual choice and competition, whereas ascribed statuses are assigned to people by their group or society.

Although there are no societies that are entirely open or entirely closed, the United States provides a good example of a relatively open system. The American dream portrays a society in which all people can alter and improve their lot. The American folk hero is Abe Lincoln, the "poor boy who made good," the "rail-splitter" who through hard work managed to move "from log cabin to the White House." The United States is founded not on the idea that all people should enjoy equal status, nor on the notion of a classless society. Rather, the democratic creed holds that all people should have an equal opportunity to ascend to the heights of the class system. In theory, the rewards of social life flow to people in accordance with their merit and competence and in proportion to their

Subject Matter

open and closed systems (of social stratification)

Main Idea

A system in which people can change their status relatively easily is an open system, whereas a closed system is one in which it is difficult for people to change their status.

Subject Matter

the United States as an example of an open system

Main Idea

Although there are no societies that are entirely open or entirely closed, the United States provides a good example of a relatively open system.

contribution to the larger social enterprise. However, in practice the ideal is not realized, since the American system places some measure of reliance on ascription, particularly in assigning statuses on the basis of sex, age, and race.

When we think of a closed system, the Hindu caste arrangement often comes to mind, particularly as it operated in India prior to 1900. Under the traditional Hindu system, life was ordered in terms of castes in which people inherited their social status at birth from their parents and could not change it in the course of their lives. Historically there have been thousands of castes in India, although all of them have fallen into four major castes: the Brahmins, or priestly caste, who represent about 3 percent of the population; the Kshatriyas, allegedly descendants of warriors, and the Vaisyas, the traders, who together account for about 7 percent of Indians; and the Sudras, peasants and artisans, who constitute about 70 percent of the population. The remaining 20 percent are the Harijans, or Untouchables, who have traditionally served as sweepers, scavengers, leatherworkers, and swineherds.

Sociology
by James Vander Zanden

Subject Matter

Hindu castes as an example of a closed system

Main Idea

When we think of a closed system, the Hindu caste arrangement often comes to mind, particularly as it operated in India prior to 1900.

Overall subject matter: _____

_____

Overall main idea: _____

_____

_____

_____

Did you combine the three subject matters of these paragraphs into one overall subject matter? The overall subject matter that they have in common is the *open and closed systems of social stratification*. The overall main idea can be expressed this way: *In an open system of social stratification, such as in the United States, it is relatively easy for people to change status; in a closed system, such as India's Hindu caste system, it is difficult to change status.*

The final example is taken from a psychology textbook. You have seen both paragraphs in previous chapters. Before you reread them, remember to turn the heading into a question. Ask yourself, "What are memory disorders?" Then read the passage to answer your question. The subject matter and main idea for each paragraph have been provided for you. Your task is to formulate the overall subject matter and overall main idea for the passage.

Memory Disorders

Amnesia is the general term for a variety of memory disorders that arise from different causes and affect the memory in different ways. A number of neurologic conditions that cause damage to the brain produce memory deficits of one kind or another. They're probably the most frequent complaint of patients who have suffered strokes, infectious diseases of the brain, and traumatic injuries. In addition, memory disorders are often the earliest signs of a number of neurologic illnesses, including Alzheimer's disease, a progressive degenerative disease of the brain that usually occurs in old age.

There are two basic kinds of memory loss. In *anterograde amnesia,* the inability to create new permanent memories, patients typically cannot learn the names of their doctors, the hospitals they're in, or any other new information they're exposed to after the traumatic event or illness that

Subject Matter

amnesia

Main Idea

Amnesia is the general term for a variety of memory disorders that arise from different causes and affect the memory in different ways.

Subject Matter

two basic kinds of memory loss

Main Idea

There are two basic kinds of memory loss: anterograde and retrograde.

caused the amnesia. In *retrograde amne-sia,* the inability to recall information that had been learned before the onset of the amnesia, patients may not remember experiences in their earlier life or the name of the president of the United States. . . .

Psychology
by Diane Papalia and Sally Olds

amnesia (ăm nē′ zhə) n. Partial or total loss of memory.

neurologic (nōor ə lŏj′ ĭk) adj. Of or pertaining to the nervous system and its disorders.

deficit (dĕf′ ĭ sĭt) n. A shortage.

traumatic (trou mă′ tĭk) adj. Pertaining to an emotional shock that creates substantial damage to the mind of the individual.

Overall subject matter: _____

_____

Overall main idea: _____

_____

_____

_____

_____

When you examine the subject matter of the two paragraphs to determine the topic they have in common, you can see that they both concern *memory disorders (amnesia).* This is the overall subject matter. The overall main idea, formulated from the main ideas from the two paragraphs, can be expressed: *Amnesia, or memory disorders, can be divided into two types: anterograde amnesia and retrograde amnesia.* When you

ă pat ā pay â care ä father ĕ pet ē be ĭ pit ī tie î pier ŏ pot ō toe
ô paw oi noise ŏŏ took ōō boot ou out th thin *th* this ŭ cut û urge
yōō abuse zh vision ə *a*bout, it*e*m, ed*i*ble, gall*o*p, circ*u*s

formulate the overall subject matter and overall main idea of a longer passage, you are taking an important step toward organizing and remembering the material in an entire section, and not simply a single paragraph.

EXPLANATION AND EXAMPLE OF SUMMARIZING A SECTION OF A TEXTBOOK

A *summary* is a way of condensing into one paragraph all of the main ideas in a textbook section. If you have correctly identified the main ideas in a textbook section, then you have already selected the contents of your summary. Creating a summary requires you to identify the main points and condense this information. The very act of writing a summary helps you transfer the information into your memory.

Once you have prepared a summary, you will have a valuable tool for studying the material in that section. It can be extremely useful if you know that you will be taking an essay test over the material. Often, when you summarize a section of a textbook, you are practicing an answer you will write on an essay test.

> A **summary** is a way of condensing into one paragraph all of the main ideas an author presents in a section of a textbook.

There are several characteristics to a good "study summary."

- It includes the title of the textbook section.

- It includes all of the author's main ideas in that section.

- It includes supporting details only if the main idea cannot be understood without them.

- It does not contain anything beyond the author's ideas. (In other words, you should not include your opinions or reactions to what you are summarizing.)

- It keeps the author's organization in sequence. (In other words, you must present the ideas in the same order as the author does.)

Steps in Summarizing a Section of a Textbook

1. Read the material you want to summarize. Do not try to write a summary until you have read the entire section.

2. Write a one-sentence summary of each paragraph. This, of course, means you must locate or formulate the main idea for each paragraph.

3. Present the author's main points (preferably in your own words) in the same order in which they appear in the textbook. You must include *all* of the main ideas.

4. Check your summary to see that you can follow the ideas clearly and easily.

Here is an sample summary for the selection you read earlier in this chapter about open and closed systems of social stratification:

Open and Closed Systems of Social Stratification

A system in which people can change their status relatively easily is an open system, whereas a closed system is one in which it is difficult for people to change their status. Although there are no societies that are entirely open or entirely closed, the United States provides a good example of a relatively open system. When we think of a closed system, the Hindu caste arrangement often comes to mind, particularly as it operated in India prior to 1900.

As you can see, this summary simply consists of the author's three main ideas. While a summary can consist entirely of main ideas, it can include certain important supporting details if they make the main ideas clearer. Of course, you should include a supporting detail if the main idea cannot be understood without it. For example, if the main idea sentence includes a new or complex term, you would want to define the term.

CHAPTER
6

APPLYING COMPREHENSION SKILLS TO LONGER PASSAGES
Chapter Summary

1. A Systematic Way to Read Textbook Assignments

It is important for you to have a systematic way to read college textbook passages so that you can locate, comprehend, and recall significant information. It is equally important to have a systematic way to approach reading *longer assignments* or even *entire chapters* in a college textbook. The following boxes summarize a method that is effective because it is based on principles of efficient learning.

Get Ready to Read

Overview the chapter by reading the

- title
- introduction
- headings
- pictures, charts, and diagrams
- summary

If the assignment or chapter is long, divide it into smaller parts.

Read to Understand Each Passage

Determine what you want to understand by

- turning headings into questions
- reading the chapter questions

- using questions given to you by your instructor

- using questions that appear in a study guide

Read by actively searching for main ideas and supporting details in each passage that answer the questions.

Follow-Up

After you read, organize and rehearse the material to transfer it into long-term memory by using these techniques:

- answering out loud the questions you created or used to guide your reading

- underlining and annotating the textbook selection

- writing a summary based on the main idea of the selection and writing the overall main idea

- outlining or mapping

- making study cards

2. Overall Subject Matter and Overall Main Idea

When you read, you know that you must look for the subject matter and main idea of individual paragraphs. But when you are reading longer passages and textbook sections, you should also determine the *overall subject matter* and the *overall main idea* of the passage.

The *overall subject matter* is the topic that all of the paragraphs of a longer passage have in common.

Keep in mind:

- The overall subject matter must be broad enough to cover all the subject matters of the paragraphs in the passage.

- The overall subject matter may be given in the *heading* of the passage.

- The overall subject matter may be given in *bold print* within the passage.

> The **overall main idea** is a sentence that summarizes the main ideas of the paragraphs of a longer passage.

Remember that:

- The overall main idea must be a complete sentence.

- The overall main idea must be general enough to cover the main ideas of each of the separate paragraphs.

- The overall main idea of a textbook section may appear at the *beginning* of the section.

- The overall main idea of a textbook section may be given at the *end* of the section.

Seeing how the subject matters and the main ideas fit together in an overall way is important for several reasons. First, you are grasping *both* the significant information *and* the organization of the entire section. This prepares you to move ahead to the next section of your text. If you do not understand how the subject matters and main ideas fit together in an overall way, then you should not move on to the next section.

When you are studying a textbook passage, it is not enough to understand individual main ideas, although this is an essential starting point. You must understand how the main ideas fit together to form an overall main idea.

3. Summarizing a Section of a Textbook

> A **summary** is a way of condensing into one paragraph all of the main ideas an author presents in a section of a textbook.

Keep these guidelines in mind when preparing a summary:

- Include a title.

- Include *all* of the author's main ideas in the section.

- Include a supporting detail if the main idea cannot be understood without it.

- Do not add anything beyond the author's ideas (such as your own opinion).

- Keep the author's organization and sequence (in other words, present the ideas in the same order the author does).

Writing summaries is an excellent way to remember what you have read. It is an especially effective way to put long, complex material into a manageable form that you can understand and remember. When preparing for essay tests, use summaries as a means of "practicing" answers to questions you expect to be asked.

APPLYING COMPREHENSION SKILLS TO LONGER PASSAGES
Practice Exercises

Read the following selections carefully. In these exercises, you are given the subject matter and main idea for each paragraph. Your task is to combine the subject matters and main ideas to formulate an overall subject matter and an overall main idea for each passage. If the passage has a heading, mentally turn the heading into one or more questions. Then read the passage to answer your questions.

1.   This selection comes from a human development textbook.

Sudden Infant Death Syndrome

Each year some 7,000 to 10,000 American families experience a devastating tragedy. They put their seemingly healthy baby down in the crib and return to find that the infant has died. Typically there is no warning. The disorder, termed *Sudden Infant Death Syndrome* (SIDS), is the number-one cause of death for infants between one month and one year. It frequently results in acute agony for parents, who blame themselves and each other for permitting the baby to smother in bed. Yet suffocation from bedding is not the cause of the baby's death.

Through the years there has been an endless proliferation of theories as to what goes wrong (Mackintosh, 1982). In the broadest sense, the difficulty appears to be a respiratory problem. The babies simply stop breathing while asleep.

Subject Matter

Sudden Infant Death Syndrome (SIDS)

Main Idea

The disorder termed Sudden Infant Death Syndrome (SIDS) is the number-one cause of death for infants between one month and one year. (stated main idea)

Subject Matter

respiratory problems as a cause of SIDS

Main Idea

Although there have been many theories about the cause of SIDS, it appears to be a respiratory problem. (implied main idea)

301

One theory is that death results from abnormalities in respiratory control (Naeye, 1980). According to this view, the infants suffer from *apnea*—spells in which interruptions or pauses occur in breathing during sleep. Some adults experience a similar disorder, but adults have better reflexes to survive and can go longer without suffering severe oxygen deprivation. Autopsies reveal that in about 60 percent of SIDS cases, there is evidence pointing to the underventilation of the lungs.

In some cases bacterial or viral infection may trigger sudden death. Babies who have had a cold or runny nose appear to be more susceptible to the disorder. The problem may also be maturational. Some centers of the brain may mature more rapidly than others, resulting in a temporary "misprogramming" of respiration. In addition, recent studies of SIDS victims suggest that they have unusually high levels of thyroid hormone—triiodothyonine, or T-3. But the significance of the finding remains to be determined. Unhappily, progress in understanding SIDS remains heartbreakingly slow.

Human Development
by James Vander Zanden

Subject Matter

apnea as a cause of SIDS

Main Idea

One theory is that death results from abnormalities in respiratory control (apnea), spells in which interruptions or pauses occur in breathing during sleep. (implied main idea)

Subject Matter

other theories about the cause of SIDS

Main Idea

SIDS may also be caused by bacterial or viral infections, maturational "misprogramming" of respiration, or too high levels of thyroid hormone, but progress in understanding SIDS remains heartbreakingly slow. (implied main idea)

---

acute (ə kyo͞ot′) adj. Extremely severe or sharp; intense.

proliferation (prə lĭf ə rā′ shən) n. Reproduction or production of new growth or parts rapidly and repeatedly.

respiratory (rĕs′ pə rə tôr ē) adj. Of or pertaining to respiration (breathing).

ă pat   ā pay   â care   ä father   ĕ pet   ē be   ĭ pit   ī tie   î pier   ŏ pot   ō toe
ô paw   oi noise   o͞o took   o͞o boot   ou out   th thin   *th* this   ŭ cut   û urge
yo͞o abuse   zh vision   ə *a*bout, it*e*m, ed*i*ble, gall*o*p, circ*u*s

abnormality (ăb nôr măl′ ĭ tē) n. The state or condition of not being normal.

apnea (ăp′ nē ə) n. Temporary or short suspension of breathing.

deprivation (dĕp rə vā′ shən) n. The condition of being deprived; being without.

autopsy (ô′ tŏp sē) n. The examination of a dead body to determine the cause of death.

susceptible (sə sĕp′ tə bəl) adj. Easily influenced or affected. _____

Now write the overall subject matter and the overall main idea.

Overall subject matter: _____

_____

Overall main idea sentence: _____

_____

_____

_____

_____

_____

Here is a sample summary for the selection.

Sudden Infant Death Syndrome

The disorder termed Sudden Infant Death Syndrome (SIDS) is the number-one cause of death for infants between one month and one year of age. Although there have been many theories about the cause of SIDS, it appears to be a respiratory problem. One theory is that death results from abnormalities in respiratory control that result in apnea, spells in which interruptions or pauses occur in breathing during sleep. SIDS may also be caused by bacterial or viral infections, maturational "misprogramming" of respiration, or too high levels of thyroid hormone. The exact cause or causes remain unknown, and progress in understanding SIDS remains heartbreakingly slow.

ă pat ā pay â care ä father ĕ pet ē be ĭ pit ī tie î pier ŏ pot ō toe
ô paw oi noise o͝o took o͞o boot ou out th thin *th* this ŭ cut û urge
yo͞o abuse zh vision ə *a*bout, it*e*m, ed*i*ble, gall*o*p, circ*u*s

2. This passage comes from a United States history textbook. It is taken from a section on the Civil War.

Inequities of the Confederate Draft

As their fortunes declined, these people of once-modest means looked around them and found abundant evidence that all classes were not sacrificing equally. They saw that the wealthy curtailed only their luxuries, while many poor people went without necessities. They saw that the government contributed to these inequities through policies that favored the upper class. Until the last year of the war, for example, prosperous southerners could avoid military service by furnishing a hired substitute. Prices for substitutes skyrocketed, until it was common for a man of means to pay $5,000 or $6,000 to send someone to the front. Well over fifty thousand upper-class southerners purchased such substitutes: Mary Boykin Chesnut knew of one young aristocrat who had "spent a fortune in substitutes. Two have been taken from him [when they were conscripted], and two he paid to change with him when he was ordered to the front. He is at the end of his row now, for all able-bodied men are ordered to the front. I hear he is going as some general's courier."

As Chesnut's last remark indicates, the rich also traded on their social connections to avoid danger. "It's a notorious fact," complained an angry Georgian, that "if a man has influential friends—or a little money to spare he will never be enrolled." The Confederate senator from Mississippi, James Phelan, informed Jefferson Davis that apparently "nine tenths of the youngsters of the land whose relatives are con-

Subject Matter

southerners' hiring military substitutes

Main Idea

The classes did not all sacrifice equally during the war, since wealthy southerners could avoid military service by hiring a substitute to serve for them. (implied main idea)

Subject Matter

rich southerners' use of social connections and money

Main Idea

Rich southerners also used their social connections and money to avoid danger when serving in the army. (implied main idea)

spicuous in society, wealthy, or influential obtain some safe perch where they can doze with their heads under their wings."

A People and a Nation
by Mary Beth Norton et al.

Confederate (kən fĕd′ ər ĭt) adj. Pertaining to the Confederate States of America, the eleven southern states that seceded from the United States (1860–1861).

curtail (kər tāl′) v. To cut short.

aristocrat (ə rĭs′ tə krăt) n. A member of the nobility or aristocracy.

conscript (kən skrĭpt′) v. To force to enlist in military service.

notorious (nō tôr′ē əs) adj. Known widely and usually unfavorably.

Now write the overall subject matter and the overall main idea.

Overall subject matter: _____

_____

Overall main idea sentence: _____

_____

_____

_____

_____

Here is a sample summary for the selection.

Inequities of the Confederate Draft

The wealthy and the poor did not sacrifice equally [during the Civil War] since wealthy southerners could avoid military service by hiring a substitute to serve for them. In particular, they often paid

ă pat ā pay â care ä father ĕ pet ē be ĭ pit ī tie î pier ŏ pot ō toe
ô paw oi noise o͝o took o͞o boot ou out th thin *th* this ŭ cut û urge
yo͞o abuse zh vision ə *a*bout, it*e*m, ed*i*ble, gall*o*p, circ*u*s

substitutes high prices to serve for them at the front. When they did have to serve in the military, some rich southerners used their social connections and money to avoid danger.

3.   This passage is taken from a marine science textbook.

Since European exploration and colonization of the newly discovered continents in the sixteenth century, the ocean has been largely free to all nations. Hugo Grotius (1583-1645) formulated the legal basis in the doctrine of *mare liberum* in 1635. For more than 300 years the ocean, outside of a narrow territorial sea extending 3 nautical miles (5 kilometers) from the shore, was freely used by all nations.

National interest in the potential of immense quantities of petroleum on the continental margins and metal-rich manganese nodules from the deep-ocean floor challenged this concept. Uncertainties about the legal status of these deposits greatly inhibited the investments necessary to exploit them.

In 1974 the United Nations convened a Conference on the Law of the Sea. The nations of the world negotiated their many conflicting needs in order to develop a consensus, often fuzzy, to divide the ocean among them. The treaty was completed in 1981. Its implementation . . . markedly [changed] the legal status of the ocean.

First, the territorial sea was extended to 12 nautical miles (22 kilometers) from the shore. Within this zone the coastal state has rights and responsibilities equal to those it has over the land. Consequently, some major straits through which ships must pass in going from one ocean to another came within the territories of coastal states. Negotiations were necessary to

Subject Matter

free use of the ocean (the doctrine of mare liberum)

Main Idea

Since European exploration and colonization of the newly discovered continents in the 16th century, the ocean has been largely free to all nations, a doctrine known as mare liberum.

Subject Matter

reasons the mare liberum doctrine was challenged

Main Idea

Uncertainties about the legal status of mineral deposits in the ocean and national interest in these resources caused the doctrine of mare liberum to be challenged.

Subject Matter

the U.N. Conference on the Law of the Sea

Main Idea

The 1974 U.N. Conference on the Law of the Sea resulted in a treaty that markedly changed the legal status of the ocean.

ensure the right of ships to navigate these areas.

More dramatic was the recognition of a 200-nautical mile (370 kilometer) Exclusive Economic Zone. In this zone the coastal state regulates fisheries and resource exploration and exploitation. About one-third of the ocean falls in the Exclusive Economic Zone of some coastal state. And many important seas—North Sea, Mediterranean, Gulf of Mexico, Caribbean—are totally divided among the coastal states.

Enormous areas of ocean thus come under national jurisdictions. The United States, for instance, assumed responsibility for an ocean area approximately 80% of its land area. New programs were required to regulate the fisheries on a much larger scale than ever tried before. And new—largely unknown—mineral resources were opened for future exploitation as their legal status was clarified, thus encouraging investment.

Oceanography
by M. Grant Gross

Subject Matter

extension of the territorial sea

Main Idea

The extension of the territorial sea resulted in negotiations to ensure the rights of ships to navigate these areas.

Subject Matter

Exclusive Economic Zone

Main Idea

The recognition of the E.E.Z. was of dramatic importance.

Subject Matter

increase of ocean areas under national jurisdictions

Main Idea

Enormous areas of ocean thus come under national jurisdictions.

Now write the overall subject matter and the overall main idea.

Overall subject matter: _____

_____

Overall main idea sentence: _____

_____

_____

_____

_____

Here is a sample summary for the selection.

Mare Liberum and the Use of the Ocean

From the time of the sixteenth century, the use of the ocean was largely free to all nations. The legal basis for this was the doctrine of mare liberum, which held that the ocean—outside a narrow strip of the sea 3 nautical miles from the shore—could be freely used by all nations. More than 300 years later, this doctrine was challenged because nations became interested in the petroleum and mineral deposits located in the ocean floor. They were afraid to invest in them because the legal status was unclear. A United Nations Conference on the Law of the Sea resulted in a 1981 treaty that markedly changed the legal status of the ocean. Nations' territorial seas were extended further from the shore, which meant that nations had to negotiate to ensure the rights of ships to navigate in these areas. The creation of a 200–nautical mile Exclusive Economic Zone placed the fisheries and resources of about one-third of the ocean under the control of various coastal states. Thus, enormous areas of the ocean came increasingly under the control of national jurisdictions.

4.   This passage was taken from a marketing textbook.

The psychoanalytic school of thought, founded by Sigmund Freud and later modified by his followers and critics, has had a tremendous impact on the study of human personality and behavior. Freud contended that there are three parts to the mind—the id, the ego, and the superego. The id houses the basic instinctive drives, many of which are antisocial. The superego is the conscience, accepting moral standards and directing the instinctive drives into acceptable channels. The id and the superego are sometimes in conflict. The ego is the conscious, rational control center that maintains a balance between the uninhibited instincts of the id and the socially oriented, constraining superego.

Subject Matter

Freud's theory of the three parts of the mind

Main Idea

Freud contended that there were three parts of the mind: the id, the ego, and the superego. (stated main idea)

Freud's behavioral thesis was that we enter the world with certain instinctive biological drives that cannot be satisfied in a socially acceptable fashion. As we learn that we cannot gratify these needs in a direct manner, we develop other, more subtle means of seeking satisfaction. These other means require that the basic drives be repressed, and consequently, inner tensions and frustrations develop. Also, feelings of guilt or shame about these drives cause us to suppress and even sublimate them to the point where they become subconscious. For satisfactions of these drives, we substitute rationalizations and socially acceptable behavior. Yet the basic urges are always there. The net result is very complex behavior. Sometimes even we ourselves do not understand why we feel or act as we do.

One significant marketing implication of psychoanalytic theory is that a person's real motive for buying a given product or shopping at a certain store may well be hidden. The usual research techniques, which are adequate for determining demographic and economic data, normally prove fruitless in uncovering the real reasons for a person's buying behavior.

Psychoanalytic theory has caused marketers to realize that they must provide buyers with socially acceptable rationalizations for their purchasing. Yet we also can appeal subconsciously to buyers' dreams, hopes, and fears.

Fundamentals of Marketing
by William J. Stanton

Subject Matter

Freud's behavioral thesis

Main Idea

Freud's behavioral thesis was that because we cannot gratify certain instinctive drives in a socially acceptable manner, we develop other, more subtle means of seeking satisfaction. (implied main idea)

Subject Matter

people's real motives for buying a product or shopping at a certain store

Main Idea

Because a person's real motive for buying a given product or shopping at a certain store may be hidden, normal marketing research techniques may prove fruitless in uncovering the real reason for a person's buying behavior. (implied main idea)

Subject Matter

implications of psychoanalytic theory for marketers

Main Idea

Psychoanalytic theory has caused marketers to realize they must provide buyers with socially acceptable rationalizations for their purchasing, as well as appeal subconsciously to their dreams, hopes, and fears. (implied main idea)

psychoanalytic (sī kō ăn ə lĭt′ ik) adj. Pertaining to psychoanalysis.

antisocial (ăn tĭ sō′ shəl) adj. Pertaining to behavior that violates the rights of others.

rational (răsh′ ən əl) adj. Having or exercising the ability to reason; logical.

thesis (thē′ sĭs) n. A proposition that is supported by argument.

subtle (sŭt′l) adj. So slight as to be difficult to detect; elusive.

repress (rĭ prĕs′) v. To hold back; restrain.

demographic (dĕm ə grăf′ ĭk) adj. Of or pertaining to demography (the study of characteristics of human populations).

rationalization (răsh ən əl ə zā′ shən) n. The act or process of rationalizing; devising self-satisfying but incorrect reasons for one's behavior.

Overall subject matter: _____

Overall main idea sentence: _____

_____

_____

_____

Prepare a one-paragraph summary of this selection. Be sure to include a title.

_____
_____
_____
_____
_____
_____
_____
_____
_____

ă pat ā pay â care ä father ĕ pet ē be ĭ pit ī tie î pier ŏ pot ō toe
ô paw oi noise o͝o took o͞o boot ou out th thin *th* this ŭ cut û urge
yo͞o abuse zh vision ə *a*bout, it*e*m, ed*i*ble, gall*o*p, circ*u*s

_____

_____

_____

_____

_____

_____

_____

_____

_____

_____

_____

_____

_____

_____

_____

_____

_____

_____

_____

_____

CHAPTER

6

APPLYING COMPREHENSION
SKILLS TO LONGER PASSAGES
Answer Key for Practice Exercises

Compare your answers for the practice exercises on page 301–311 with the answers below.

1. *Overall subject matter:* Sudden Infant Death Syndrome (SIDS).

   Overall main idea: Sudden Infant Death Syndrome (SIDS), the number-one cause of death for infants, appears to be a respiratory problem whose precise cause has not yet been determined.

   (Did you remember to write the overall main idea as a sentence?)

2. *Overall subject matter:* inequities of the Confederate draft

   or

   wealthy southerners' avoidance of military service

   Overall main idea: Wealthy southerners were able to avoid the Confederate draft by paying substitutes, and they used their social connections to avoid danger if they did have to enlist.

3. *Overall subject matter: mare liberum* and use of the sea

   or

   changes in the use of the sea since the 16th century doctrine of *mare liberum*

   Overall main idea: Jurisdiction of the ocean has evolved from the 1635 doctrine of *mare liberum* to the present-day treaty that defines national jurisdictions.

4. *Overall subject matter:* psychoanalytic theory and marketing

   or

   the implications of pscyhoanalytic theory for marketing

   Overall main idea: To market effectively, marketers must provide buyers with socially acceptable rationalizations for their purchasing and appeal subconsciously to their dreams, hopes, and fears.

(Here, the main idea of the last paragraph also serves as the overall main idea.)

Here is a sample summary for the selection:

Psychoanalytic Theory and Marketing

Freud's psychoanalytic school of thought has had a great impact on the study of human personality and behavior. Freud contended that there were three parts to the personality: the id, which consists of instinctive and sometimes antisocial drives; the superego, or conscience; and the ego, the control center that maintains conscious, rational balance between the other two components. Freud's behavioral thesis was that because we cannot gratify certain instinctive drives in a socially acceptable manner, we develop other, more subtle means of seeking satisfaction. The result is complex behavior that sometimes causes us to have feelings and behaviors that even we ourselves do not understand. Psychoanalytic theory suggests that because a person's real motive for buying a given product or shopping at a certain store may be hidden, normal marketing research techniques may prove futile in uncovering the real reason for a person's buying behavior. Psychoanalytic theory has caused marketers to realize that they must provide buyers with socially acceptable rationalizations for their purchasing, as well as appeal subconsciously to their dreams, hopes, and fears.

APPLYING COMPREHENSION SKILLS TO LONGER PASSAGES
Review Test

Read each of the following passages carefully. Using a dictionary, define the words listed below each passage. Next, write the subject matter and main idea of each paragraph, and then write the overall subject matter and overall main idea for each passage.

1. This selection is from a United States history textbook.

Settlers of the Plains also had to contend with social isolation. The European pattern, whereby farmers lived together in a village and traveled each day to their nearby fields, was rare in the American West. Instead, various peculiarities of land division compelled rural dwellers to live apart from each other. The Homestead Act of 1862 and other measures adopted to facilitate western settlement offered free or cheap plots to people who would live on and improve their property. Because most homesteads and other plots acquired by small farmers were rectangular—usually encompassing 160 acres—at most four families could live near each other, but only if they congregated around the same four-corner boundary intersection. In practice, farmers usually lived back from their boundary lines, and at least a half-mile separated farmhouses. Often adjacent land was unoccupied, making neighbors even more distant.

Many observers wrote about the loneliness and monotony of life on the Plains.

Subject Matter

_____

Main Idea

_____

_____

Subject Matter

_____

Main Idea

_____

_____

315

Men escaped the oppressiveness by working outdoors and taking occasional trips to sell crops or buy supplies. But women were more isolated, confined by domestic chores to the household, where, as one writer remarked, they were "not much better than slaves. It is a weary, monotonous round of cooking and washing and mending and as a result the insane asylum is $1/3$ filled with wives of farmers."

A People and a Nation
by Mary Beth Norton et al.

social isolation: _____

facilitate: _____

monotony: _____

oppressive: _____

Now write the overall subject matter and the overall main idea.

Overall subject matter: _____

_____

Overall main idea sentence: _____

_____

_____

_____

_____

Prepare a one-paragraph summary of this selection. Be sure to include a title:

_____

_____

_____

_____

_____

_____

_____

_____

_____

_____

_____

_____

_____

2. This passage comes from an economics textbook.

Precisely what do we mean by "material wants?" We mean, first, the desires of consumers to obtain and use various goods and services which give pleasure or satisfaction. An amazingly wide range of products fills the bill in this respect: houses, automobiles, toothpaste, pencils, pizzas, sweaters, and the like. In short, innumerable products which we sometimes classify as necessities (food, shelter, clothing) and luxuries (perfumes, yachts, mink coats) are all capable of satisfying human wants. Needless to say, what is a luxury to Smith may be a necessity to Jones, and what is a commonplace necessity today may have been a luxury a few short years ago.

But services satisfy our wants as much as do tangible products. A repair job on our car, the removal of our appendix, a

Subject Matter

_____

Main Idea

_____

_____

_____

Subject Matter

_____

Main Idea

_____

_____

_____

haircut, and legal advice have in common with goods the fact that they satisfy human wants. On reflecting, we realize that we indeed buy many goods, for example, automobiles and washing machines, for the services they render. The differences between goods and services are often less than they seem to be at first.

Material wants also include those which businesses and units of government seek to satisfy. Businesses want factory buildings, machinery, trucks, warehouses, and other things that assist them in realizing their production goals. Government, reflecting the collective wants of its citizenry or goals of its own, seeks highways, schools, hospitals, and military hardware.

As a group, these material wants are, for practical purposes, insatiable, or unlimited, which means that material wants for goods and services are incapable of being completely satisfied. A simple experiment will help to verify this point: Suppose we are asked to list those goods and services we want but do not now possess. If we take time to ponder our unfilled material wants, chances are our list will be impressive. And over a period of time, wants multiply so that, as we fill some of the wants on the list, at the same time we add new ones. Material wants, like rabbits, have a high reproductive rate. The rapid introduction of new products whets our appetites, and extensive advertising tries to persuade us that we need countless items we might not otherwise consider buying. Not too many years ago, the desire for color television, air conditioners, video recorders, digital watches, and tubeless tires was nonexistent. Furthermore, we often cannot stop with simple satisfaction:

Subject Matter

_____

Main Idea

_____

_____

_____

Subject Matter

_____

Main Idea

_____

_____

_____

The acquisition of an Escort or Chevette has been known to whet the appetite for a Cadillac or Mercedes.

In summary, we may add that at any given time the individuals and institutions which constitute society have innumerable unfulfilled material wants. Some of these wants—food, clothing, shelter—have biological roots. But some are also influenced by the conventions and customs of society: The specific kinds of food, clothing, and shelter we seek are frequently determined by the general social and cultural environment in which we live. Over time, wants change and multiply, abetted by the development of new products and by extensive advertising and sales promotion.

Economics
by Campbell McConnell

Subject Matter

_____

Main Idea

_____

_____

_____

consumer: _____

innumerable: _____

tangible: _____

collective: _____

insatiable: _____

whet: _____

constitute: _____

abet: _____

Now write the overall subject matter and the overall main idea.

Overall subject matter: _____

_____

Overall main idea sentence: _____

_____

_____

_____

_____

_____

Prepare a one-paragraph summary of this selection. Be sure to include a title.

_____

_____

_____

_____

_____

_____

_____

_____

_____

_____

_____

_____

_____

APPLYING COMPREHENSION SKILLS TO LONGER PASSAGES
Supplemental Exercises

1. This passage is from a computer science textbook.

The Computer Criminal: Who and Why?

Here is what a computer criminal is apt to be like. He (we will use *he* here, but of course *he* could be *she*) is usually someone occupying a position of trust in an organization. Indeed, he is likely to be regarded as the ideal employee. He has had no previous lawbreaking experience and, in fact, will not see himself as a thief but as a "borrower." He is apt to be young and to be fascinated with the challenge of beating the system. Contrary to expectations, he is not necessarily a loner: he may operate in conjunction with other employees to take advantage of the system's weaknesses.

What motivates the computer criminal? The causes are as varied as the offenders. However, a few frequent motives have been identified. A computer criminal is often the disgruntled employee, possibly a longtime loyal worker out for revenge after being passed over for a raise or promotion. In another scenario an otherwise model employee may commit a crime while suffering from personal or family problems. Not all motives are emotionally based. Some people simply are attracted to the challenge of the crime. In contrast, it is the ease of the crime that tempts others.

Subject Matter

_____

Main Idea

_____

_____

_____

Subject Matter

_____

Main Idea

_____

_____

_____

An experienced security consultant noted that computer crime is nothing but white-collar crime with a new medium: each employee who is trained to use a computer is also trained—potentially—to use the computer to rob the company.

In many cases the criminal activity is unobstrusive; it fits right in with regular job duties. One offender noted that his colleagues would never ask what he was doing; instead, they would make comments like, "That turkey, that technician, all he ever does is talk his buzzwords, can't talk to him," and walk away. So the risk of detection is often quite low. Computer criminals think they can get away with it. And they do—some of the time.

Computers: Tools for an Information Age by H.C. Capron

Subject Matter

_____

Main Idea

_____

_____

_____

Now write the overall subject matter and the overall main idea.

Overall subject matter: _____

_____

Overall main idea sentence: _____

_____

_____

_____

_____

_____

Prepare a one-paragraph summary of this selection. Be sure to include a title.

_____

_____

_____

_____

_____

_____

_____

_____

_____

_____

_____

_____

_____

_____

_____

2. This selection is from a sociology textbook.

Picture a "college student." Most likely, you will imagine someone under 25 years of age. This reflects the belief that education is something experienced and completed during the first two or three decades of life and rarely supplemented after that. However, many colleges and universities have witnessed a dramatic increase in the number of older students pursuing two-year, four-year, and graduate degrees. For example, during the 1970s, the number of women in college aged 35 and over doubled; a 1981 magazine article featured six sets of mothers and daughters who were classmates at colleges across the nation (Sweet, 1981).

In 1981, one-third of all students taking credit courses in colleges were 25 years old

Subject Matter

_____

Main Idea

_____

_____

_____

or older. [During] the 1990s, there will be almost as many college students over 25 years of age as under. Obviously, sociological models of the collegiate subculture will have to be revised significantly in light of such changes. Moreover, as the age of the "typical" college student increases, there is growing need for on-campus day care. This is especially true in community colleges, where the median age of students is 31. According to a 1983 estimate, 40 percent of all two- and four-year colleges currently offer some type of child care on campus (Gilinsky, 1983).

It should be noted that American colleges need older students. Given the expected decrease in population in the age group 18 to 24 years old over the period 1980 to 1995, institutions of higher learning will have to find new consumers for their services in order to survive financially. This need has led colleges across the nation to develop adult education programs. Currently, about half of all adults in the United States take part in some type of adult education. In the words of Dr. Anad Mohan of Queens College: "Adult education has become both popular and profitable—and everyone wants to get in on the bucks."

Ironically, a 1984 report issued by the Commission on Higher Education and the Adult Learner argued that the current structures and curricula of colleges and universities were a "major impediment" to meeting the educational needs of American adults. The Commission recommended that colleges reorient their programs to adult learners rather than simply try to fit prospective adult students into the existing curricula. At the same time, the Commis-

Subject Matter

_____

Main Idea

_____

_____

_____

Subject Matter

_____

Main Idea

_____

_____

_____

Subject Matter

_____

Main Idea

_____

_____

_____

sion called for a comprehensive national program of institutional grants, financial aid, individual tax incentives, and information services for adult learners (*Chronicle of Higher Education,* 1984).

One aspect of the adult education boom involves the rapidly changing nature of the business world in an age of technological innovation. Business firms have come to accept the view of education as a lifelong process and may encourage (or require) employees to learn job-related skills. Thus, secretaries are sent to special schools to be trained to use word-processing systems and video display units. Realtors attend classes to learn about alternative forms of financing for prospective home buyers. In occupation after occupation, longtime workers and professionals are going back to school to adapt to the new demands of their jobs.

Not all these adult learners receive their additional schooling in conventional settings. While about 12 million persons attend colleges and universities in the United States, another 46 million adults are being educated by other service providers. These include train-for-profit schools, such as Bell and Howell's 11 DeVry schools, and instructional programs offered by the military and the U.S. Department of Agriculture. Consequently, the nation now has a "second system" of postsecondary education whose total annual investment—about $50 billion—equals the annual investment in colleges and universities (Hodgkinson, 1983; Zigli, 1984a).

Sociology
by Richard Schaefer

Subject Matter

_____

Main Idea

_____

_____

_____

Subject Matter

_____

Main Idea

_____

_____

_____

Now write the overall subject matter and the overall main idea.

Overall subject matter: _____

_____

Overall main idea sentence: _____

_____

_____

_____

_____

_____

Prepare a one-paragraph summary of this selection. Be sure to include a title.

_____

_____

_____

_____

_____

_____

_____

_____

_____

_____

_____

_____

_____

_____

_____

_____

_____

_____

_____

_____

_____

_____

_____

_____

_____

_____

_____

3. This selection comes from an art appreciation textbook.

The social role of artists has changed over time, but their function remains basically the same. Like their counterparts in earlier times, contemporary artists fulfill a practical function, designing virtually every structure and object in the environment. Today this practical role is carried out by artists with specialized, often technical, training—industrial and graphic designers, architects, craft artists, and fashion designers, among others. But what about the painters and sculptors, the photographers and cinematographers? What needs do they meet in our computer age? We can identify at least four basic functions for the artist—all of them age-old, all expanding in complexity.

First, artists *record*. They give us visual images that can be preserved for historical reference. This idea is so obvious that we take it for granted, forgetting how over whelming our ignorance otherwise would be.

Subject Matter

_____

Main Idea

_____

_____

_____

Were it not for artists, we would have no idea what people from the past looked like. Thomas Jefferson was one of the founders of our country, principal author of the Declaration of Independence, and third president of the United States. He is well known to us from his extensive writings. His splendid architecture stands today and is still admired. But Jefferson died more than a decade before the invention of photography, and were it not for artists' portraits, including the sensitive one by Rembrandt Peale, we would have no visual image of the man to match the achievement. Nor could we form any visual image of historical places and events. Before the invention of the camera in the early 19th century, artists recorded images mainly through painting and sculpture. Today we rely more heavily on photography, cinema, and television to keep our history, but of course the people behind these media are also artists. Even with the prevalence of mechanical recording, there is a renewed interest in the painted portrait, and a great many well-known artists are thriving on portrait commissions.

Second, artists *give tangible form to the unknown.* In other words, they attempt to record what cannot be seen with the eyes or what has not yet occurred. This role has been important throughout the history of art, and it is no less vital today. Ancient artists had a somewhat different list of unknowns to contend with. They puzzled over and feared such things as tornadoes, floods, eclipses, and the wrath of spirits. Even in an age when satellites predict the weather and spirits have been tamed, there still are certain unknowns, and artists still are struggling to give them tangible form.

Subject Matter

_____

Main Idea

_____

_____

_____

Subject Matter

_____

Main Idea

_____

_____

_____

What would a nuclear holocaust be like? We do not know and dare not find out. What exists at the edge of our universe? Scientists will know eventually, but not soon. What do our dreams and nightmares really mean? None of us can analyze them definitely. These unknowns are frightening to us, just as the Thunder God must have been to our ancestors. If artists can present them to us in some concrete form, we can tame them and go about our business.

Third, artists *give tangible form to feelings.* These may be the artist's own feelings that are expressed in paint or marble or whatever the medium. But surely they are feelings shared by many people—love, hate, despair, fear, exhilaration, anger, admiration, the terror of nightmares. When we respond to a work of art, when we pay attention to the emotions it evokes, we are communicating in a way with the artists and with other people who share these responses.

Fourth, artists *offer an innovative way of seeing,* a unique visual perspective. When we experience a work of art, we confront the artist's perspective, compare it to our own, and take note of both the similarities and differences. Art encourages us to think, to question, to imagine, to explore, to dream. It stretches our own horizons by confronting us with someone else's.

To sum up, then, artists perform at least four important functions in society: they record, they visualize the unknown, they portray feelings, and they stretch one's ability to see. All of these functions have to do with communication. Artists are able to fill these roles because they create new visual images.

Subject Matter

_____

Main Idea

_____

_____

_____

Subject Matter

_____

Main Idea

_____

_____

_____

Subject Matter

_____

Main Idea

_____

_____

_____

Now write the overall subject matter and the overall main idea.

Overall subject matter: _____

_____

Overall main idea sentence: _____

_____

_____

_____

_____

Prepare a one-paragraph summary of this selection. Be sure to include a title.

_____

_____

_____

_____

_____

_____

_____

_____

_____

_____

_____

_____

_____

_____

_____

_____

_____

_____

_____

_____

_____

_____

_____

_____

_____

_____

_____

_____

_____

APPLYING COMPREHENSION SKILLS TO LONGER PASSAGES
Textbook Excerpt and Comprehension Quiz

"The Primates" from *Anthropology,* 6th ed., by Conrad Phillip Kottak, McGraw-Hill, Inc., 1994, pp. 132–138.

Prepare Yourself to Read

Before you read this selection, read and think about its title. Then, in one or two sentences, write a few of the things that you already know about primates.

_____

_____

_____

_____

Complete your preview of this selection by reading

- the first paragraph
- the headings of each section
- any diagrams, illustrations, and photographs
- all of the last paragraph

Ask and answer questions as you read.

Use questions to guide your reading. Turn section headings into questions. If there are no headings, create questions based on what the paragraphs or sections seem to be about.

Read actively to find answers to your questions.

THE PRIMATES

SIMILARITIES BETWEEN HUMANS AND OTHER PRIMATES

There is a large gap between primate society and fully developed human culture. However, studies of primates in varied circumstances have revealed more similarities than were once imagined. Scholars used to contend that learned (versus instinctive) behavior separates humans from other animals. We know now that monkeys and apes also rely extensively on learning. Differences between humans and other primates are quantitative rather than qualitative: They are differences in *degree* rather than in kind. For example, chimpanzees make tools for specific tasks, but human reliance on tools is much greater.

Adaptive Flexibility Through Learning

Common to monkeys, apes, and humans is the fact that behavior and social organization aren't rigidly programmed by the genes. All anthropoids learn throughout their lives. In several cases, an entire troop has learned from the experiences of some of its members. In one group of Japanese macaques, a three-year-old female developed the habit of washing dirt off sweet potatoes before she ate them. First her mother, then her age peers, and finally the entire troop started washing sweet potatoes, too. The direction of learning was reversed when members of another macaque troop learned to eat wheat. Dominant males first tried the new food; within four hours the practice had spread throughout the troop. Changes in learned behavior seem to spread more quickly from the top down than from the bottom up.

For monkeys as for people, the ability to learn, to profit from experience, confers a tremendous adaptive advantage, permitting them to avoid fatal mistakes. Faced with environmental change, primates don't have to wait for a genetic or physiological response, since learned behavior and social patterns can be modified. Thus behavioral flexibility facilitates adaptation to diverse environments, although this occurs to a lesser degree than it does in humans.

Tools

Anthropologists used to distinguish humans from other animals as tool users, and there is no doubt that *Homo* does employ tools more than any other animal does. However, tool use also turns up among several nonhuman species. For example, in the Galápagos Islands off western South America there is a "woodpecker finch" that selects twigs to dig out insects and grubs from tree bark. Sea otters use rocks to break open mollusks, which are important in their diet. Beavers are famous for dam construction.

When it became obvious that people weren't the only tool users, anthropologists started contending that only humans manufacture tools with foresight, that is, with a specific purpose in mind. Chimpanzees show that this, too, is debatable. The research of many primatologists, particularly Jane Goodall (1986), has increased our knowledge of chimp behavior in natural settings. In 1960 Goodall began observing chimps in Gombe Stream National Park in Tanzania, East Africa. More than any other primate, chimps share the human capacity for deliberate tool manufacture, although in chimps the capacity remains rudimentary. Nevertheless, wild chimps regularly make tools. To get water from places their mouths can't reach, thirsty chimps pick leaves, chew and crumple them, and then dip them into the water. Thus, with a specific purpose in mind, they devise primitive "sponges."

More impressive is "termiting." Chimps make tools to probe termite hills. They choose twigs, which they modify by removing leaves and

Learned behavior among wild chimps includes rudimentary tool making. Here, a chimpanzee uses a specially prepared twig to "fish" for termites.

peeling off bark to expose the sticky surface beneath. They carry the twigs to termite hills, dig holes with their fingers, and insert the twigs. Finally they pull out the twigs and dine on termites that were attracted to the sticky surface.

Termiting isn't as easy as it might seem. Learning to termite takes time, and many Gombe chimps never master it. Twigs with certain characteristics must be chosen. Furthermore, once the twig is in the termite hill and the chimp judges that termites are crawling on its surface, the chimp must quickly flip the twig as it pulls it out so that the termites are on top. Otherwise they fall off as the twig comes out of the hole. This is an elaborate skill that neither all chimps nor human observers have been able to master.

Chimps have other abilities essential to culture. When they are trained by humans, their manipulatory skills flower, as anyone who has ever seen a movie, circus, or zoo chimp knows. Wild chimps aim and throw objects. The gorilla, our other nearest relative, lacks the chimp's proclivity for tool making. However, gorillas do build nests, and they throw branches, grass, vines, and other objects. Hominids have considerably elaborated the capacity to aim and throw, which is a likely homology passed down from the common ancestor of humans and apes. Without it we would have never developed projectile technology, weaponry, and baseball.

Communication Systems

Only humans speak. No other animal has anything approaching the complexity of language. However, evidence is accumulating that linguistic ability is also a quantitative rather than qualitative difference between humans and other primates, especially gorillas and chimps. The natural communication systems of other primates—their **call systems**—which are composed of sounds that vary in intensity and duration, are much more complex than used to be supposed. Goodall (1986*a*) identified twenty-five distinct calls used by Gombe chimps. Each had a distinct meaning and was used only in particular situations. Calls are much less flexible than language because they are automatic and can't be combined. When primates encounter food and danger simultaneously, they can make only one call. They can't combine the calls for food and danger into a single utterance, indicating that both are present. If by chance they did so, others would probably not understand the message. At some point in hominid evolution, however, our ancestors began to combine calls and understand the combinations. The number of calls also expanded, eventually becoming too great to be transmitted even partly through the genes. Hominid communication came to rely almost totally on learning.

Although wild primates use call systems, the vocal tract of apes is not suitable for speech. Until the 1960s attempts to teach spoken language to apes suggested that they lack linguistic abilities. In the 1950s a couple raised a chimpanzee, Viki, as a member of their family and systematically tried to teach her to speak. However, Viki learned only four words ("mama," "papa," "up," and "cup").

More recent experiments have shown that apes can learn to use, if not speak, true language (Miles 1983). Several apes have learned to converse with people through means other than speech. One such communication system is American Sign Language, or **Ameslan,** which is widely used by deaf and mute Americans. Ameslan employs a limited number of basic gesture units that are analogous to sounds in spoken language. These units combine to form words and larger units of meaning.

The first chimpanzee to learn Ameslan was Washoe, a female. Captured in West Africa, Washoe was acquired by R. Allen Gardner and Beatrice Gardner, scientists at the University of Nevada in Reno, in 1966, when she was a year old. Four years later she moved to Norman, Oklahoma, to a converted farm that had become the Institute for Primate Studies. Washoe's experiences in Reno revolutionized the discussion of the language-learning abilities of apes. Washoe lived in a trailer and heard no spoken language. The researchers always used Ameslan to communicate with each other in her presence. The chimp gradually acquired a vocabulary of 132 signs representing English words (Gardner, Gardner, and Van Cantfort 1989). At the age of two, Washoe began to combine as many as five signs into rudimentary sentences such as "you, me, go out, hurry."

The second chimp to learn Ameslan was Lucy, Washoe's junior by one year. Lucy died, or was murdered by poachers, in 1986, after having been carefully introduced to "the wild" in Africa in 1979 (Carter 1988). From her second day of life until her move to Africa, Lucy lived with a family in Norman, Oklahoma. Roger Fouts, a researcher from the nearby Institute for Primate Studies, came two days a week to test and improve Lucy's knowledge of Ameslan. During the rest of the week Lucy used Ameslan to converse with her foster parents. After acquiring language, Washoe and Lucy expressed several human traits: swearing, joking, telling lies, and trying to teach language to others.

When irritated, Washoe has called her monkey neighbors at the institute "dirty monkeys." Lucy insulted her "dirty cat." On arrival at Lucy's place, Fouts once found a pile of excrement on the floor. When he asked the chimp what it was, she replied "dirty, dirty," her expression for feces. Asked whose "dirty, dirty" it was, Lucy named Fouts's coworker, Sue. When Fouts refused to believe her about Sue, the chimp blamed the excrement on Fouts himself.

Cultural transmission of a communication system through learning is a fundamental attribute of language. Both Washoe and Lucy have tried to teach Ameslan to other animals, including their own offspring. Washoe has taught gestures to other institute chimps, including her son Sequoia, who died in infancy (Fouts, Fouts, and Van Cantfort 1989). There have been other cases of cultural transmission of Ameslan from chimp to chimp.

Because of their size and strength as adults, gorillas are less likely subjects than chimps for such experiments. Lean adult male gorillas in the wild weigh 400 pounds (180 kilograms), and full-grown females can easily reach 250 pounds (110 kilograms). Because of this, psychologist Penny Patterson's work with gorillas at Stanford University seems more daring than the chimp experiments. Patterson raised her now full-grown female gorilla, Koko, in a trailer next to a Stanford museum. Koko's vocabulary surpasses that of any chimp. She regularly employs 400 Ameslan signs and has used about 700 at least once.

Koko and the chimps also show that apes share still another linguistic ability with humans—**productivity.** Speakers routinely use the rules of their language to produce entirely new expressions that are comprehensible to other native speakers. I can, for example, create "baboonlet"

to refer to a baboon infant. I do this by analogy with English words in which the suffix *-let* designates the young of a species. Anyone who speaks English immediately understands the meaning of my new word. Koko, Washoe, and Lucy have shown that apes also use language productively. Lucy used gestures she already knew to create "drinkfruit" for watermelon. Washoe, seeing a swan for the first time, coined "waterbird." Koko, who knew the gestures for "finger" and "bracelet," formed "finger bracelet" when she was given a ring.

Chimps and gorillas have at least a rudimentary capacity for language. They may never have invented a meaningful gesture system in the wild. However, given such a system, they show many humanlike abilities in learning and using it. Of course, language used by apes is a product of human intervention and teaching. The experiments mentioned here do not suggest that apes can invent language (nor are human children ever faced with that task). However, young apes have managed to learn the basics of gestural language. They can employ it productively and creatively, although not with the sophistication of human Ameslan users.

Apes, like humans, may also try to teach their language to others. Lucy, not fully realizing the difference between primate hands and feline paws, once tried to mold her pet cat's paw into Ameslan signs. Koko has taught gestures to Michael, a male gorilla six years her junior.

Apes also have the capacity for linguistic **displacement.** Absent in call systems, this is a key ingredient in language. Each call is tied to an environmental stimulus such as food. Calls are uttered only when that stimulus is present. Displacement permits humans to talk about things that are not present. We don't have to see the objects before we say the words. Human conversations are not bounded by place. We can discuss the past and future, share our experiences with others, and benefit from theirs.

Patterson has described several examples of Koko's capacity for displacement (Patterson 1978). The gorilla once expressed sorrow about having bitten Penny three days earlier. Koko has used the sign "later" to postpone doing things she doesn't want to do. Thus, she can reconstruct events, including emotional states. She imagines the future and uses language to express her thoughts.

Certain scholars still doubt the linguistic abilities of chimps and gorillas (Terrace, 1979; Sebeok and Umiker-Sebeok 1980). These people contend that Koko and the chimps are comparable to trained circus animals and don't really have linguistic ability. However, in defense of Patterson and the other researchers, whose findings are impressive (Hill 1978; Van Cantfort and Rimpau 1982), only one of their critics has worked with an ape. This was Herbert Terrace, whose experience teaching a chimp sign language lacked the continuity and personal involvement that have contributed so much to Patterson's success with Koko.

No one denies the huge difference between human language and gorilla signs. There is a major gap between the ability to write a book or say a prayer and the few hundred gestures employed by a well-trained chimp. Apes aren't people, but they aren't just animals either. Let Koko express it: When asked by a reporter whether she was a person or an animal, Koko chose neither. Instead, she signed "fine animal gorilla" (Patterson 1978).

The capacity to remember and combine linguistic expressions is latent in the apes (Miles 1983). In hominid evolution the same ability flowered into language. Language did not appear miraculously at a certain moment in human history. It developed over hundreds of thousands of years, as our ancestor's call systems were gradually transformed. Language offered a tremendous adaptive advantage to *Homo.* Along with technology, language is a basic part of our cultural, nonbodily, or **extrasomatic**, means of adaptation. Language permits the information stored by a human society to exceed by far that of any nonhuman group. Language is a uniquely effective vehicle for learning. Because we can speak of things we have never experienced, we can anticipate responses before we encounter the stimuli. Adaptation can occur more rapidly in *Homo* than in the other primates because our adaptive means are more flexible. Humans routinely rely on biological, social, and cultural means of adaptation.

Predation and Hunting

Like tool making and language, hunting has been cited as a distinctive human activity that is not shared with our ape relatives. Again, however, primate research shows that what was previously thought to be a difference of kind is a difference of degree.

The diets of other terrestrial primates are not exclusively vegetarian, as was once thought. Baboons kill and eat young antelopes, and researchers have observed hunting by chimpanzees. Geza Teleki (1973) has provided a detailed report based on twelve months of observing predation among chimps at Tanzania's Gombe Stream National Park. He recorded thirty cases of chimpanzee hunting, twelve of which led to a kill. About a hundred kills were recorded during a decade of research by Goodall (1986*b*) and her associates at Gombe.

Generally, chimps simply lunged at and seized their prey, but they also did more complex hunting. Groups of five or six sometimes patiently stalked a prey animal. Stalking was silent; vocalization occurred only when they seized the prey. Nor did the chimps use gestures to co-ordinate the hunt. After seizing an infant baboon, the hunter would bite or wring the baboon's neck or bash its head against the ground or a tree. Occasionally, young baboons were ripped apart when two chimps seized them simultaneously. For a few moments after the kill, chimps that had not taken part in the hunt could grab part of the carcass. Once this initial division occurred, however, meat sharing became more intri-cate. Chimps used a variety of gestures to request meat from their fel-lows. The hunters granted the requests about one-third of the time. Chimpanzee hunting is predominantly a male activity; insect eating is more common in females (McGrew 1979).

Predation, Aggression, and Resources

The potential for predation may be generalized in monkeys and apes, but its expression seems to depend on the environment. Hunting by chimpanzees might have developed in response to changes in their environment. Humans have been encroaching on their natural habitat.

Goodall specifically linked chimpanzee predation to human en-croachment. The Gombe chimps are divided into a northern group and a smaller group of southerners. Parties from the north have invaded southern territory and killed southern chimps. Infant victims were par-tially eaten by the assailants (Goodall 1986). John MacKinnon's research (1974) among orangutans on the Indonesian islands of Borneo (Kali-mantan) and Sumatra shows that orangutans have also suffered as a re-sult of human encroachment, particularly farming and timbering. On Borneo, in response to nearby human activities, orangs have developed a pattern of extreme sexual antagonism which may further endanger their survival. During MacKinnon's field work, Bornean orangs rarely had sex. Their limited sexual encounters were always brief rapes, often with screaming infants clinging to their mothers throughout the ordeal.

As MacKinnon did his field work, logging operations were forcing orangs whose territory was destroyed into his research area, swelling the population it had to support. The response to this sudden overpopula-tion was a drastic decline in the local orang birth rate. Primates respond in various ways to encroachment and population pressure. A change in sexual relationships that reduces the birth rate is one way of easing pop-ulation pressure on resources.

We see that primate behavior is not rigidly determined by the genes. It is plastic (flexible), capable of varying widely as environmental forces change. Among humans, too, aggression increases when resources are threatened or scarce. What we know about other primates makes it reasonable to assume that early hominids were neither uniformly aggressive nor consistently meek. Their aggression and predation reflected environmental variation.

DIFFERENCES BETWEEN HUMANS AND OTHER PRIMATES

The preceding sections emphasized similarities between humans and other primates. The differences discussed so far have been of degree rather than kind. Thus *Homo* has elaborated substantially on certain tendencies shared with the apes. A unique concentration and combination of characteristics makes humans distinct. However, the early hominid savanna niche also selected certain traits that are not so obviously foreshadowed by the apes.

Sharing, Cooperation, and Division of Labor

Early humans lived in small social groups called bands, with economies based on hunting and gathering. Some band-organized societies survived into the modern world, and ethnographers have studied them. From those studies we can say that in such groups the strongest and most aggressive members do not dominate, as they do in a troop of terrestrial monkeys. Sharing and curbing of aggression are as basic to technologically simple humans as dominance and threats are to baboons.

Monkeys fend for themselves in the quest for food. However, among human foragers, men generally hunt and women gather. People bring resources back to the camp and share them. The most successful hunters are expected to be generous. Everyone shares the meat from a large animal. Older people who did not engage in the food quest receive food from younger adults. Nourished and protected by younger band members, elders live past the reproductive age. They receive special respect for their age and knowledge. The amount of information stored in a human band is far greater than that in any other primate society. Sharing, cooperation, and language are intrinsic to information storage.

Among all primates except *Homo,* most food comes from individual foraging, usually for vegetation. The rarity of meat eating and the concentration on vegetation are fundamental differences between apes and humans. Through millions of years of adaptation to an omnivorous diet, hominids have come to rely on hunting, meat eating, food sharing, and cooperative behavior. These are universal features in human adaptive strategies.

Mating, Exogamy, and Kinship

Another difference between humans and other primates concerns mating. Among baboons and chimpanzees, sexual intercourse occurs when females "go into heat" or enter **estrus**, a period of sexual receptivity. Estrus is signaled by swelling and coloration of the vaginal skin. Receptive females form temporary bonds with males. Among humans, sexual activity occurs throughout the year. Related to this more constant sexuality, all human societies have some form of marriage. Marriage gives mating a reliable basis and grants to each spouse special, though not always exclusive, sexual rights in the other.

Marriage creates another major contrast between humans and non-humans: exogamy and kinship systems. Most cultures have rules of exogamy requiring marriage outside one's kin or local group. Coupled with the recognition of kinship, exogamy confers adaptive advantages. It creates ties between the spouses' groups of origin. Their children have relatives, and therefore allies, in two kin groups rather than just one. The key point here is that ties of affection and mutual support between members of different local groups are absent among primates other than *Homo.* There is a tendency among primates to disperse at adolescence. Among chimps and gorillas, females tend to migrate, seeking mates in other groups. Both male and female gibbons leave home when they become sexually mature. Once they find mates and establish their own territories, ties with their native groups cease. Long-term studies of terrestrial monkeys reveal that males leave the troop at puberty, eventually finding places elsewhere. The troop's core members are females. They sometimes form **uterine** groups made up of mothers, sisters, daughters, and sons that have not yet emigrated. This dispersal of males reduces the incidence of incestuous matings. Females mate with males born elsewhere, which join the troop at adolescence. Although kin ties are maintained between female monkeys, no close lifelong links are preserved through males.

Humans choose mates from outside the native group (the family), and at least one spouse moves. However, *humans maintain lifelong ties with sons and daughters.* The systems of kinship and marriage that preserve these links provide a major contrast between humans and other primates.

"The Primates" from *Anthropology*, 6th ed., by Conrad Phillip
Kottak, McGraw-Hill, Inc., 1994, pp. 132–138.

COMPREHENSION QUIZ

True or False

Directions: In the blank provided, indicate whether each statement is true or
false.

_____ 1. Studies revealed that there are more similarities between primates and humans than once imagined.

_____ 2. Primates are not tool users.

_____ 3. Unlike humans, each monkey fends for itself in the quest for food.

_____ 4. For monkeys, as with people, the ability to learn permits adaptation to diverse environments.

_____ 5. The differences in degree between humans and other primates are quantitative rather than qualitative.

_____ 6. The communication system of primates is much less flexible because primates cannot combine their calls.

_____ 7. The first chimp to learn Ameslan was named Lucy.

_____ 8. *Estrus* occurs in all primates.

Multiple Choice

Directions: For each item, select the best answer.

_____ 9. Ameslan
   a. is American Sign Language
   b. is used by many deaf and mute Americans
   c. employs a limited number of basic gestures
   d. all of the above

_____10. All of the following are similarities between humans and other primates except
   a. the ability to adapt through learning
   b. mating and kinship practices
   c. linguistic displacement
   d. the ability to transmit culture

_____11. A *call* system of primates is
   a. a system of hand signals
   b. a communication system composed of sounds that vary in intensity and duration
   c. a system used in hunting
   d. body language

_____12. *Productivity* means
   a. the ability to produce new expressions in language that are understood to others in the group
   b. to work more efficiently
   c. a component of linguistic ability
   d. both a. and c.

_____13. *Exogamy* involves
   a. marriage outside one's kin or local group
   b. mating practices of primates
   c. both a. and b.
   d. none of the above

_____14. All of the following characteristics make humans distinct from other primates except
   a. the sharing, cooperation, and division of labor
   b. mating and exogamy practices
   c. predation and hunting practices
   d. the maintenance of lifelong ties with sons and daughters

_____15. *Uterine* groups refers to
   a. primates who have migrated to seek mates
   b. primates who are related such as mothers, sisters, daughters, and sons who have not emigrated
   c. primates who live in certain areas
   d. all of the above

_____16. A specific difference between primates and humans is
    a. the absence of affection and support between members of local primate groups
    b. the tendency of adolescent primates to disperse when they are sexually mature
    c. the relatively small amount of information shared by primates
    d. the rarity of meat eating by primates

_____17. Which of the following conclusions can be drawn about primates and language?
    a. Chimps and gorillas have a rudimentary capacity for language.
    b. Apes, like humans, try to teach their language to other apes.
    c. Apes' linguistic ability includes productivity.
    d. All of the above can be concluded.

_____18. Linguistic displacement is not characterized as
    a. a key ingredient in language
    b. a key component of the primate call system
    c. the ability to talk about things that are not present
    d. the ability to discuss the past, present, and future and share experiences

_____19. *Cultural transmission* of a communication system through learning was evident among primates when
    a. Washoe taught gestures to other chimps at the institution
    b. Lucy and Washoe tried to teach Ameslan to their offspring
    c. Koko taught Michael, a male gorilla, Ameslan gestures
    d. all of the above

_____20. Language development in humans
    a. appeared at a certain moment in history
    b. developed quickly
    c. offered little adaptive advantage to *Homo*
    d. none of the above

CHAPTER

7

REMEMBERING COLLEGE TEXTBOOK MATERIAL THROUGH ORGANIZING

1 Determining Subject Matter

2 Locating Directly Stated Main Ideas

3 Formulating Implied Main Ideas

4 Identifying Supporting Details

5 Recognizing Authors' Writing Patterns

6 Applying Comprehension Skills to Longer Passages

7 Remembering College Textbook Material through Organizing

8 Thinking Critically as You Read

349

What I began by reading, I must finish by acting.
Henry David Thoreau (1817–1862)

INTRODUCTION

You have worked through the longer passages presented in Chapter 6, and you are now ready to learn several study strategies. *You will use every comprehension skill you have learned so far* in this book as you apply these study strategies. These strategies include *memory techniques, textbook annotation and underlining, outlining and mapping,* and *making study cards.* What you do with the material *after* you have read it determines whether or not you will remember it. Indeed, you must "finish by acting."

THE IMPORTANCE OF EFFICIENT STUDY TECHNIQUES

All of us have had the experience of completing a task, realizing that we have done it the "hard way." It can be frustrating to feel that we worked harder than we needed to; we wonder if there isn't an easier, more efficient way. The techniques in this chapter will enable you to study smarter—not just harder—and to read your textbooks more efficiently. Some of the skills in this chapter may already be familiar to you, although you may not have used them systematically in the past. Often, the difference between an effective student and the less successful one is *applying these study skills in a systematic way.*

Of course, effective students also know that they must allow plenty of time in order to master the information in their textbooks. Many beginning college students have completely unrealistic expectations about the amount of time necessary for studying their textbooks and preparing for tests. In fact, they are sometimes shocked when they discover just how much time studying requires. Also, many students mistakenly believe that they are the only ones who have to spend this much time in order to master information in a textbook. But investing this amount of time is exactly what effective, successful students are doing.

However, the *amount of study time* itself does not guarantee success. It is what you *do* during this study time that is important. Many students think that if they are sitting at their desk, casually looking at their book, they are "studying." But sitting at a desk is not the same as studying, and looking at a book is not the same as reading it.

The truth is that being an effective, responsible student demands time, effort, and dedication. If you are willing to invest the time and effort, you can become a more effective student. Semester by semester, you will become a better and better student.

The exercises in this chapter will take you longer to complete than any of the previous exercises in this book. The Practice Exercises will give you some idea of the amount of time that is required in order to *master* the information in a textbook assignment. Not every course will require you to master the information in the textbook in this way, but if it does, you will know how to master it, and you will feel confident that you *can* master the information in courses in which this is necessary.

The study skills in this chapter will not only serve you well as you study for each of your courses, but will also help you in various learning situations. There will always be situations in which you must organize, learn, and remember information.

PREPARING FOR TESTS: MEMORIZING COLLEGE TEXTBOOK MATERIAL

Many students have the mistaken belief that if they read and understand a textbook passage, they should automatically be able to remember it for the test. They feel that there is something wrong with them if they can't recall the information after merely reading it. The fact is that *reading and remembering are two separate tasks.* Successful students know that good concentration and effective study techniques are needed to understand *and remember* textbook material. Just because you read (comprehend) textbook material does not mean that you will remember it. You will have to take some additional steps to transfer the information into long-term memory.

Understanding

Understanding *what you read is the critical first step to remembering what you read.* That is why this book emphasizes comprehension as the heart of the reading process. You have learned techniques for understanding the subject matter, main idea, and supporting details, thinking critically, recognizing the author's writing pattern, and recognizing the overall subject matter and overall main idea.

Selectivity

A second essential step to remembering is *selectivity.* Too many students think that they can and must remember *everything* they read in their textbooks—and this is a source of great frustration to them. These students are mistaken, of course, since *it is generally necessary to remember only the main ideas and their important supporting details.* Throughout this book, you have practiced reading selectively, focusing on main ideas and details, and thinking about and noting how they are organized.

Organization

Organization is a third critical step to remembering what you have read. When you can see the relationship between the main idea and its supporting details, for example, or when you can detect the author's writing pattern, you have made the task of remembering easier. *Organized material is easier to memorize and to recall than material that is not organized.* In this chapter you will learn how to organize textbook material by underlining and annotating your textbook, by outlining and mapping, and by preparing study cards.

Rehearsal and Review

The fourth step to remembering complex textbook material is *rehearsal and review* of the information in order to put it into memory.

Once you have selected the most important information and organized it, *you should rehearse and review the material by reciting it (saying it aloud) and writing it down.* You should review the material several times, and you should begin to review long before the test.

As you work through this chapter, you will learn how to apply these steps as you read and study your college textbooks. These techniques for remembering go hand in hand with the effective comprehension strategies you have learned so far in this book. You can become a more successful student by using the powerful combination of understanding, selecting, organizing, and rehearsing your college textbook material.

EXPLANATION AND EXAMPLES

The skills of underlining and annotating, outlining and mapping, and making study cards will be explained and demonstrated below. As you work through this section, pay particular attention to the benefits of each technique and when each is appropriate to use; you will want to be able to select the combination that works best for you in a particular course. Although you may want to experiment with several techniques at first to see which ones work best for you, you will probably find that you will not need to use each technique every time you study. This chapter simply allows you to become familiar with each of these techniques.

To illustrate exactly what you should do as you study textbook material that you need to remember, the same passage has been used throughout this chapter. (This textbook passage is about marriage; it is from a human development textbook.) As you examine the techniques in this section, you will be "looking over the shoulder" of a successful student who is going through the steps of studying textbook material effectively.

In both the Practice Exercises and Review Test sections of this chapter, you will have the opportunity to apply these skills. As you have learned, it is important to understand the key terms in textbook passages. In this chapter, unlike the previous chapters, vocabulary has not been identified for you. Instead, *you* are expected to identify and define any key terms and any other unknown words that are essential for you to understand the passage.

Remembering Textbook Material
by Underlining and Annotating

It has been estimated that 80 percent of the material teachers select for tests comes from textbooks. For this reason, it can be extremely helpful to you to be able to underline and annotate your textbook effectively.

Underlining refers to identifying and marking the subject matter, main idea, and important definitions as you read. *Annotation* refers to words, phrases, and symbols that you write *in the margin* that help you organize and remember the important supporting details in each paragraph. When you are reading a difficult textbook, you may find it helpful to concentrate on one paragraph at a time.

The biggest mistake students make in underlining their textbooks is that they underline too much. The reason they underline too much is that they try to mark the textbook as they are reading it for the first time. Underlining should be a *selective* process. You cannot know what is important in a paragraph *until you have finished reading all of it.* For example, the main idea may not appear until the end of the paragraph. Also, you may not understand the paragraph until you have read all of it and see how the "parts" fit together. The rule is this: *Read first and then underline,* after you have identified the important ideas.

What should you underline? Underline the subject matter and the main idea, if it is directly stated in the paragraph. Often, you will not need to underline every word in the main idea sentence to capture the idea it is expressing. Also, you will want to underline important definitions. (You may find it helpful to *circle* important terms as well.) You will not want to underline supporting details in the paragraph since this generally leads to *over*marking. (As you will see, annotations can be effectively used to indicate the supporting details.)

Here is the sample passage on marriage. It has been marked for you. In the first paragraph, *marriage* (the subject matter) and the main idea have been marked.

In the second paragraph, the main idea, *(Societies differ in how they structure marriage relationships)* and the four marriage patterns (structures of marriage relationships) have been marked.

In the third and fourth paragraphs, the main ideas have been marked. Study the example, noticing that the underlining is extremely selective.

That is, *only* the most important ideas have been underlined and only the most important terms and phrases have been circled.

Marriage

A life-style that apparently exists in all societies is (marriage) — a socially sanctioned union between a woman and a man with the expectation that they will play the roles of wife and husband. After studying extensive cross-cultural data, the anthropologist George P. Murdock (1949) concluded that reproduction, sexual relations, economic cooperation, and the socialization of offspring are functions of families throughout the world. We now recognize that Murdock overstated the matter, since there are a number of societies—for instance, Israeli kibbutz communities—in which the family does not encompass all four of these activities (Spiro, 1954; Gough, 1960). What Murdock describes are commonly encountered (tendencies in family functioning) in most cultures.

Societies differ in how they structure marriage relationships. Four patterns are found: (monogamy,) one husband and one wife; (polygyny,) one husband and two or more wives; (polyandry,) two or more husbands and one wife; and (group marriage,) two or more husbands and two or more wives. Although monogamy exists in all societies, Murdock discovered that other forms may be not only allowed but preferred. Of 238 societies in his sample, only about one-fifth were strictly monogamous.

(Polygyny) has been widely practiced throughout the world. The Old Testament reports that both King David and King Solomon had several wives. In his cross-cultural sample of 238 societies, Murdock found that 193 of them permitted husbands to take several wives. In one-third of these polygynous societies, however, less than one-fifth of the married men had more than one wife. Usually it is only the rich men in a society who can afford to support more than one family.

In contrast with polygyny, (polyandry) is rare among the world's societies. And in practice, polyandry has not usually allowed freedom of mate selection for women; it has often meant simply that younger brothers have sexual access to the wife of an older brother. Thus where a father is unable to afford wives for each of his sons, he may secure a wife for only his oldest son.

Human Development
by James Vander Zanden

After underlining the main ideas and circling the important terms of your textbook paragraphs, you will want to *annotate* the paragraph. Remember that annotation refers to words, phrases, and symbols that you write in the margin to help you organize and remember important information. (Since the width of the margins varies from textbook to textbook, some students prefer to write their annotations on notebook paper because they have more room.)

You may be wondering why it is necessary to do more than underline. There are several reasons for annotating: First, writing an important term and its definition in the margin helps you focus your attention on it, helps you pay attention to the spelling, and helps you remember it. When your instructor uses these important terms in a lecture that you are taking notes on, you will recognize the terms. You will also need to know these terms for a test.

The second reason for using annotations is that they are an effective and convenient way to organize the supporting details in a concise (clear and brief) way. This also makes them easier to remember. In your annotations, you would include words or phrases that give you more information about the main idea (in other words, the supporting details). For example, in the paragraph below, you will see an annotation that lists the tendencies in family functioning.

A third reason for annotations is that you will have to formulate a main idea for a paragraph when it is not directly stated. Your formulated main idea sentence should be written in the margin beside the paragraph.

There are a few key abbreviations and symbols that you might find helpful in annotating your textbooks. These include:

def	A definition is given for an important term
?	You do not understand something and will need to study it again or get help on it
1, 2, 3, . . .	The author gives you items in a series

Now examine the passage with both underlining and annotations.

Marriage

A life-style that apparently exists in all societies is (marriage) —a socially sanctioned union between a woman and a man with the expectation that they will play the roles of wife and husband. After studying extensive cross-cultural data, the anthropologist George P. Murdock (1949) concluded that reproduction, sexual relations, economic cooperation, and the socialization of offspring are functions of families throughout the world. We now recognize that Murdock overstated the matter, since there are a number of societies—for instance, Israeli kibbutz communities—in which the family does not encompass all four of these activities (Spiro, 1954; Gough, 1960). What Murdock describes are commonly encountered (tendencies in family functioning) in most cultures.

Societies differ in how they structure marriage relationships. Four patterns are found: (monogamy,) one husband and one wife; (polygyny,) one husband and two or more wives; (polyandry,) two or more husbands and one wife; and (group marriage,) two or more husbands and two or more wives. Although monogamy exists in all societies, Murdock discovered that other forms may be not only allowed but preferred. Of 238 societies in his sample, only about one-fifth were strictly monogamous.

(Polygyny) has been widely practiced throughout the world. The Old Testament reports that both King David and King Solomon had several wives. In his cross-cultural sample of 238 societies, Murdock found that 193 of them permitted husbands

def. marriage: socially sanctioned union of a woman and a man with the expectation they will play the roles of wife and husband

4 tendencies in functions of families:
—*reproduction*
—*sexual relations*
—*economic cooperation*
—*socialization of offspring*

defs. four patterns of marriage:
—*monogamy: one husband/one wife*
—*polygyny: one husband/2+ wives*
—*polyandry: 2+ husbands/1 wife*
—*group marriage: 2+ husbands/2+ wives*

Old Testament kings with several wives:
—*Solomon*
—*David*

—*Murdock study: 193/238 societies permitted polygamy*
—*Usually only rich were polygynous*

to take several wives. In one-third of these polygynous societies, however, less than one-fifth of the married men had more than one wife. Usually it is only the rich men in a society who can afford to support more than one family.

In contrast with polygyny, (polyandry) is rare among the world's societies. And in practice, polyandry has not usually allowed freedom of mate selection for women; it has often meant simply that younger brothers have sexual access to the wife of an older brother. Thus where a father is unable to afford wives for each of his sons, he may secure a wife for only his oldest son.

—women not usually allowed to choose mates
—often simply means younger brothers have sexual access to wife of older brother

Human Development
by James Vander Zanden

Organizing Textbook Material by Outlining or Mapping

Outlining is nothing more than a formal way of organizing main ideas and the supporting details that go with them. Even though you have underlined main ideas and key terms in your textbook and have listed the supporting details in annotations in the margin, there may be times when it is helpful to outline a section or chapter in your textbook. If you choose to make an outline, you will need to decide at what point (either at the end of a section or at the end of a chapter) it would be helpful to stop and outline. One difference between an outline and textbook annotations is that outlining is done on separate paper and annotations are usually written in the textbook.

Obviously, it will not always be necessary to outline every selection or chapter. Outlining can be useful, though, whenever you are dealing with complex material. It is especially useful for material that is written in a simple listing pattern, cause-effect pattern, or comparison-contrast pattern. It is also helpful when you need to create an overview of a lengthy section or chapter by condensing it. Because outlining allows you to understand and see the organization of an entire chapter, it makes it easier to remember the material. Seeing the important information of the chapter condensed into a shorter, more manageable way often makes it easier to memorize.

OUTLINING TEXTBOOK PASSAGES

How do you prepare a study outline for a textbook paragraph or section? For a paragraph, you will need to write its main idea and then indent beneath it on separate lines the supporting details that go with it, like this:

   I. First main idea sentence
     A. Supporting detail
     B. Supporting detail
     C. Supporting detail
     D. Supporting detail

For longer passages with several paragraphs, continue your outline in this manner:

   I. First main idea sentence
     A. Supporting detail
     B. Supporting detail
     C. Supporting detail
     D. Supporting detail
  II. Second main idea sentence
     A. Supporting detail
     B. Supporting detail
 III. Third main idea sentence
     A. Supporting detail
     B. Supporting detail
     C. Supporting detail

The *overall subject matter* will be the title of the outline.

It is less important that your study outline look perfect than that your outline be clear to *you.* In other words, your outline should show you how the ideas are organized. Main ideas should stand out, and it should be clear which details go with each main idea. The roman numerals and letters are simply guides to help you see how the ideas are related.

Here is a paragraph-by-paragraph outline of the sample passage on marriage.

Marriage

I. Marriage apparently exists in all societies.

    A. Marriage is a socially sanctioned union between a woman and a man with the expectation that they will play the roles of wife and husband.

    B. Families have four common tendencies.

        1. Reproduction

        2. Sexual relations

        3. Economic cooperation

        4. Socialization of offspring

II. Although societies differ in how they structure marriage relationships, there are four common patterns.

    A. Monogamy—one husband, one wife

    B. Polygyny—one husband, two or more wives

    C. Polyandry—two or more husbands, one wife

    D. Group marriage—two or more husbands, two or more wives

III. Polygyny has been widely practiced throughout the world for many centuries.

    A. Old Testament—King David and King Solomon had several wives.

    B. Murdock's study—193 out of 238 societies permitted polygyny.

    C. Usually only rich men were polygynous.

IV. Polyandry is rare among the world's societies.

    A. In practice, women are usually not allowed to choose mates.

    B. Often it means younger brothers have sexual access to the wife of an older brother, if the father is unable to afford wives for each of his sons.

Notice how easy it is to see the author's four main points and the details that support each of them. Information that is organized in this way is more manageable; it is clear that there are four functions of marriage, four types of marriage structures, etc.

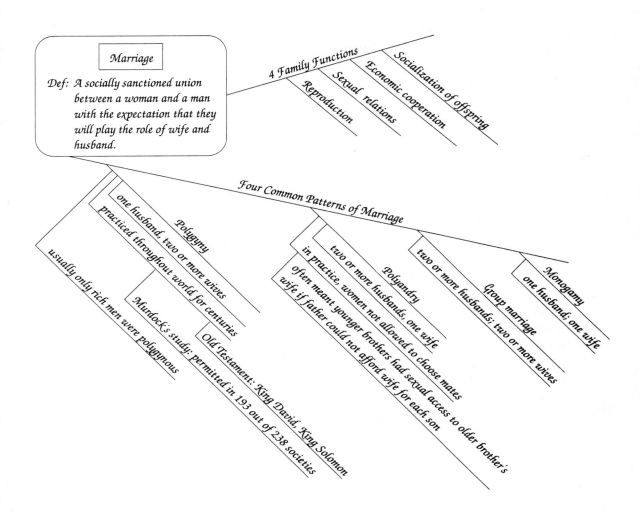

Marriage

Def: A socially sanctioned union between a woman and a man with the expectation that they will play the role of wife and husband.

4 Family Functions
- Reproduction
- Sexual relations
- Economic cooperation
- Socialization of offspring

Four Common Patterns of Marriage
- Polygyny — one husband, two or more wives
  - practiced throughout world for centuries
  - usually only rich men were polygynous
  - Murdock's study: Permitted in 193 out of 238 societies
  - Old Testament: King David, King Solomon
- Polyandry — two or more husbands, one wife
  - in practice, women not allowed to choose mates
  - often meant younger brothers had sexual access to older brother's wife if father could not afford wife for each son
- Group marriage — two or more husbands; two or more wives
- Monogamy — one husband, one wife

MAPPING TEXTBOOK PASSAGES

Mapping is an alternate way of organizing information on paper. The passage on marriage could be mapped as shown above.

Notice that the map shows the relationships among the important ideas in the passage. How can you decide when to create an outline and when to create a map? Your decision to use one or the other will depend on how comfortable you are with each of these techniques, as well as how the passage itself is written.

361

Keep in mind that mapping is an informal study technique, whereas outlining is also used in more formal or conventional situations. When you are to prepare a formal outline in a college course, do not assume that you can substitute a map.

PREPARING FOR TESTS: STUDY CARDS

Making Study Cards

When you take notes of any kind from a textbook or a lecture, your goal is to follow the author's or the speaker's train of thought. This means that you are following that person's main ideas as he or she moves from one point to the next and from one topic to the next.

Just as in outlining and mapping, making study cards allows you to organize material in a clear, concise way. Most students prefer to buy $3'' \times 5''$ or $4'' \times 6''$ index cards to make into study cards. Because these cards are available in different colors, some students find it helpful to use a different color card for each course, or to put vocabulary terms on a different color card. Because study cards are a convenient size, they are easy to carry with you so that you can review them when you have spare moments.

Each study card will usually focus on a single main idea and its supporting details. These study cards are an efficient, effective, and convenient way to review for tests. The very act of preparing the study cards (by writing out the information) helps you "rehearse" the information and put it into memory.

Using Study Cards

Using individual study cards enables you to concentrate on one small, manageable part of the material at a time. Reviewing these study cards by yourself or with a study partner is an especially powerful technique when preparing for a test. What would seem overwhelming to do all at once before a test or at the end of the semester is quite manageable when done in small parts.

Study cards can also be used to help you memorize key terms or formulas. For example, a college professor might require students to learn several math or chemistry formulas, or to memorize a set of key terms. Learning ten definitions a week is much easier than trying to learn 150 definitions for the final exam. You will need to decide when to use the study card technique; you will also have to decide the ways in which you want to use it.

Effective students often try to anticipate test questions. They find it helpful to formulate questions based on important information and terms in the passage. They then write the answers to the questions on the back of the study cards. These study cards allow you to test yourself on the material before the professor has a chance to test you on it.

These cards can help you monitor your learning by seeing what you know and what you still need to learn or review. Do not assume, though, that making the study cards is a substitute for thinking about and learning the information that is on them. If you make your study cards carefully and use them to rehearse and review information, they can be an important key to success.

Here are some study cards for the sample passage on marriage:

FRONT OF THE CARD   BACK OF THE CARD

QUESTION: 1.
What is the definition of marriage?

ANSWER:
Marriage is a socially sanctioned union between a woman and a man with the expectation that they will play the roles of wife and husband.

QUESTION: 2.
What are the four functions of families found in most societies?

ANSWER:
1. Reproduction
2. Sexual relations
3. Economic cooperation
4. Socialization of offspring

QUESTION: 3.

What are the four patterns of marriage relationships found in various societies?

ANSWER:
1. Monogamy—one husband and one wife
2. Polygyny—one husband, two or more wives
3. Polyandry—two or more husbands, one wife
4. Group marriage—two or more husbands, two or more wives

QUESTION: 4.

Discuss polygyny and its historical background.

ANSWER:

Polygyny has been widely practiced throughout the world for centuries. In the Bible, King David and King Solomon had several wives. In a recent study, Murdock found 193 out of 238 societies permitted polygyny, although usually only rich men are polygynous.

QUESTION: 5.

Discuss polyandry.

ANSWER:
Polyandry is rarely found among the world's societies. When practiced, women are not allowed to choose mates; instead younger brothers have sexual access to the wife of an older brother when the father is unable to afford wives for each of his sons.

Be sure to make study cards *as you study each chapter.* Number your study cards so that they can be easily rearranged and put back in order. You may also wish to go through them and set aside those cards with difficult questions. In this way, before the test, you can give them the special attention they will require.

REMEMBERING COLLEGE TEXTBOOK MATERIAL THROUGH ORGANIZING
Chapter Summary

MEMORY

You can improve your recall of textbook material if you use these four keys to remembering: *understanding, selecting, organizing,* and *rehearsing.* First, be sure you have comprehended the material. Second, select the author's main points and essential supporting details. Third, organize this information by underlining and annotating your textbook or by outlining or mapping the material. Fourth, rehearse and review the material to put it into memory. You can accomplish this by:

- rereading and reciting the information in your outlines and maps

- making study cards and reciting aloud from them

- writing a summary of the information on a blank sheet of paper from memory

TECHNIQUES FOR REMEMBERING THROUGH ORGANIZING

While textbook underlining and annotation are essential techniques for studying *any* textbook, you will need to decide which additional techniques are necessary in courses in which you must *master* textbook material.

Remembering Textbook Material by Underlining and Annotating

One of the first steps in organizing textbook information that is to be learned is to underline the main idea and important definitions in each paragraph. There are a few abbreviations and symbols (such as *def* and *1, 2, 3, . . .*) that may prove helpful as you underline the paragraphs of your textbook. You may want to use a question mark (?) to remind you

365

that you need additional help or information about a passage. Use marginal annotations (or take notes on notebook paper) to isolate supporting details of the passage.

Organizing Textbook Material by Outlining or Mapping

Outlining and mapping can be useful when you need an overview of a longer section of an entire chapter or when you are dealing with complex material. Outlines and maps are concise ways of showing the relationships between main ideas and their supporting details.

Preparing for Tests: Making Study Cards

Writing out questions and answers on study cards can be an effective way to prepare for tests. A study card has a question about a main idea on the front and its answer (usually the supporting details) on the back. Study cards can also be prepared for key terms by listing a vocabulary word on one side and its definition on the other.

REMEMBERING COLLEGE TEXTBOOK MATERIAL THROUGH ORGANIZING
Practice Exercises: Part A

In these practice exercises, you will be applying all the techniques presented in this chapter, unless your instructor asks you to do only certain ones. As noted earlier, you would probably not apply all these techniques (underlining, annotating, outlining, mapping, and preparing study cards) every time you study a textbook, but you should be familiar with each of the techniques.

DIRECTIONS

1. Read this human development passage carefully. For each paragraph, *underline* the subject matter and main idea. *Circle* important terms.

2. Add marginal annotations to organize the supporting details for each paragraph and to define important terms. When appropriate, use *def, ?,* or numbers *(1, 2, 3)*.

Characteristics of Piaget's Cognitive Stages

Piaget distinguished four stages in the development of cognition or intelligence. Although teaching and experience can speed up or slow down development, he believed that neither can change the basic order of the stages (Piaget, 1970).

Sensorimotor stage (birth to two years).   During this period, infants are busy discovering the relationships between sensations and motor behavior. They learn, for instance, that their hands are part of themselves, whereas a ball is not. They learn how far they need to reach in order to grasp a ball. Perhaps the main feature of this stage is the child's mastery of the *principle of object permanence*. Piaget observed that when a baby of four or five months is playing with a ball and the ball rolls out of sight behind another toy, the child does not look for it even though it remains within reach. Piaget contended that

367

this is because infants do not realize that objects have an independent existence. This explains a baby's delight in playing peek-a-boo. Around the age of eight months, the child grasps the fact of object constancy and will search for toys that disappear from view (Elkind, 1968b). Hence, during the sensorimotor stage, infants become able to distinguish between various objects and experiences and to generalize about them. This ability lays the groundwork for later intellectual and emotional development.

Preoperational stage (two to seven years).   A key part of the preoperational stage is the child's developing capacity to employ *symbols,* particularly language. Symbols enable people to deal with things in another time and place. Because of symbols, children are no longer limited to the stimuli that are immediately present here and now. Children use symbols to portray the external word internally—for instance, to talk about a ball and form a mental image of it. They do not have this capacity earlier. In the sensorimotor stage, children "know" about a ball in that they can roll it, throw it, or grasp it, but they cannot conceive of a ball as an entity apart from these activities. Now they learn the word "ball" and use it more or less appropriately to refer to round objects (Gardner, 1979).

  Egocentrism is another characteristic of the preoperational stage. By this term Piaget does not mean that the child is self-serving or selfish. Rather, children four and five years of age consider their own point of view to be the only possible one. They are not yet capable of putting themselves in another's place. They are unaware that the other person has a point of view. A five-year-old who is asked why it snows will answer by saying, "So children can play in it."

Stage of concrete operations (seven to eleven years).   This is the beginning of rational activity in children. They come to master various logical operations, including arithmetic, class and set relationships, measurement, and conceptions of hierarchical structures. Probably the aspect of this stage that has been most thoroughly investigated is the child's growing ability to "conserve" mass, weight, number, length, area, and volume. Before this stage, for instance, children do not appreciate that a ball of clay can change to a sausage shape and still remain the same in amount.

  Further, before the stage of concrete operations, children cannot understand that when water is poured out of a full glass into a wider glass that the water fills only halfway, the amount of water remains unchanged. Instead, children "concentrate" on only one aspect of reality at a time. They see that the second glass is half empty and conclude that there is less water in it. In the stage of concrete operations, children come to understand that the quantity of water remains the same. Piaget refers to this ability as the *conservation of quantity*. This ability is usually achieved between six and eight years of age.

Stage of formal operations (eleven years and older).   In stage three, the child's thought remains fixed upon the visible evidence and concrete properties of objects and events. Now children acquire a greater ability to deal with abstractions. The adolescent can engage in hypothetical reasoning based on logic. When younger children are confronted with the problem, "If coal is white, snow is _____," they insist that coal is black. Adolescents, however, respond that snow is black (Elkind, 1968a). In other words, the adolescent acquires the capacity for adult thinking.

Human Development
by James Vander Zanden

3.   Prepare a map or an outline of this selection. If you create an outline, be sure to include the author's main ideas (written as sentences), and beneath each one, indent its supporting details. Remember to include a title.

_____

_____

_____

_____

_____

_____

_____

_____

_____

_____

_____

_____

_____
_____
_____
_____
_____
_____
_____
_____
_____
_____
_____
_____
_____
_____
_____
_____

4. Prepare study cards by writing a possible test question on the front of a card
    and its answer on the back. You may also wish to prepare vocabulary study
    cards by writing an unfamiliar term on the front of a card and its definition
    on the back.

FRONT   BACK

QUESTION: 1.	ANSWER:

QUESTION: 2.

ANSWER:

QUESTION: 3.

ANSWER:

QUESTION: 4.

ANSWER:

QUESTION: 5.

ANSWER:

QUESTION: 6.

ANSWER:

QUESTION: 7.

ANSWER:

QUESTION: 8.

ANSWER:

REMEMBERING COLLEGE TEXTBOOK MATERIAL THROUGH ORGANIZING
Answer Key for Practice Exercises: Part A

Compare your responses to the practice exercises on pages 367–374 with the acceptable answers given below.

1.–2.   Here is the passage underlined and annotated.

Characteristics of Piaget's Cognitive Stages

(Piaget) distinguished four stages in the development of cognition or intelligence. Although teaching and experience can speed up or slow down development, he believed that neither can change the basic order of the stages (Piaget, 1970).

(*1*) (Sensorimotor stage) (birth to two years).   During this period, infants are busy discovering the relationships between sensations and motor behavior. They learn, for instance, that their hands are part of themselves, whereas a ball is not. They learn how far they need to reach in order to grasp a ball. Perhaps the main feature of this stage is the child's mastery of the (principle of object permanence.) Piaget observed that when a baby of four or five months is playing with a ball and the ball rolls out of sight behind another toy, the child does not look for it even though it remains within reach. Piaget contended that this is because infants do not realize that objects have an independent existence. This explains a baby's delight in playing

—*Teaching/experience can speed up or slow down development of cognition or intelligence.*

—*Order of stages cannot be changed.*

—*They learn what is part of their body and what is not.*

def. principle of object permanence: A baby learns that an object still exists even when it is out of sight.

peek-a-boo. Around the age of eight months, the child grasps the fact of object constancy and will search for toys that disappear from view (Elkind, 1968b). Hence, during the sensorimotor stage, infants become able to distinguish between various objects and experiences and to generalize about them. This ability lays the groundwork for later intellectual and emotional development.

(2) **Preoperational stage** (two to seven years). A key part of the preoperational stage is the child's developing capacity to employ symbols, particularly language. Symbols enable people to deal with things in another time and place. Because of symbols, children are no longer limited to the stimuli that are immediately present here and now. Children use symbols to portray the external world internally—for instance, to talk about a ball and form a mental image of it. They do not have this capacity earlier. In the sensorimotor stage, children "know" about a ball in that they can roll it, throw it, or grasp it, but they cannot conceive of a ball as an entity apart from these activities. Now they learn the word "ball" and use it more or less appropriately to refer to round objects (Gardner, 1979).

Egocentrism is another characteristic of the preoperational stage. By this term Piaget does not mean that the child is self-serving or selfish. Rather, children four and five years of age consider their own point of view to be the only possible one. They are not yet capable of putting themselves in another's place. They are unaware that the other person has a point of view. A five-year-old who is asked why it

—Infants learn to distinguish between various objects and experiences and to generalize about them.

—By using symbols, particularly language, they're no longer limited to stimuli that are present.

def. egocentrism: Children age 4-5 see their own point of view as the only possible one.

snows will answer by saying, "So children can play in it."

(3) **Stage of concrete operations** (seven to eleven years).   This is the beginning of rational activity in children. They come to master various logical operations, including arithmetic, class and set relationships, measurement, and conceptions of hierarchical structures. Probably the aspect of this stage that has been most thoroughly investigated is the child's growing ability to "conserve" mass, weight, number, length, area, and volume. Before this stage, for instance, children do not appreciate that a ball of clay can change to a sausage shape and still remain the same in amount.

Further, before the stage of concrete operations, children cannot understand that when water is poured out of a full glass into a wider glass that the water fills only halfway, the amount of water remains unchanged. Instead, children "concentrate" on only one aspect of reality at a time. They see that the second glass is half empty and conclude that there is less water in it. In the stage of concrete operations, children come to understand that the quantity of water remains the same. Piaget refers to this ability as the *conservation of quantity.* This ability is usually achieved between six and eight years of age.

(4) **Stage of formal operations** (eleven years and older).   In stage three, the child's thought remained fixed upon the visible evidence and concrete properties of objects and events. Now children acquire a greater ability to deal with abstractions. The adolescent can engage in hypothetical reasoning based on logic. When younger

def. conservation of quantity: Between age 6–8, children learn that the quantity doesn't change just because the shape of the container does.

—Adolescents can engage in hypothetical reasoning based on logic and adult thinking.

children are confronted with the problem, "If coal is white, snow is _____," they insist that coal is black. Adolescents, however, respond that snow is black (Elkind, 1968a). In other words, the adolescent acquires the capacity for adult thinking.

Human Development
by James Vander Zanden

3. Here is an outline of this selection. Notice the author's five main ideas (written as sentences).

Characteristics of Piaget's Cognitive Steps

I. Piaget distinguished four stages in the development of cognition (intelligence).

A. Teaching and experience can speed up or slow down development.

B. The order of stages cannot be changed.

II. In the sensorimotor stage (birth to two years), infants discover the relationships between sensations and motor behavior.

A. They learn what is part of their body and what is not.

B. At about 8 months, a baby learns that an object still exists even when out of sight (principle of object permanence).

C. Infants learn to distinguish between various objects and experiences and to generalize about them.

III. In the preoperational stage (two to seven years), the child develops the capacity to employ symbols, particularly language.

A. Being able to use symbols means a child is no longer limited only to the stimuli that are present.

B. Egocentrism refers to children of ages four to five seeing their point of view as the only possible one.

IV. In the concrete operations stage, children (ages seven to eleven) master various logical operations, including arithmetic, class and set relationships, measurement, and conceptions of hierarchical structures.

A. Conservation of quantity refers to the realization of children (ages six to eight) that the quantity of something does not change just because its shape changes.

Piaget's Four Stages in the Development of Cognition (Intelligence)

Can be speeded up or slowed down (by experience and learning), but the order cannot be changed

Formal Operations Stage (11 yrs and older)

adolescents learn to engage in hypothetical reasoning based on logic

acquire the capacity for adult thinking

acquire ability to deal with abstractions

Concrete Operations Stage (7–11 yrs)

learn that quantity does not change because shape does (conservation of quantity)

between ages of 6–8 yrs.

master various logical operations

Preoperational Stage (2–7 yrs)

see their point of view as only possible one (egocentrism)

develop the ability to employ symbols, especially language

not limited to stimuli that are present

Sensorimotor Stage (birth–2 years)

can distinguish between various objects and experiences and generalize about them

discover objects continue to exist even when out of sight (principle of object permanence)

discover relationships between sensations and motor behavior

379

V. In the formal operations stage (ages eleven and older) children acquire
   more ability to deal with abstractions.

   A. Adolescents can engage in hypothetical reasoning based on logic.

   B. They acquire the capacity for adult thinking.

A study map of this selection appears on page 379.

4. On the following pages are study cards that represent some of the major
    points of this selection.

FRONT   BACK

QUESTION: 1.	ANSWER:
What are the four stages Piaget proposed for the development of cognition (intelligence)?	1. Sensorimotor stage (birth to 2 yrs.) 2. Preoperational stage (2–7 yrs.) 3. Concrete operations stage (7–11 yrs.) 4. Formal operations stage (11–older)

QUESTION: 2.	ANSWER:
Can the basic order of the cognitive stages be changed?	No. Teaching and experience can speed up or slow down development, but the basic order of development will not be changed.

QUESTION: 3.

What occurs during the sensorimotor stage (birth–2 yrs.)?

ANSWER:

During the sensorimotor stage (birth–2 yrs.), infants discover the relationships between sensations and motor behavior (e.g., babies discover their hands).

QUESTION: 4.

What is the principle of object permanence?

ANSWER:

Objects continue to exist even when they are out of sight (e.g., a baby does not look for a ball that has rolled out of sight).

QUESTION: 5.

What critical development occurs during the sensorimotor stage?

ANSWER:

Infants become able to distinguish between various objects and experiences and to generalize about them.

QUESTION: 6.

What occurs during the preoperational stage (2–7 yrs.)?

ANSWER:

During the preoperational stage (2–7 yrs.), a child develops a capacity to employ symbols, particularly language.

QUESTION: 7.

What do we mean by egocentrism?

ANSWER:

Egocentrism (a characteristic of the preoperational stage) means that a child of four or five considers his or her own point of view to be the only one possible.

QUESTION: 8.

What occurs during the concrete operational stage (7–11 yrs.)?

ANSWER:

During the concrete operational stage (7–11 yrs.) children begin to master logical operations:
    Arithmetic
    Class/set relationships
    Measurements
    Concept of hierarchy

QUESTION: 9.

What do we mean by the term "conservation of quantity"?

ANSWER:

Between the ages 6–8, children learn that the quantity of something doesn't change just because its shape does.
Examples:
    —clay
    —water

QUESTION: 10.

What occurs during the formal operations stage (11–older)?

ANSWER:

During the formal operations stage (11–older), children acquire a greater ability to deal with abstraction, and acquire the capacity for adult thinking.

REMEMBERING COLLEGE TEXTBOOK MATERIAL THROUGH ORGANIZING
Practice Exercises: Part B

DIRECTIONS

1. Read this humanities textbook passage carefully. For each paragraph, *underline* the subject matter and main idea. *Circle* important terms.

2. Add marginal annotations to organize the supporting details for each paragraph and to define important terms. When appropriate, use *def, ?,* or numbers *(1, 2, 3).*

The French Revolution

Causes of the Revolution

The most populous country in Europe and among the most prosperous, France in the last half of the eighteenth century was a troubled society. All phases of French life were dominated by an outmoded social structure that endured primarily because it was legally defined and protected. All Frenchmen except the royal family were divided into three classes: the clergy, the nobility, and the third estate, by far the largest of the three, comprising the peasants, the artisans of the towns, and the middle class or bourgeois. Of France's 24,000,000 people, only about 2 percent belonged to the clergy and nobility. Yet in a society where land remained the greatest form of wealth, the other 98 percent owned only 60 percent of the landed property. This was the social group from which the revolution came.

But there was a greater source of discontent among the third estate. The clergy and nobility paid almost no taxes. Moreover, while giving little or nothing to support it, the nobility enjoyed all the highest offices in the government; they also constituted the officer corps of the army. As for the clergy, this class had the right to levy a tax, for its maintenance, on all agricultural goods produced by the third estate.

What made the situation volatile was that for most of the eighteenth century the economy was expanding. Bankers, merchants, and other members of the middle class had accumulated great wealth, and many of the peasants were prosperous. Traditionally there had been various avenues by which successful members of the third estate could work their way into the nobility, but in the course of the eighteenth century these avenues had gradually been shut off by an aristocracy resolved not to dilute its membership further. The upper bourgeois, therefore, felt excluded from the social and financial privileges to which their success entitled them.

Economic prosperity also entailed rising prices and higher living costs. The nobility and clergy, barred by law from entering commerce or industry to reap the profits of the boom, increasingly came to insist on their economic rights over the third estate. Indeed, this was the heyday of lawyers employed by the upper classes to dredge up old, long-neglected rights over the peasantry.

Moreover, although the bourgeois and the upper peasantry were profiting throughout most of the eighteenth century, the lower classes, at least in the last half of the century, saw their wages rise more slowly than prices and their standard of living fall.

The most immediate cause of the revolution, which began in the summer of 1789, was the government's financial crisis. Because some of the wealthiest elements in the country were exempt from taxation, the state could not balance its budget. An important element in the French public debt was the expense incurred by helping the Americans in their revolt against England. For years the enlightened advisers of the French king had endeavored to abolish the tax privileges of the clergy and the nobility, but these two orders had solidly resisted the effort. The king could proclaim the necessary laws, but the courts, completely controlled by the nobility, would never enforce them. Finally, in 1788, the royal government simply abolished the old court system and created a new one.

The result was an aristocratic revolt: the army officers and the king's officials at Paris and in the provinces refused to serve, and the whole state was brought to a halt. Unable to persevere in the attempt at reform, the king (Louis XVI) acceded to noble demands that, for the first time since 1614, a National Assembly be called to settle the nation's problems. The nobility clearly intended to gain a larger control over the king's government through an assembly that, by tradition, gave them and the clergy (dominated by the aristocracy) two votes against one for the third estate.

The Humanities
by M. A. Witt et al.

3. Prepare a map or an outline of this selection. If you create an outline, be
    sure to include the authors' main ideas (written as sentences), and beneath
    each one, indent its supporting details. Remember to include a title.

_____

_____

_____

_____

_____

_____

_____

_____

_____

_____

_____

_____

_____

_____

_____

_____

_____

_____

_____

_____

_____

_____

_____

_____

_____

4. Prepare study cards by writing a possible test question on the front of a card and its answer on the back. You may also wish to prepare vocabulary study cards by writing an unfamiliar term on the front of a card and its definition on the back.

FRONT   BACK

QUESTION: 1.	ANSWER:

QUESTION: 2.	ANSWER:

QUESTION: 3.

ANSWER:

QUESTION: 4.

ANSWER:

QUESTION: 5.

ANSWER:

QUESTION: 6.

ANSWER:

QUESTION: 7.

ANSWER:

QUESTION: 8.

ANSWER:

QUESTION: 9.

ANSWER:

QUESTION: 10.

ANSWER:

QUESTION: 11.

ANSWER:

QUESTION: 12.

ANSWER:

REMEMBERING COLLEGE TEXTBOOK MATERIAL THROUGH ORGANIZING
Answer Key for Practice Exercises: Part B

1.–2. Here is the passage from pages 385–386 underlined and annotated.

The French Revolution

Causes of the Revolution

The most populous country in Europe and among the most prosperous, France in the last half of the eighteenth century was a troubled society. [1]All phases of French life were dominated by an outmoded social structure that endured primarily because it was legally defined and protected. All Frenchmen except the royal family were divided into three classes: the [a] clergy, the [b] nobility, and the [c] third estate, by far the largest of the three, comprising the peasants, the artisans of the towns, and the middle class or bourgeois. Of France's 24,000,000 people, only about 2 percent belonged to the clergy and nobility. Yet in a society where land remained the greatest form of wealth, the other 98 percent owned only 60 percent of the landed property. This was the social group from which the revolution came.

But there was a greater source of discontent among the third estate. The [2]clergy and nobility paid almost no taxes. Moreover, while giving little or nothing to support it, the nobility enjoyed all the highest offices in the government; they

Although the most populous European country and very prosperous, France in last half of 18th century was troubled.

(1) All phases of life dominated by outmoded social structure. French society divided into

(a) Clergy ⎫ this 2% owned
(b) Nobility ⎭ 40% of the land

def. (c) Third estate—largest—98% peasants/artisans/middle class— This group was the source of the revolution

(2) Clergy/nobility paid almost no taxes, and yet nobility:
—Held all highest government offices
—Comprised officer corps
   the clergy:
—Could levy tax on agricultural goods produced by third estate

395

also constituted the officer corps of the army. As for the clergy, this class had the right to levy a tax, for its maintenance, on all agricultural goods produced by the third estate.

What made the situation volatile was that for most of the eighteenth century [3]the economy was expanding. Bankers, merchants, and other members of the middle class had accumulated great wealth, and many of the peasants were prosperous. Traditionally there had been various avenues by which successful members of the third estate could work their way into the nobility, but in the course of the eighteenth century these avenues had gradually been shut off by an aristocracy resolved not to dilute its membership further. The upper bourgeois, therefore, felt excluded from the social and financial privileges to which their success entitled them.

Economic prosperity also entailed [4]rising prices and higher living costs. The nobility and clergy, barred by law from entering commerce or industry to reap the profits of the boom, increasingly came to insist on their economic rights over the third estate. Indeed, this was the heyday of lawyers employed by the upper classes to dredge up old, long-neglected rights over the peasantry. Moreover, although the bourgeois and the upper peasantry were profiting throughout most of the eighteenth century, the lower classes, at least in the last half of the century, saw their wages rise more slowly than prices and their standard of living fall.

The most immediate cause of the revolution, which began in the summer of 1789, [5]was the government's financial crisis. Because some of the wealthiest

(3) Economy was expanding. Middle class had wealth, but was excluded from social and financial privileges.

(4) Prices and cost of living were rising; therefore
   —Nobility and clergy were more insistent on their money rights over the third estate.
   —Lower classes saw their wages rise more slowly and their standard of living fall.

(5) Government's financial crisis of unbalanced budget
   —wealthiest went untaxed
   —helping finance Amer. Rev. added to debt

elements in the country were exempt from taxation, the state could not balance its budget. An important element in the French public debt was the expense incurred by helping the Americans in their revolt against England. For years the enlightened advisers of the French king had endeavored to abolish the tax privileges of the clergy and the nobility, but these two orders had solidly resisted the effort. The king could proclaim the necessary laws, but the courts, completely controlled by the nobility, would never enforce them. Finally, in 1788, the royal government simply abolished the old court system and created a new one.

King could make laws, but courts, controlled by nobility, would not enforce them.

Govt finally abolished old court system and created new one.

(6)The result was an aristocratic revolt: the army officers and the king's officials at Paris and in the provinces refused to serve, and the whole state was brought to a halt. Unable to persevere in the attempt at reform, the king (Louis XVI) acceded to noble demands that, for the first time since 1614, a National Assembly be called to settle the nation's problems. The nobility clearly intended to gain a larger control over the king's government through an assembly that, by tradition, gave them and the clergy (dominated by the aristocracy) two votes against one for the third estate.

(6) Aristocratic revolt
Army officers and king's officials refused to serve and brought the state to a halt.
Louis XVI acceded to nobles' demands for a Nat'l Assembly which the two upper classes (aristocracy) controlled. (The third estate revolted against the aristocracy's control of the National Assembly.)

The Humanities

3. Here is an outline of this selection written in complete sentences. Notice the authors' six main ideas.

Causes of the French Revolution

I. Although it was a very populous and prosperous country, France in the last half of the eighteenth century was dominated by an outmoded social structure of three classes.

    A. The clergy and the nobility, the two upper classes, comprised 2 percent of the population but owned 40 percent of the land.

    B. The third estate (peasants, artisans, middle class) comprised 98 percent of the population but owned only 60 percent of the land, and it was the source of the revolution.

II. The clergy and nobility paid almost no taxes.

    A. The nobility, however, held all the highest government offices and comprised the army officer corps.

    B. The clergy could levy taxes on agricultural goods produced by the third estate.

III. The French economy was expanding.

    A. Members of the middle class had accumulated wealth, yet were denied the social and financial privileges their success entitled them to.

IV. Prices and living costs were rising.

    A. The nobility and clergy increasingly insisted on their economic rights over the third estate.

    B. The lower classes saw their wages rise more slowly and their standard of living fall.

V. The most immediate cause of the revolution was the government's financial crisis (its unbalanced budget).

    A. The wealthiest went untaxed.

    B. The government incurred debt from helping America finance its revolt against England.

    C. Although the king could proclaim the needed tax laws, the courts, which were controlled by the nobility, did not enforce them, and eventually the government abolished the old court system and created a new one.

VI. The aristocracy revolted and brought the state to a halt.

    A. Army officers and the king's officials refused to serve.

    B. King Louis XVI acceded to the nobles' demands to call a National Assembly to settle the nation's problems.

    C. The upper classes controlled the National Assembly.

A study map of this selection appears on page 399.

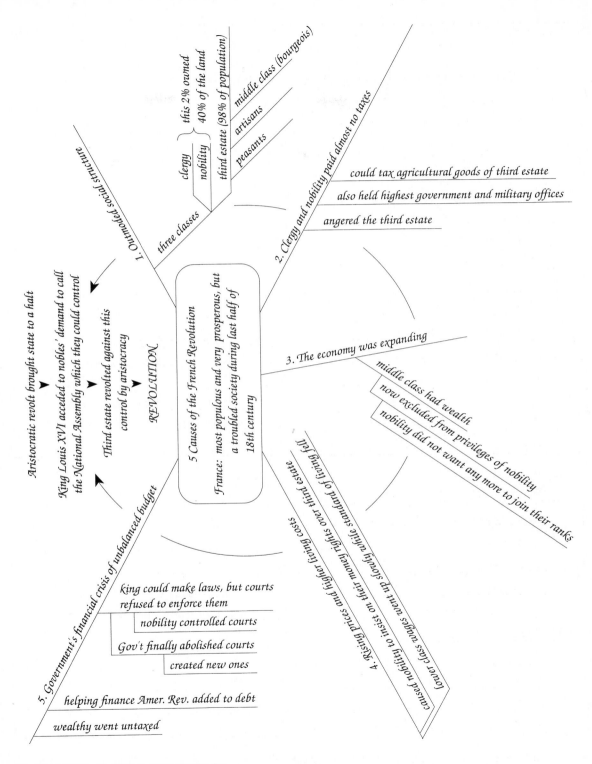

5 Causes of the French Revolution

France: most populous and very prosperous, but a troubled society during last half of 18th century

1. Outmoded social structure

three classes
- clergy
- nobility } this 2% owned 40% of the land
- third estate (98% of population)
  - middle class (bourgeois)
  - artisans
  - peasants

2. Clergy and nobility paid almost no taxes
- could tax agricultural goods of third estate
- also held highest government and military offices
- angered the third estate

3. The economy was expanding
- middle class had wealth
- now excluded from privileges of nobility
- nobility did not want any more to join their ranks

4. Rising prices and higher living costs
- rising prices and higher living costs over third estate
- caused nobility to insist on their money rights while standard of living fell
- (lower class wages went up slowly

5. Government's financial crisis of unbalanced budget
- king could make laws, but courts refused to enforce them
  - nobility controlled courts
  - Gov't finally abolished courts
    - created new ones
- helping finance Amer. Rev. added to debt
- wealthy went untaxed

REVOLUTION
- Aristocratic revolt brought state to a halt
- King Louis XVI acceded to nobles' demand to call the National Assembly which they could control
- Third estate revolted against this control by aristocracy

4.   Here are study cards that represent the major points of this selection.

FRONT

BACK

QUESTION: 1.

Describe France in the last half
of the 18th century before the
French Revolution.

ANSWER:

1.   Most populous country in
     Europe
2.   Among the most
     prosperous countries in
     Europe
3.   Troubled because of its
     outmoded social structure

QUESTION: 2.

List the three classes of
French society.

ANSWER:

1.   The clergy
2.   The nobility
3.   The third estate

QUESTION: 3.

What is meant by the term "third estate"?

ANSWER:

The third estate was one of the classes of French society. It was the largest class consisting of the peasants, the artisans, and the bourgeois (middle class).

QUESTION: 4.

Discuss the discontent among the third estate prior to the French Revolution.

ANSWER:

1. Imbalance of land ownership in favor of clergy and nobility.
2. Inequity of taxation (the clergy and nobility paid almost no taxes).
3. The clergy could levy taxes to support itself.
4. Nobility held all the highest offices.
5. Even wealth would not allow the third estate to join the ranks of nobility.

QUESTION: 5.

Discuss problems related to economic prosperity prior to the French Revolution.

ANSWER:

1. The clergy and nobility wanted part of the profits made by the third estate.
2. The lower class of peasants suffered from rising costs of living and poor wages.

QUESTION: 6.

What was the most immediate
cause of the French
Revolution?

ANSWER:

The most immediate cause was
the state's inability to balance
the budget.

QUESTION: 7.

Who was the French king during
the turmoil that led to the
revolution?

ANSWER:

Louis XVI

QUESTION: 8.

Define the terms "bourgeois"
and "artisan."

ANSWER:

bourgeois: the French middle
class
artisan: hand craftsman

REMEMBERING COLLEGE TEXTBOOK MATERIAL THROUGH ORGANIZING
Review Test

EXERCISE I

Directions

1. Read this selection from an art appreciation textbook carefully. For each paragraph, *underline* the subject matter and main idea. *Circle* important terms.

2. Add marginal annotations to organize the supporting details for each paragraph and to define important terms. When appropriate, use *def, ?,* or numbers *(1, 2, 3).*

Style

There are styles of music, styles of dress, styles of interior design, even styles of speaking and walking. When an automobile manufacturer changes the way its cars look from year to year, we speak of the "new style." If a person we know always wears jeans and cowboy boots, or always wears long flowing dresses and flowered prints, we identify that person with his or her particular style of dress. Furthermore, we may say of someone, "She really has style!" Or we might describe the décor of a particular home as "stylish." In the latter two cases, we mean the person or place shows a *desirable* style, one we admire, because everybody and everything has *some* style or other. But what exactly *is* style?

Above all, *style* is a characteristic or group of characteristics that we can identify as constant, recurring, or coherent. For instance, suppose you have a friend who has very long hair and always wears it in braids; then your friend gets a short haircut. You would call this a sudden change of style. Or perhaps you know a family whose home is entirely decorated with antiques, except for one very modern chair and table in the living room. You would recognize a mix of styles— not necessarily bad, but obvious.

403

In the visual arts, just as in any other area of life, style indicates a series of choices an artist has made. *Artistic style* is the sum of constant, recurring, or coherent traits identified with a certain individual or group. In painting, for example, a particular style could be composed of many elements—the materials used, the type of brush strokes, the colors, the way forms are handled, the choice of subject matter, the degree of resemblance to the natural world (representational *vs.* abstract style), and so on.

Style may be associated with a whole artistic culture (the Song dynasty style in China); with a particular time and place (the early Renaissance style in Rome); with a group of artists whose work shows similar characteristics (the Abstract Expressionist style); with one artist (Van Gogh's style); or with one artist at a certain time (Picasso's Blue Period style). In all these instances there are common elements—constant, recurring, coherent—that we can learn to recognize. Once you become familiar with Van Gogh's mature style, with its licking, flamelike brush strokes and vivid color, you will probably be able to identify other paintings by Van Gogh, even if you have never seen them before. Some artists develop a style and stick to it; others work in several styles, simultaneously or sequentially.

One way to think of style is to consider it an artist's personal "handwriting." You know that if you give ten people identical pieces of paper and identical pens and tell them to write the same sentence, you'll get ten very different results, because no two people have the same handwriting. Penmanship styles are interesting. Each is absolutely unique, yet there are characteristics we can identify, even if we don't know the person who did the writing. If you study handwriting at all, a given sample should be able to tell you if the writer is male or female, old or young, American or European, and so forth. Much the same is true of artistic styles. Every one is individual, but we may find similarities among artists of a particular time, place, or group.

Living with Art
by Rita Gilbert and William McCarter

3. Prepare a map or an outline of this selection. If you create an outline, be sure to include the authors' main ideas (written as sentences), and beneath each one, indent its supporting details. Remember to include a title.

_____
_____
_____
_____
_____
_____
_____
_____
_____
_____
_____
_____
_____
_____
_____

4. Prepare study cards by writing a possible test question on the front of a card and its answer on the back. You may also wish to prepare vocabulary study cards by writing an unfamiliar term on the front of a card and its definition on the back.

FRONT   BACK

QUESTION: 1.	ANSWER:

QUESTION: 2.

ANSWER:

QUESTION: 3.

ANSWER:

QUESTION: 4.

ANSWER:

QUESTION: 5.

ANSWER:

QUESTION: 6.

ANSWER:

QUESTION: 7.

ANSWER:

QUESTION: 8.

ANSWER:

QUESTION: 9.

ANSWER:

QUESTION: 10.

ANSWER:

EXERCISE II

Directions

1. Read the passage from a sociology textbook carefully. For each paragraph, *underline* the subject matter and main idea. *Circle* important terms.

2. Now add marginal annotations to organize the supporting details for each paragraph and to define important terms. When appropriate, use *def, ?,* or numbers *(1, 2, 3).*

Erik H. Erikson: The Eight Ages of Man

In the late 1940s and early 1950s, Erik H. Erikson, one of Freud's greatest students, began to expand both the scope and content of his teacher's theory of human development. One of Erikson's most significant contributions to the study of socialization is his vivid description of the problems of adolescence and young adulthood. It is he who gave us the familiar term *identity crisis.* But this concept is only a small part of Erikson's comprehensive theory of human development, which brings Cooley, Mead, and Freud together, integrating the physiological, psychological, and social elements of the process. Erikson does this by focusing on the ego in its role as mediator between the individual and society.

Erikson's central concern is with the feelings people develop toward themselves and the world around them. He describes socialization as a lifelong process, beginning at birth and continuing into old age. In *Childhood and Society* (1950) Erikson describes eight stages of human development. Each stage constitutes a crisis, brought on by physiological changes and new social environments, to which the growing person must adapt. Erikson describes positive and negative responses to these crises, but emphasizes that elements of both exist in most people. When things go well, the maturing ego works out solutions to these crises that build up to a stable identity.

Trust vs. Mistrust (Infancy)

During their first year children are totally dependent on adults, primarily their mothers. Even their own sensations of comfort and discomfort are unfamiliar, unpredictable. Children whose mothers respond warmly and consistently to their needs begin to develop feelings of *basic trust.* Comfort becomes what Erikson calls an inner certainty, and children come to believe that the world is reliable. If mothers are patient when infants bite while nursing or grasp so hard that it hurts, allowing children to develop control at their own pace, they also begin to trust themselves. Infants whose mothers are undependable and rejecting find the world a fearful place; there is no one they can count on to ease their discomforts. If mothers are erratic about caring for them, children may be afraid to let mother out of their sight, fearing that she might never return. The quality of maternal care in this first year shapes infants' basic orientation toward themselves and other people.

Autonomy vs. Shame and Doubt (Early Childhood)

For the first two years of life children spend endless hours trying to make their bodies do what they want them to do. By the age of three, their muscles and nerves have developed to the point where they are capable of grasping, reaching, crawling, controlling their bowels, and so on—delightful accomplishments from their point of view. However, while these accomplishments bring new autonomy, they raise doubts as well. A child crawls around the corner to another room, then realizes he is alone and cries out. Besides the doubts of going it alone, there is the shame of losing self-control, as when a toilet-trained toddler wets the neighbor's rug.

Much depends on children's parents. If adults allow the young ones to explore and develop at their own pace, they gain confidence in their ability to govern themselves—what Erikson calls *autonomy*. On the other hand, if children interpret constant supervision as a sign that they cannot take care of themselves, they may begin to overdiscipline themselves to avoid punishment or ridicule and shame (the feeling of being exposed). Neglected children, whose parents allow them to get into situations where they are hurt, may experience similar feelings of self-doubt. Erikson suggests that to develop self-confidence, children should be encouraged to "stand on their own feet," but they must also be protected from experiences of shame and doubt.

Initiative vs. Guilt (The Play Stage)

At four or five, children begin to extend their mastery over their own bodies to the world around them (if, that is, they have developed some sense of autonomy). They enjoy attacking and conquering the material world; in their play and fantasies they begin to act out adult roles, transforming (and hence mastering) the world in their imaginations. Most important, in Erikson's view, children begin to *initiate* purposeful activities on their own. Earlier, their play consisted mostly of exploring and imitating others.

Children's feelings of self-worth grow if their parents and others who are important to them respect their efforts. Ridicule and disinterest make children wonder about the values of their actions and goals; they may punish themselves for their failures. There is a danger, then, of children developing more or less permanent *guilt* feelings about any self-initiated activities at this age. Ideally, children begin to turn from their attachments to their parents to the world beyond—without losing the exuberance of early childhood.

Industry vs. Inferiority (School Age)

The social setting now shifts from home to school and the larger community. At six, if not earlier, children enter the impersonal world of unrelated children and adults, of rules and organized games. As they begin to acquire the skills and technology of their society, they "learn to win recognition by producing things." Ideally, they come to enjoy the exercise of mental and physical skills, and take pride in *industry*. However, if they are not emotionally prepared for school, if they fail to do well in school, if they find that their race or family background or looks or even the way they dress automatically disqualifies them in other people's eyes, the experience will be negative. Some children develop a deep sense of *inferiority* in this stage, a fear of being required to perform and failing. Some overcommit themselves to the sphere of work, trying to compensate for feelings of inadequacy.

Identity vs. Role Confusion (Adolescence)

With childhood drawing to a close and adulthood looming ahead, adolescents become preoccupied with the question of *identity*. It is not that they don't know who they are before this time, but rather that they have been changing and shaping themselves in many different ways. The time has come to draw together all that has made up their lives, to give a more permanent shape to who they are and where they are going as adults. What Erikson means by *identity* is being able to derive a sense of continuity about one's past, present, and future, coordinating feelings about the self with the image reflected in the social looking-glass. There is also the danger, however, that a person will not be able to integrate his or her various roles into a clear identity. The self, then, remains diffuse.

Intimacy vs. Isolation (Young Adulthood)

Erikson sees young adulthood, like each of the stages before it, as a turning point. Think how many young people fall madly in love at twenty, only to find that after a few months they feel stifled by so much closeness. The other person seems to be taking over their life, swallowing them up. They can't find that comfortable sense of self anymore, someone sees through their acts—and they pull back. This is true in close friendships as well as in love affairs. As Erikson suggests, *intimacy* requires vulnerability; caring deeply for another person always involves some risk—the risk of being hurt, of losing that person. Without a clear sense of identity, without an ability to trust, it may be difficult to take these risks. Young people who are unsure of themselves, who fear commitment, find intimate relationships anxious and stormy—however much they desire love and companionship. Isolation—keeping to oneself or moving from one intense but short-lived relationship to another—may feel safer, but it limits personal and social growth.

Generativity vs. Stagnation (Young Adulthood and Middle Age)

In young adulthood, there is still time for exploring and dreaming; the future is still an open book. In middle age, however, realistic alternatives seem limited; a way of life has been chosen. Erikson identifies the "need to be needed" as the central theme of adulthood. Perhaps nothing satisfies this need so much as an infant, whose helplessness seems to cry out for intimacy and giving. This is one of the points where the needs and desires of one stage mesh with those of another. An infant satisfies an adult's desire to give, while an adult satisfies the infant's needs for warmth and security. This is why Erikson speaks of a *life cycle*.

Generativity is the feeling that one is making a significant contribution, that one is guiding new generations—either directly, as a parent, or indirectly, by working to better society. The better people feel about themselves, the closer they are to other people, the more likely they are to feel productive or industrious, to work creatively, to take on social commitments. For some people, however, middle age is painful. Childish self-absorption and "early invalidism, physical or psychological" are signs that a person has not found generativity. It is almost as if they were reliving unresolved crises of earlier stages. Yet as with all stages, Erikson points out that elements of both resolutions—generativity and stagnation—are found in even the healthiest person.

Integrity vs. Despair (Old Age)

The last stage in Erikson's "Eight Ages of Man" is one of reflection and evaluation. In a very real way, coming to terms with death means coming to terms with life—with where one has been, with what one has done with one's time on earth. By *integrity* Erikson means that a person sees meaning in both the good and bad, the joys and pain of his or her life; that he or she has arrived at a higher level of self-acceptance. The despair that comes from looking back and seeing one's life as a series of missed opportunities and realizing that it is too late to start over is difficult for a younger person to imagine.

In describing the "Eight Ages of Man," Erikson focuses on the potential for negative as well as positive developments in each stage, and how the growing person's adjustment in one stage affects his orientation in the next. Thus, gaining a sense of initiative aids a person in being industrious, though the sequence is not rigid. Erikson believes that the concerns of every stage are present throughout a person's life though each pair has its time of prominence. This means that a person can overcome an early sense of shame or mistrust by working at it later, or that a person can lose an early strength like initiative through great strain later on. No crisis is completely resolved once and for all; the most the growing person can do is to achieve a positive balance of healthy and pathological tendencies. Moreover, no one can maintain feelings of trust, autonomy, or initiative in isolation. Positive feelings toward the self and the world must be verified and reinforced in each stage.

Sociology
by Donald Light, Jr., and Suzanne Keller

3. Prepare a map or an outline of this selection. If you create an outline, be sure to include the authors' main ideas (written as sentences), and beneath each one, indent its supporting details. Remember to include a title.

_____

_____

_____

_____

4. Prepare study cards by writing a possible test question on the front of a card and its answer on the back. You may also wish to prepare vocabulary study cards by writing an unfamiliar term on the front of the card and its definition on the back.

FRONT   BACK

QUESTION: 1.   ANSWER:

QUESTION: 2.   ANSWER:

QUESTION: 3.   ANSWER:

QUESTION: 4.

ANSWER:

QUESTION: 5.

ANSWER:

QUESTION: 6.

ANSWER:

QUESTION: 7.	ANSWER:

QUESTION: 8.	ANSWER:

QUESTION: 9.	ANSWER:

QUESTION: 10.

ANSWER:

QUESTION: 11.

ANSWER:

QUESTION: 12.

ANSWER:

REMEMBERING COLLEGE TEXTBOOK MATERIAL THROUGH ORGANIZING
Supplemental Exercises

EXERCISE I

Directions

1. Read this selection from a business textbook carefully. For each paragraph, *underline* the subject matter and main idea. *Circle* important terms.

2. Add marginal annotations to organize the supporting details for each paragraph and to define important terms. When appropriate, use *def, ?,* or numbers *(1, 2, 3,).*

Why Are Microcomputer Systems Important?

Microcomputers have great importance to today's business students primarily for one monumental reason—microcomputers are already widely used by managers in business, and the extent of their use is increasing at a phenomenal rate. Companies that in 1982 had no microcomputers for managerial use now may have hundreds, or, in a few cases, thousands. All business students of today should study and gain experience with microcomputers for the simple but compelling reason that they will be using microcomputers for managerial analysis.

Microcomputers help managers extend their thinking; to an extent, they become an extension of managers' minds. At a microcomputer the manager's thoughts often can be quickly translated and placed in the computer system via the keyboard, and they are then processed almost as if the manager were mentally processing them. While this may be an exaggeration, nevertheless managers with extensive microcomputer experience report that they do think of the microcomputer as an extension of their own thinking capabilities.

There is little doubt at this time that the microcomputer revolution's effect on society and on business will be roughly comparable in magnitude to that of many major technological developments of the past, such as the steam engine and the airplane. Some observers believe that the microcomputer is bringing about an information systems equivalent of the industrial revolution.

Two analogies dramatize the microcomputer's importance to our society. The first involves the telegraph and the telephone. For the first time, the telegraph enabled people to communicate almost instantly over long distances. The telegraph was somewhat specialized and isolated, though, in that sending a telegram required traveling to a telegraph station to give the message to the operator for transmission. At the receiving end, the telegram had to be delivered or picked up. The telephone, a later invention, uses a similar technology consisting of lines across the country, but it allows an individual to use a telephone at home to directly dial another person with a home telephone. The telegraph is still in service and is still useful. However, the telephone popularized personal telecommunications, and hundreds of millions of telephones now exist, whereas telegraph stations are rather restricted in number. In information systems the mainframe computer is analogous to the telegraph, and the microcomputer is analogous to the telephone.

The second analogy uses trains as the mainframe computer equivalent and automobiles as the microcomputer equivalent. Both trains and automobiles transport people over long distances on wheels using a mechanical apparatus combined with a power system. But individuals do not own trains; they only ride on them, and relatively few trains have come into existence. Automobiles, however, popularized the mechanical mode of transportation, and hundreds of millions of them now travel the world's roads.

Principles of Management Information Systems
George M. Scott

3. Prepare a map or an outline of this selection. If you create an outline, be sure to include the author's main ideas (written as sentences), and beneath each one, indent its supporting details. Remember to include a title.

_____

_____

_____

_____

_____

_____
_____
_____
_____
_____
_____
_____
_____
_____
_____
_____
_____
_____
_____
_____
_____
_____
_____
_____
_____
_____
_____
_____
_____

4. Prepare study cards by writing a possible test question on the front of a card and its answer on the back. You may also wish to prepare vocabulary study cards by writing an unfamiliar term on the front of a card and its definition on the back.

FRONT   BACK

QUESTION: 1.

ANSWER:

QUESTION: 2.

ANSWER:

QUESTION: 3.

ANSWER:

QUESTION: 4.

ANSWER:

QUESTION: 5.

ANSWER:

QUESTION: 6.

ANSWER:

QUESTION: 7.

ANSWER:

QUESTION: 8.

ANSWER:

QUESTION: 9.

ANSWER:

QUESTION: 10.

ANSWER:

QUESTION: 11.

ANSWER:

QUESTION: 12.

ANSWER:

EXERCISE II

Directions

1. Read this biology textbook passage carefully. For each paragraph, *underline* the subject matter and main idea. *Circle* important terms.

2. Add marginal annotations to organize the supporting details for each paragraph and to define important terms. When appropriate, use *def, ?,* or numbers *(1, 2, 3).*

Channels of Communication

Communication signals are based on diverse sensory modes. For example, nasute termites make use of tactile senses (when they transmit alarm vibrations through wood) and olfactory senses (in the release of alarm pheromones). Humans are more familiar with acoustical signals (as in speech) and visual displays (as in facial expressions like smiles and frowns). Let's consider a few examples of signals in these major sensory modes.

Visual Signals

Visual signals are nearly universal among species of animals that are active by day. Often male baboons "yawn" at each other when they are both interested in a receptive female or some other resource. This facial movement is a visual display, designed to threaten a rival, and often precedes an attack on the rival.

How can it be advantageous for a baboon to signal an intention to attack or for a receiver to "accept" this information? Here, the signaler benefits if the receiver backs down after perceiving the threat signal, rather than physically attacking and possibly injuring the signaler. The receiver also benefits if, after mulling over the threat signal, he can accurately judge that his opponent can inflict a real beating unless he gives ground.

Visual communication is essential in the courtship of many animal species. For example, male and female albatross have a battery of visual displays, each with its own message. As is true for many birds, the albatross adopts exaggerated and sometimes contorted postures that convey readiness to mate, to take over incubation duties from the partner sitting on the eggs, and so on. Possibly, these highly distinctive poses represent unambiguous messages for the intended receiver and minimize the chance of confusion.

Visual communication is limited at night, but a number of organisms use *bioluminescent* signals (based on special metabolic reactions that are accompanied by a release of light energy). For example, fireflies (beetles, really) have light-generating organs at the tip of the abdomen. Each male produces a signal characteristic of his species and one that a receptive female may answer. After seeing his signal, she waits a standard time and replies with a single flash. A male approaches an answering female, engaging her in a visual "dialogue" until he precisely locates and mates with her.

Females of a predatory species of firefly have "broken the code" of their prey. When they detect a signaling male, they wait the appropriate interval and then give the "come-hither" answering flash. The male approaches and is embraced by the predator, which consumes her victim.

Chemical Signals

Chemical signals abound among the insects, which use them as sex attractants, trail markers, alarm calls, and so on. Male hangingflies lure females to themselves with sex pheromones. More often, a receptive female insect releases sex pheromones and waits for the male. The male insects have large antennae, packed with specialized receptors. After detecting the pheromone, males fly upwind, tracking the odor in a race to be the first to reach the chemically beckoning female.

Chemical signaling is also notable among some of the primates. A female baboon uses chemical and visual signals to announce her readiness to mate. Her external genitalia become swollen and she produces distinctive sex pheromones that elicit mating behavior from the males. In humans, male pheromones may influence the physiological health of the female's reproductive system.

Tactile Signals

Many animals communicate over short ranges, where tactile signals (distinct patterns of touch) become important.

When a foraging honeybee returns from several successful trips to a rich nectar or pollen source, she may begin to "dance" on the vertical surface of the comb in the darkness of the beehive. The forager moves in circles, jostling her way through the crowded mass of workers on the comb. Other individuals may follow her, keeping in physical contact with the dancer and, in doing so, acquiring information about the distance and direction of the food source.

Karl von Frisch was the first to discern the message encoded in this tactile signaling. In one set of experiments, he trained marked foragers to come to stations baited with concentrated sugar water. He then set out a series of stations with identical baits at different distances or directions from the hive. Generally, the station closest to the original training site attracted by far the greatest number of new (unmarked) bees in a short time. The trained bees apparently were acting as recruiters, directing new bees to the general area where they had found so much food.

By observing marked bees and knowing where they had been trained, von Frisch was able to break the code of the dancing bees. He saw that bees trained at stations close to a hive performed a round dance. Worker bees trailing the round-dancing bees were stimulated to fly out of the hive in search of nearby food but they did not learn which direction to fly. If, however, the station was more than eighty meters distant, the foragers trained at this station performed waggle dances. The frequency with which they waggled their abdomen during the straight runs of the dance and the speed with which they completed each loop of the dance conveyed information about the distance to the food. *The more waggles and the faster the dance, the closer the food source* (down to about eighty meters, at which point bees switch to round dancing).

The angle of the straight run with respect to vertical provided information about the direction of the food source relative to the sun and the hive. If a dancer went straight up the comb surface on her straight runs, followers learned that food could be found by flying from the hive in the direction of the sun. If, however, a dancer made her straight run 90° to the right of vertical, she was trained at a food station located at 90° to the right of a line drawn between the hive and the sun. Thus dancing bees transpose information about the position of the sun, hive, and food source into a code, and they convey the symbolic message via tactile stimulation to their hivemates.

Acoustical Signals

Both chemical and visual signals travel long distances in air (and water), and the same is true for acoustical messages (distinctive sounds). Bird song . . . is a familiar example of acoustical signaling. Male frogs also use acoustical signals to communicate with rival males and receptive females. As is true for bird song, calling is primarily a male activity, and each frog or toad species has its own distinctive call.

Frog calling is complicated for many species because (1) some predators use the calls of their amphibian prey to locate victims, and (2) many rival males may be concentrated in the same relatively small area, creating intense competition for space on the "air waves." For example, a tropical frog *(Physalaemus pustulosus)* is a favorite prey of a bat that tracks down calling individuals and snatches them from the water with its formidable jaws. The frog call has two parts, a whine followed by a "chuck." A frog calling all by itself often drops the "chuck" which, because of its acoustical properties, gives better information about his location than the initial whine. Although the male thereby makes himself less attractive to females, he is more likely to live to call another day. He gives the complete call when part of a male chorus; being one of many that could be grabbed that evening by a frog-eating bat, he may live *and* get to mate.

Biology: The Unity and Diversity of Life
by Cecie Starr and Ralph Taggart

3. Prepare a map or an outline of this selection. If you create an outline, be sure to include the authors' main ideas (written as sentences), and beneath each one, indent its supporting details. Remember to include a title.

_____

_____

_____

_____

_____

_____

_____

_____

_____

_____

_____

_____

_____

_____

4. Prepare study cards by writing a possible test question on the front of a card and its answer on the back. You may also wish to prepare vocabulary study cards by writing an unfamiliar term on the front of a card and its definition on the back.

FRONT   BACK

QUESTION: *1.*	*ANSWER:*

QUESTION: 2.

ANSWER:

QUESTION: 3.

ANSWER:

QUESTION: 4.

ANSWER:

QUESTION: 5.

ANSWER:

QUESTION: 6.

ANSWER:

QUESTION: 7.

ANSWER:

QUESTION: 8.

ANSWER:

QUESTION: 9.

ANSWER:

QUESTION: 10.

ANSWER:

QUESTION: 11.

ANSWER:

QUESTION: 12.

ANSWER:

CHAPTER 7

REMEMBERING COLLEGE TEXTBOOK MATERIAL THROUGH ORGANIZING
Textbook Excerpt and Comprehension Quiz

"The Nature of Life: An Introduction" from *The Nature of Life*, 3d ed., by John H. Postlethwait and Janet L. Hopson, McGraw-Hill, Inc., 1995, pp. 2–24.

Prepare Yourself to Read

Before you read this biology chapter, read and think about its title. What are the characteristics of living things? List any you know.

_____

_____

_____

_____

Complete your preview of this selection by reading

- the first paragraph

- the headings of each section

- any diagrams, illustrations, and photographs

- all of the last paragraph

Ask and answer questions as you read.

Use questions to guide your reading. Turn section headings into questions. If there are no headings, create questions based on what the paragraphs or sections seem to be about.

Read actively to find answers to your questions.

THE NATURE OF LIFE

THE EARTH SUMMIT: ISSUES IN MODERN BIOLOGY

In 1954, a plant researcher for Eli Lilly and Company, one of the world's largest pharmaceutical manufacturers, made a fateful discovery. In his laboratory in Switzerland, Dr. Gordon Svoboda extracted two compounds with distinct anticancer properties from an exotic tropical flower. He isolated both compounds from the delicate pink petals of *Catharanthus roseus,* the rosy periwinkle of Madagascar. In the four decades since Svoboda's discovery, the drugs made from these compounds have saved the lives of many children and young adults who might have died from Hodgkin's lymphoma and leukemia, two forms of cancer. Despite the life-saving benefits, the drugs and their source have become controversial symbols of a complex international problem. These symbols garnered considerable attention at a historic event in the summer of 1992.

That year official delegations from 177 countries met in Rio de Janeiro, Brazil, for the largest biology class ever held. At the United Nations Conference on Environment and Development, better known as the Earth Summit, politicians and scientists carried out a massive discussion of how biology affects people's lives. The urgent issues on the agenda included pollution, overpopulation, resource use, economic development, global climate change, and the imminent loss of many of earth's species and natural habitats. World leaders were concerned about their people's current and future physical and economic well-being. They left the conference agreeing that the quality of life cannot be separated from the quality of the environment. They learned, too, that biology and ecology cannot be separated from politics, and that's where the rosy periwinkle comes in.

This small flower exemplifies the vast untapped biological resources in rain forests and other remote regions of the earth, including the oceans. But the representatives at the Earth Summit disagreed strongly on whether these remote regions, such as the rain forests, should be preserved or exploited. The rich countries of North America, Europe, and Asia have relatively small populations, but they use a disproportionate amount of the world's energy and other resources and contribute a disproportionately large amount to its pollution. At the Earth Summit, representatives of these countries argued for vigorous preservation of areas like tropical rain forests, since such regions naturally release large amounts of oxygen into the atmosphere, they house a tremendous diversity of species, and they contain huge numbers of organisms that, like the rosy periwinkle, may be of benefit to humankind.

At the same time, the large and rapidly growing populations of the developing countries are pressing in on the rain forests. People want to harvest the trees for lumber and to clear the land for farms and homes. Some peoples indigenous to these otherwise uninhabited areas also attended the Earth Summit. They live in the earth's few remaining natural areas much as their ancestors did for generations, but their ways of life are disappearing along with the rain forests and other natural habitats. Besides trying to preserve their native lands, they wanted to receive compensation, through patents and royalties, for any commercial exploitation of indigenous plants, including the rosy periwinkle. The governments of countries such as Madagascar and Brazil, which contain large undeveloped areas, made similar financial claims. Pharmaceutical companies, in turn, pointed out that without sufficient return on investment, they would be unable to mount the huge research and development efforts required to bring a life-saving drug to market.

Delegates to the Earth Summit, therefore, faced a major question: How can humanity balance the need to retain natural environments and the resources they provide with the rapidly expanding human popula-

---

MESSAGES

1. Living organisms are highly ordered, and maintaining order requires energy and materials from the environment.

2. Individual organisms eventually die, but life continues via reproduction and heredity.

3. Over long periods of time, life forms change due to evolution. Natural selection—the ability of individuals with certain traits to reproduce more successfully than those lacking the traits—is a mechanism of evolution.

4. Science is a way of learning how nature functions. Scientists perform tests that might rule out possible explanations for a particular phenomenon. Explanations that have been repeatedly tested and not disproven are tentatively accepted.

5. The principles of biology can be applied to world problems such as overpopulation, disease, environmental degradation, famine, and drug addiction.

---

tion and the rights of native peoples? The current human population of 5.5 billion people will swell to 11 billion within our lifetimes. Can 11 billion people share this small planet with flowers such as the rosy periwinkle growing in obscure tropical forests? What about plants, animals, and other organisms with no specific utility other than their small roles in nature?

The issues raised by the Earth Summit require an understanding of **biology,** the study of life. Our introduction to this chapter, and our detailed discussions of biology throughout this book, will often center on topics of concern at the Earth Summit. These topics, which represent three of the themes of this book, include the interactions of organisms and their environments, reproduction and development, and the role of energy in life.

The Nature of Life has two other basic themes that are related to *biology:* The first is the process of *evolution,* the change in life forms over long periods of time. The theory of evolution is central to modern biology, particularly in terms of changes involving the genetic (hereditary) mechanisms that operate in an observable and testable fashion. The final theme is the scientific way of knowing, a commonsense approach to learning about and surviving in the natural world.

In each chapter of this book, we end the introduction with a brief description of the chapter's contents and organization to help orient you to the material. We begin this chapter by discussing the basic characteristics that living things share and that differentiate them from nonliving things. We will see, in general, how living organisms use energy to maintain their complex organization. Next we will see why reproduction is so fundamental to each type of living organism, and how reproduction relates to evolution. Then we will learn how, through the mechanisms of evolution, changes appear among groups of organisms and how new kinds of organisms arise. We will go on to see how the scientific way of knowing, the scientific method, can be used to investigate the natural world as well as to make decisions about complex everyday problems. Finally, we will see how biological science is helping people solve some of the world's most urgent issues.

Let's begin, now, to explore life science.

CHARACTERISTICS OF LIVING ORGANISMS

What is a living organism? How can we tell if something is alive or dead? What, in fact, is the nature of life itself? These questions have never been more important because today's biologists and physicians have unprecedented abilities to sustain the human body and individual organs on life-support machines; to freeze human embryos for later use; and to change and merge hereditary traits of microbes, plants, and animals. Perhaps, one day, this list will extend to generating life in a test tube and to creating hybrids between computers and living things. In the broadest sense, biological science probes the question, What is life?, and it takes this entire book to provide an answer.

As this fascinating story unfolds, the five themes of the book—energy, reproduction, evolution, environment, and the scientific way of knowing—will occur again and again. In this chapter, the themes help organize a set of nine observable characteristics that define life. The characteristics of living things are:

1. **Order.** Each structure or activity is in a specific relationship to all other structures and activities.

2. **Metabolism.** Organized chemical steps break down and build up molecules, making energy available or building needed parts.

3. **Motility.** Using their own power, organisms move themselves or their body parts.

4. **Responsiveness.** Organisms perceive the environment and react to it.

5. **Reproduction.** Organisms give rise to others of the same type.

6. **Development.** Ordered sequences of progressive changes result in increased complexity.

7. **Heredity.** Organisms have units of inheritance called genes that are passed from parent to offspring and control physical, chemical, and behavioral traits.

8. **Evolution.** Through evolution, species acquire new ways to survive, to obtain and use energy, and to reproduce.

9. **Adaptations.** Specific structures and behaviors suit life forms to their own environment.

Many nonliving entities have one or more of the characteristics of life; if you consider the life traits of movement, energy use, and growth, you can observe that waves move, flames use energy, and crystals grow. Only living organisms, however, display *all* the characteristics at some point during their individual life cycle or species history. For example, the petals of a periwinkle flower move as the bud unfolds; the plant supporting the flower captures energy from the sun; and the plant originally emerged from a seed and grew in size.

Let's begin, now, to consider the defining characteristics of life, one by one, in groupings that match the list above, and that reflect our bookwide themes of energy, reproduction, the environment, and evolution.

ENERGY AND ORGANIZATION IN LIVING THINGS

Many of the issues that delegates discussed at the Earth Summit centered around how people acquire and use energy. The developed countries of Europe, North America, and Asia use more than their share of global energy supplies—mainly in the form of oil. And many scientists have concluded that the burning of oil creates carbon dioxide and other waste products which contribute to the global climate change we call global warming. Human beings, in general, may use more total energy in more forms than other kinds of living organisms, but energy use is a shared trait, an essential feature of all life forms. Living systems use energy to maintain organization. Our discussions of life's characteristics, therefore, begin with those that require energy expenditure.

Order

Living organisms possess a degree of **order**—a structural and behavioral complexity and regularity—far greater than the finest Swiss clock, the fastest racing car, or anything else in the nonliving world. The eye of a fly, for example, and the spiral-packed seeds of a sunflower head consist of highly organized units repeated and arranged in precise geometric arrays. In fact, some biologists suggest that the most highly organized structure yet discovered in the universe is the human brain, such as the one allowing you to read and understand this page.

Order is apparent in both the visible and microscopic organization of living things. This organization forms a hierarchy, beginning with the individual organism and moving toward both higher and lower levels of organization, [as shown in the Concept Integrator]. An **organism** is an independent individual that shows the characteristics of life. Each elephant and each tree is a single organism. Each organism, in turn, is made up of **organ systems,** groups of body parts arranged so that together they carry out a particular function within the organism. The skeletal system, for example, supports an elephant's body.

Organ systems are made up of **organs,** structures that perform specialized functions for the organ system. Two examples are a single bone that supports part of an elephant's leg, and the leaves that produce sugars for a tree.

Each organ is made up of **tissues,** groups of similar cells that carry out the function of the organ. For example, blood (a tissue) flows in tubes, or vessels, through the bone, providing food and oxygen for the bone cells.

Tissues are made up of **cells,** the simplest entities that have all the properties of life. Cells contain within them structures known as **organelles,** which perform the functions necessary for the life of the cell.

The organization of living things is important because it identifies the various levels at which we can examine and understand biology. For example, to understand the significance of the cancer-fighting drugs made from periwinkle flowers (organism level), a biologist wants to know how the plant makes the compounds without its own tissues becoming poisoned (cell and tissue levels). He or she also wonders how the drugs affect the flower's reproductive abilities or ability to survive.

Metabolism

To understand the life characteristic of metabolism, we can consider the strawberry frog, a brightly colored animal that inhabits the damp cloud forests of Central America. This frog has two large, dark eyes, muscles and bones that allow its legs to hop and paddle, and a dazzling red skin that covers its exterior. As time passes, some of this organization can start to deteriorate. While climbing a tree one day in search of ants, the frog may slip and crash to the forest floor, puncturing its skin, bruising its legs, and becoming more disorganized.

This kind of wear and tear is not unique to living things. Rocks, stars, rivers, and mountain ranges all tend to become more disordered with passing time. You need only look as far as the nearest heap of papers on your desk and the accumulation of dirty clothes and dust balls in the corner to witness the tremendous tendency toward disorder. To combat a housekeeping disaster, you must expend energy to sort the papers and clean up the dust. Likewise, in an injured frog, broken skin is replaced and wounded muscles heal when the animal's body extracts energy and materials from the insects it catches and eats, then uses the energy and materials to generate new skin and healthy muscle tissue. In general, living things counteract the disorder that comes with time by taking energy and materials from their environment and using them for repair, growth, and other processes needed for survival.

The intricate order within an organism's body—whether it is a brilliantly colored tropical frog or a thorny desert tree such as the acacia—can only be maintained through an expenditure of energy. For that reason, organisms require a constant supply of energy and building materials. The maintenance of order, as well as growth, replacement of worn-out or damaged body parts, and the basic life processes are accomplished by a highly complex series of chemical reactions within the cells of the organism. The sum of all such reactions is the organism's **metabolism.**

Once an organism has taken in energy-containing food molecules or has manufactured its own food using sunlight and gases from the air, metabolism changes the food molecules. Food molecules taken from the environment tend to be large and complex, and these molecules are broken down by metabolism into smaller and simpler molecules that can be used by the cells. Metabolism also rearranges these simpler molecules and builds new ones, which are used for repair and growth. Some food molecules are broken down by a series of reactions that gradually releases their chemical energy. This energy is used by the cells to maintain themselves and the organism as a whole. Light striking a palm leaf initiates a series of metabolic steps that causes the plant to make high-energy compounds, move organelles around inside cells, produce new leaves, and break down worn-out cells and tissues.

Motility

Energy released by metabolic reactions allows materials to be moved to areas where they can be used to replace worn parts, increase size, and generally combat disorganization. Self-propelled movement, or *motility,* is characteristic of many kinds of organisms. Even organisms as simple as bacteria can move on their own. Organisms such as plants, which cannot move from place to place, nonetheless show various kinds of movement. For example, water carrying dissolved materials moves through the plant, and the material that fills the living cells is in constant motion. The flowers of some plants open in the morning and close at night. Animals, of course, have elevated movement to an art form in their pursuit of food, their escape from enemies, and their social relations.

Responsiveness

To survive, an organism must respond to changes in its environment. It must be able to detect food, water, or enemies, and to react appropriately. The response can be an instantaneous one, as when a moth hears the high-pitched whine of a swooping bat, or it can be gradual, as when trumpeter swans detect the shortening days of autumn and respond by flying to warmer regions. Plants, too, respond to their environments, conserving water during times of drought and capturing sunlight when it is available. Some plants even show instantaneous responses, reacting to external signals rapidly enough to trap an unsuspecting fly.

The life characteristics of metabolism, motility, and responsiveness allow an organism to obtain energy and materials from the environment and use them to maintain order and organization within their bodies. Nevertheless, as organisms age, they can no longer stop the disorganization that inevitably occurs, and eventually all individual organisms die. Life continues to exist, however, because organisms perpetuate themselves, and three characteristics of life are directly involved in the perpetuation of species: reproduction, development, and heredity.

REPRODUCTION OF LIVING THINGS

While all individual organisms die, many generate new individuals like themselves during their lifetimes. If they didn't, organisms of their type would disappear. The life process by which organisms give rise to others of the same kind is called **reproduction.** The two basic modes of reproduction are asexual and sexual.

Modes of Reproduction

Asexual Reproduction In **asexual reproduction,** there is a single parent, and the offspring are all identical to the parent and to each other. Asexual reproduction occurs most commonly in one-celled organisms, and the new cells are produced when the parent cell simply splits in half, producing two identical daughter cells.

Sexual Reproduction Most complex organisms reproduce sexually. In **sexual reproduction,** the offspring generally contain hereditary material from two different parents and are not identical either to the parent or to each other. The first cell of the new individual is formed when two specialized cells called the egg and sperm unite.

Many sexually reproducing organisms have special adaptations for reproduction. A male golden toad, for example, increases his chances of reproducing if he advertises his location and amorous intent by a distinctive song attractive to females of his species. In another example, tube-shaped scarlet gilia flowers produce stores of energy-rich nectar, and both the flaming red petals and the nectar attract hummingbirds. The iridescent birds feed on the nectar and inadvertently assist in the plant's reproduction. The hummingbirds' feathers pick up sticky pollen grains, which contain the flower's sperm, and when the bird deposits the pollen on the next plant it visits, these sperm cells can reach the eggs of another flower and lead to the formation of a new plant generation.

Development

When an organism reproduces, the young start out smaller, and usually much simpler in form, than the parents. The offspring then grow in size and increase in complexity, a process known as **development**. Eventually, they themselves can become parents.

One of the most intriguing questions in all biology is how a fertilized egg cell develops into the millions of cells of various types that function as a viable organism. The answer lies in the remarkable process of heredity.

Genes: The Units of Heredity

Identical twins make a convincing argument that some kind of information must direct the development of each individual in a fairly precise manner so that two very similar organisms result. When we contrast a set of identical twins with their different-looking brothers and sisters, however, we can see that there are also variations in hereditary information. The units of inheritance that control the development of specific physical, chemical, and behavioral traits in a living organism are the **genes.**

Genes are made of a remarkable molecule called DNA. Each of your cells contains 46 of these twisting, threadlike molecules, and each DNA molecule in your cells contains about 4000 genes. The DNA in eggs and sperm carries hereditary information from the parents that is passed on to their offspring. Specific genes, inherited from parents, determine whether a strawberry frog has big, bright red splashes of color or small, pale pink patches; whether a rosy periwinkle produces a lot of the cancer-stopping drug or only a little; and whether a person has blue, brown, or hazel eyes.

DNA has the unique ability to make identical copies of itself within a cell. This process, called *replication,* makes it possible for one cell to divide, yielding two identical cells. In this way, organisms can grow and also replace damaged or worn-out cells, the cells can expand and the organism can grow, and eventually, reproduction can take place and whole new organisms can form.

Reproduction allows life to continue even though the bodies of individual organisms become disorganized over time and die, and as we saw, the processes of development and heredity—fundamental characteristics of living things—are completely integral to reproduction.

►Concept Challenge

An automobile uses energy, is highly organized, is motile, and responds when the accelerator is pushed. Why wouldn't you consider an automobile to be alive?

THE HIERARCHY OF LIFE

Picture, for a moment, some of your favorite organisms. You may envision your dog playfully returning a frisbee on a grassy lawn. Or a flock of geese flying in a vee-shaped formation. Or a gnarled pine tree growing atop a rocky summit. Regardless of whether an organism lives alone, lives as a member of a group, or lives attached to or inside of another organism, it must interact with its physical and biological environment. The branch of biology that studies the relationships between living organisms and their environment is **ecology.**

Ecologists study individual organisms, but also several levels of the hierarchy of life *above* the level of the organism. Recall from our discussion of the hierarchy of life *below* the level of the organism that living things are composed of organs, which are made up of cells, which are in turn made up of molecules. When an ecologist or a beginning student of biology considers life and the environment, he or she must focus on the higher orders of organization that include and impinge upon any given organism.

Take, for example, life in the African savanna environment—a collection of elephants, acacia trees, tussock grasses, and arid plains. The hierarchy of life on the savanna proceeds from small to large in the following sequence: **Organisms** are individual independent living things: an elephant is an organism and so is an acacia tree. Groups of a particular type of organism that live in the same area and actively interbreed with one another are called **populations**—for example, an elephant herd or a field of grass. All the populations that live in a particular area make up a **com-**

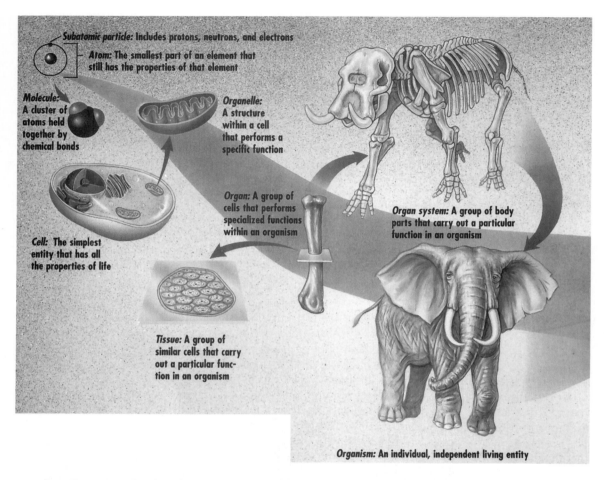

Subatomic particle: Includes protons, neutrons, and electrons

Atom: The smallest part of an element that still has the properties of that element

Molecule: A cluster of atoms held together by chemical bonds

Organelle: A structure within a cell that performs a specific function

Cell: The simplest entity that has all the properties of life

Organ: A group of cells that performs specialized functions within an organism

Organ system: A group of body parts that carry out a particular function in an organism

Tissue: A group of similar cells that carry out a particular function in an organism

Organism: An individual, independent living entity

munity—for example, the plants, animals, and other organisms at a certain location on the savanna. The living community together with its non-living physical surroundings is called an **ecosystem.** The savanna ecosystem includes elephants, the egrets that pick insects off their skin, and the coarse grass they chew and trample, as well as the water in clouds, the sandy soil underfoot, and the hot African sunshine. All the ecosystems of the earth make up the **biosphere,** that portion of the earth on which life exists. The biosphere is a relatively thin layer about 6 ½ to 13 kilometers (6 to 8 miles) thick, and includes unimaginably remote places that nevertheless still teem with life, including the deepest parts of the ocean floor, deep-sea vents spewing superheated water, and the tops of earth's highest mountains where the air is thin and freezing cold. A huge variety of organisms exists in these and the more familiar and hospitable forests,

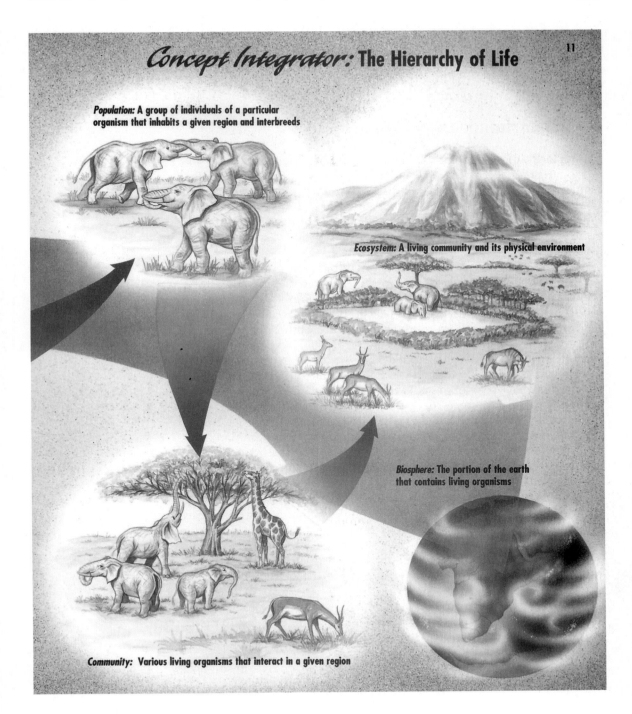

Concept Integrator: The Hierarchy of Life

11

Population: A group of individuals of a particular organism that inhabits a given region and interbreeds

Ecosystem: A living community and its physical environment

Biosphere: The portion of the earth that contains living organisms

Community: Various living organisms that interact in a given region

meadows, lakes, marshes, and grasslands we know in our own environments. Biologists have tried to make sense of life's spectacular variety by classifying organisms into various groups.

CLASSIFICATION OF LIVING THINGS

Put on a mask and snorkel, and plunge into the warm, blue waters off Hawaii and count the varieties of fish you see in just a few minutes—perhaps butterfly fish, bird wrasses, striped Moorish idols with streaming back fins, or intensely turquoise parrot fish. This same dazzling variety is evident in the colorful songbirds of eastern forests, the butterflies of midwestern weed fields, and the wildflowers of the Rocky Mountains.

To help make sense of this vast array of different organisms, biologists have created a system for categorizing organisms, separating living things into groups according to their similarities. Brightly colored tropical frogs, for example, are more similar to bullfrogs than to elephants, but frogs and elephants are more similar to each other than to mushrooms or grass. To make sense of this *diversity* of life, biologists divide organisms into the following categories:

Species (SPEE-seez; both singular and plural) are groups of structurally similar individuals that all descend from the same initial group and that have the potential to breed successfully with one another in nature.

Several related and similar species make up a **genus** (JEE-nuhss; plural, *genera*). Just as a person has a family name and a given name, biologists refer to each species by a two-part name: (1) The first part is the genus; for example, the rosy periwinkle is assigned to the genus *Catharanthus,* while the strawberry frog is assigned to the genus *Dendrobates,* along with the closely related play-actor frog and several other species. (2) The second part of the name distinguishes among several species within one genus. The rosy periwinkle is *Catharanthus roseus,* while the strawberry frog is *Dendrobates pumilio* and the related play-actor frog is *Dendrobates histrionicus.* After once mentioning the complete two-part name, biologists may subsequently abbreviate the genus, referring to *C. roseus* or *D. pumilio.*

Just as species are grouped into genera, genera are grouped into **families,** families into **orders,** orders into **classes,** and classes into **phyla** or **divisions.** In each successive grouping, similar organisms are arranged by broader and broader criteria.

Ultimately, biologists assign the dozens of divisions and phyla—and the millions of life forms they include—into **kingdoms.**

Kingdoms of Living Things

You can perform a simple exercise in classification by quickly writing down the names of about 10 organisms as they pop into your mind. Now take the organisms on your list and try grouping them into the broadest categories possible. What categories did you choose? How many categories were there? If you are like most people, you would have listed and grouped organisms in just two main categories—plants, such as roses and maple trees, and animals, such as dogs, cats, and flies.

In fact, the ancient Greeks divided all living things into those same two kingdoms, and this division into plants and animals was sufficient for most biologists and naturalists throughout most of recorded history. Not until the mid-twentieth century did the American biologist R. H. Whitaker propose that the growing number of organisms discovered and studied by life scientists be divided into a five-kingdom scheme based on cell structure. In the late 1980s, studies of DNA supported a six-kingdom scheme: Animalia, Plantae, Fungi, Protista, Eubacteria, and Archaebacteria. The five-kingdom scheme lumped Eubacteria and Archaebacteria together in the kingdom Monera, but the six-kingdom scheme better represents the family tree by which all living organisms appear to be related to each other. While your list of organisms may have included a couple of members of the kingdom Fungi (mushrooms and yeasts), it probably didn't include any members of the kingdoms Protista, Eubacteria, or Archaebacteria because the vast majority of species in these kingdoms are microscopic and are unfamiliar to most people. Biologists define kingdoms by the evolutionary relationships and cell structure of the species within them, and the ways in which these species obtain energy.

Three of the six kingdoms contain large, familiar organisms with complex cells. Members of the largest kingdom, **Animalia**—including insects, earthworms, snails, elephants, egrets, and human beings, to name but a few—consist of many cells, and get their energy and materials by ingesting other organisms, alive and dead. Members of the kingdom **Plantae,** such as ferns and maple trees, are usually green and many-celled, and they generate their own food from the energy in sunlight and the materials in air and water. The kingdom **Fungi** includes some single-celled forms like yeasts, and many-celled forms like mushrooms. Fungi obtain energy by absorbing materials from the environment after decomposing other living or dead organisms or their parts.

Most of the members of the other three kingdoms are invisible to the naked eye. The **Protista**, or *protists,* include both one-celled and many-celled species. Numerous kinds of algae are protists, as are amoe-

The Family Tree of Life.
[A] These newly divided *Streptococcus* cells (microscopic bacteria, magnification 20,750×) represent kingdom Eubacteria. [B] This *Methanobacterium ruminantium* cell (magnification 30,000×), which inhabits a cow's intestines, is from the kingdom Archaebacteria. [C] The kingdom Protista also contains microscopic single-celled organisms, but they are generally much larger and more complex than bacteria. This *Paramecium* cell, with its exterior covering of beating hairlike organelles, is a protist. [D] Fungi, such as this *Hygrophorus conicus* mushroom decomposing leaf litter on the forest floor, make up a fourth kingdom. [E] The plant kingdom includes a large group of many-celled organisms that generate their own food molecules and are often conspicuous and graceful, such as this pine. [F] The largest of the six kingdoms contains several million species of animals. Most of these lack backbones, but some, like this arctic loon, have an internal skeleton and complex behavior pattern.

[E] Plantae

[F] Animalia

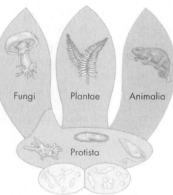

Fungi   Plantae   Animalia

Protista

Eubacteria   Archaebacteria

[D] Fungi

[C] Protista

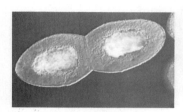

[A] Eubacteria

[B] Archaebacteria

bas and many other organisms that swim in drops of pond water. (Some biologists prefer to call this group *Protoctista.*)

The remaining two kingdoms consist of single-celled organisms whose cells are much simpler in structure than the cells of animals, plants, fungi, or protists. The kingdom **Eubacteria** (*eu-* means "true") includes small, single-celled microscopic organisms such as the organisms that turn milk into yogurt or those that cause strep throat. The kingdom **Archaebacteria** (*archae-* means "ancient") are single-celled organisms about the same size and shape as Eubacteria, but with some different cellular components. They live in very harsh environments, such as the inside of a cow's intestine, or in acidic, sulfurous hot springs. Many Archaebacteria obtain their energy from sulfur compounds, and some produce methane (swamp gas) as a waste product.

Although members of each of the six kingdoms of life play important roles in the environment, people generally think of the familiar plants and animals as the most significant groups. The delegates to the Earth Summit in Rio, for example, focused on saving species from the kingdoms Animalia and Plantae. Losing species from the other four kingdoms would change life on earth just as drastically, though. This is because members of the fungal, protist, and bacterial kingdoms are largely responsible for recycling materials in the environment. Have you ever wondered what happens to all the fingernails that people clip off and throw away? Silly as it may sound, fingernails would start to pile up in the environment if it weren't for the recycling activities of fungi and eubacteria. The important point here is that all life is interconnected. Environmentalists may focus on saving beautiful and inspiring animals such as the jaguar of the Amazon basin or the spotted owl of the Pacific Northwest. But for the natural world to go on functioning as we know it, we must preserve the widest possible spectrum of life's diversity—even organisms we have yet to discover and name.

The Unity and Diversity of Life

While biologists distinguish the six kingdoms according to their cell structures and ways of obtaining energy and materials, the kingdoms share a great number of genetic similarities. These similarities suggest that all living things on earth arose from a single group of ancestral cells present at the dawn of life. The similarities stand as powerful evidence for the *unity* of life, a unity both of origin and of basic day-to-day functioning. In the chapters to come you will see dozens of examples of common life mechanisms at the molecular level, and you will also see how these similarities unite our planet's incredible diversity of life forms at a fundamental level. A question about these underlying connections has long intrigued biologists: What mechanisms can account for the unity of life at the cellular and genetic levels, and yet still foster the vast diversity of life which we group into six large kingdoms? That mechanism is the unifying theme for all life science: evolution.

➤ Concept Challenge

By applying the rules of taxonomy, determine which two of the three following organisms are more closely related, even if their names are unfamiliar to you: *Felis domesticus, Musca domesticus, Felis concolor.* Defend your choice.

People in Biology

Darwin, Wallace, and Evolution by Natural Selection

History has not dealt equally with Charles Darwin and Alfred Russel Wallace. Yet these two men, living in the same country during the same era, proposed remarkably similar theories of evolution by *natural selection*—a central theme of this book and a unifying concept in all of biological science. To understand this historical oversight, as well as the stunning achievement evolutionary theory represents, one must consider both the social and scientific tenor of the mid-nineteenth century.

Darwin and Wallace both lived in Victorian England, an era of courtly manners, rigid social roles, and inflexible stratification by social class. In contrast to the social constraints of the day, there was excitement and progressive thinking in many areas of science, including a growing belief that the natural world is in a constant state of change.

For hundreds of years prior to the time of Darwin and Wallace, most scientists believed that all species originated about 6000 years ago and remained unchanged in form throughout history. With the careful study of fossils in the late eighteenth and early nineteenth centuries, however, biologists Georges Cuvier, Georges Louis Leclerc de Buffon, Jean Baptiste Lamarck, and others began to realize that extinct organisms were unlike those alive in the 1800s, and that the form of plants and animals seemed to change, or evolve, over the years. Simultaneously, geologists such as James Hutton and Charles Lyell were investigating rock layers and other evidence of mountain building, erosion, and volcanic eruptions and suggested that our planet must be millions—not thousands—of years old, and must be undergoing slow but continual change.

Darwin had also read the writings of Thomas Malthus (1766–1834), who pointed out that populations tend to grow geometrically (2, 4, 8, 16, etc.) and that only wars, famine, and disease keep population growth in check. Within this social and scientific context, Darwin and Wallace separately made their own observations of unfamiliar organisms half a world away. Independently, they drew nearly identical conclusions about the mechanisms of evolutionary change within the organisms on our changing planet.

Darwin was a wealthy upper-class gentleman who had studied for the clergy at Cambridge University but was passionately interested in natural history. Upon graduating, he agreed to serve as a social companion to Captain Fitzroy of the HMS *Beagle* on a five-year voyage (1831–1836) to map the coastline of South America. Throughout the voyage, Darwin had ample opportunity to explore the jungles, plains, and mountains of South America. A seminal stop on the trip was the Galápagos, a cluster of black volcanic islands 1000 kilometers (600 miles) west of Ecuador with a small but unique set of plants and animals.

Throughout his travels, Darwin was continually impressed by the variable shapes and colors that the members of a single species often showed, and he pondered the origin and significance of such variety. He returned to England with the idea of natural selection already half formed and notebooks full of observations to support the contention, but he continued studying variation in domesticated species for nearly 20 years.

Darwin had written a short summary of his theory in 1842, but it remained unpublished as late as 1858. That changed abruptly, however, when Alfred Russel Wallace's work in the arena came to light. Younger than Darwin, Wallace had sailed to South America himself in 1848 to collect plants, insects, and other natural specimens. Later Wallace visited Singapore and Borneo to make similar collections. Like Darwin, he had read the works of Malthus and Lyell, and had noticed on his travels the striking variations among populations of individual species. And

(continued on following page)

like Darwin, Wallace had returned and devised a theory of evolution by natural selection to explain what he saw (even choosing the term *natural selection* independently!). Unlike Darwin, however, Wallace was a working-class man, and perhaps because he had far less to lose and few fears of public disapproval, he was more eager to promote his ideas.

By 1858, Wallace had published four papers containing portions of a theory of evolution that included the mechanism of natural selection, the notion of descent with modification, and the idea of survival of the fittest. Wallace sent Darwin his fourth paper in 1858, and Darwin—realizing that his life's work was being scooped—rushed to prepare an abstract. Friends read this abstract before the Linnean Society later that year along with Wallace's published work. Then the following year, Darwin released his monumental and well-documented book, *On the Origin of Species by Means of Natural Selection.*

As biologist William V. Mayer points out*, the simultaneous publication of nearly identical theories in today's highly competitive scientific world would probably lead to "recrimination and lawsuits." But products of the gracious Victorian era, Darwin and Wallace instead approached their situation with courtesy and generosity, each fully acknowledging each other's contribution at every opportunity. Darwin and Wallace, in fact, became personal friends, Darwin arranging for the impoverished Wallace to receive a government pension, and Wallace serving as a pallbearer at Darwin's funeral.

The intellectual stimulation each scientist gave the other provided generations of biologists with their broadest conceptual framework for understanding the living world. Now, over 130 years after the independent contributions of Darwin and Wallace and the thorough documentation of evolutionary principles, their insights still foster lively experimental inquiry into the mechanisms of life.

*William V. Mayer, "Wallace and Darwin," *The American Biology Teacher* 49 (1987): 406–410

Darwin, C. *On the Origin of Species: A Facsimile of the First Edition.* Cambridge, Mass: Harvard University Press, 1975

EVOLUTION, ADAPTATION, AND NATURAL SELECTION

Forms of living organisms change over time. We know this partly from the fossilized imprints of early organisms. The older a fossil, the less similar it is to present-day forms, and this provides good evidence of the continued change in living species over millennia. Using fossils, analysis of DNA, and other kinds of evidence, biologists can trace the history of a group of organisms. All groups alive today are like the youngest branches of a family tree. For example, the strawberry frog and the common frog are amphibious cousins. Reaching farther back in time, frogs and salamanders would share a common ancestor, and even farther back in the history of this lineage, frogs would share a common ancestor with snakes, fish, beetles, button mushrooms, rosy periwinkles, and bacteria. Tracing the evolutionary tree of life to more remote periods, all organisms would eventually share a common ancestor in the ancient past. This family-tree concept helps explain the origin of species: All living things are descended from a common ancestor, and arose as the result of genetic modifications in species that lived before them in a process of change called **evolution.**

The amazing diversity of plants, animals, and other living organisms that the Earth Summit delegates sought to protect is a product of evolution, as is each individual species.

Adaptation

As groups of organisms evolve, genetic modifications (mutations) arise that allow them to cope with their environments in more efficient ways. Different species, for example, have different ways of extracting energy and materials from their surroundings. Because these differences help the organism adapt to their own special ways of life, they are called **adaptations.** One adaptation in an adult frog, for example, is a long, sticky tongue folded over at the tip. When an ant or fly ventures near, the frog quickly unfurls the tongue, mires the victim in the sticky coating, retracts its tongue, and devours the insect.

Not all adaptations relate to the intake of energy and materials. Some adaptations improve the organism's ability to grow; others, to reproduce, move, live in a group, or attract a mate. Some adaptations are truly wondrous and bizarre. Certain flowers, for instance, so closely resemble female wasps that male wasps try to "copulate" with them. Pollen clings to the insects' bodies, and as they move on to "mate with" new "females," they carry the pollen from one flower to the next.

Adaptation and the broader theme of evolution so pervade the way biologists think about, understand, and explain life that an evolutionary perspective will appear in virtually every chapter in this book. The next section provides an overview of evolution by natural selection, which can serve as a useful framework until we explore evolution in greater detail.

Natural Selection

On November 24, 1859, a drab little green book with a cumbersome title was published in London. Its first edition of 1250 copies was bought by booksellers in one day, and it has not been out of print since. The author was Charles Darwin. The title of the book was *On the Origin of Species by Means of Natural Selection, or The Preservation of Favoured Species in the Struggle for Life.* Today we refer to his book as *The Origin of Species.*

The Origin of Species proposed these major ideas:

1. Living things are changing constantly, producing new species that did not exist when life on earth first originated.

2. All living organisms, no matter how different they seem, evolved from a single common ancestor.

3. Within any given population, variations in shape, size, vital processes, and behavior exist among individuals of the same species. These variations can be inherited from one generation to the next.

From these ideas, Darwin concluded that individuals possessing variations that help them survive and reproduce in a competitive, changing environment have an advantage over members of their species that lack such traits. Darwin thought this last idea provided the mechanism for change in living things over time. He called this mechanism **natural selection** because nature was "selecting" the individuals with the most suitable variations to survive and become the parents of the next generation.

The principle of natural selection, now widely accepted as a main mechanism behind evolution in nature, can explain adaptations such as the long neck of giraffes. In a population of giraffes browsing on trees in the savanna many thousands of years ago, some of the giraffes probably would have had long necks and others short necks, each based on preexisting variations of the hereditary units called genes within the giraffe population. If there were too few low-hanging leaves around to feed all the giraffes in the population, then the long-necked giraffes

Natural Selection on the Savanna: Giraffes with Genetically Determined Long Necks Have Advantages for Survival and Reproduction.

Amid tall trees and long-necked neighbors, short-necked giraffes would have died and left few offspring, while long-necked giraffes would have survived, reproduced more often, and left more long-neck genes in the population.

could reach more food, harvest more energy and materials, and survive to produce more offspring—many, like their parents, possessing the genes for long necks. Natural selection, in short, results in the best adapted, best-competing individuals to be parents for the next generation.

Darwin argued that evolution by natural selection, working over long stretches of time, could have produced the millions of living forms we now observe in all their splendid diversity. Natural selection fine-tunes each species to its own environment by selecting genes that, in the broadest sense, help individual organisms overcome disorder and death for as long as possible.

Evolution by natural selection is so grand an organizing principle for all biology that it will resurface time and again in this book, in the many magazine and newspaper articles you may read on life science, and in any future biology courses you may take.

➤Concept Challenge

Darwin presented three main ideas: that species could change over time, that evolution occurs by descent with modification, and the notion of natural selection. How do those three ideas relate to each other?

SCIENCE AS A WAY OF KNOWING

An important result of the Earth Summit was a renewed focus on ecology: Participants realized that before we can decide how to preserve biological diversity, how to block climate change, and how to promote economic development without damaging the environment, we need to know more about how living things interact with each other and with the nonliving world around them. Delegates to the conference came away with a conviction that the world's nations must train more scientists to study ecology and the principles of nature in general.

Let's look now at the process of science and how scientists have coaxed, prodded, and pried the secrets of nature from living organisms. It is important to keep in mind that behind every fact and concept we present, there were people in laboratories or field stations engaged in the often tedious and frustrating, but sometimes joyful and exciting, pursuit of knowledge about what makes living things look and act the way they do. So let's look more closely at the fundamental principles behind the scientific process, as well as the general methods for problem solving that scientists employ, and that, in fact, we all use daily.

Fundamental Principles: Causality and Uniformity

A lightning bolt flashes in a cloud-darkened sky. A man eating in a restaurant becomes enraged and abusive when the waitress tells him they are out of apple pie. Modern scientists assume that events like these are due to natural causes, a principle they call **causality.** The ancient Greeks, on the other hand, believed that thunderbolts arose when the god Zeus hurled them at the earth, and that an emotionally disturbed person was possessed by evil spirits. Today's scientists may not yet fully understand the natural causes of a phenomenon like mental illness, but they firmly believe that it is based upon natural causes and that by applying the scientific process, they someday will be able to understand those causes.

A second fundamental principle of science is the **uniformity** of phenomena in time and space. Scientists contend that the laws of nature, for example, the speed of light, the laws of gravity, and so on, operate the same way today in Columbus, Ohio, as they did in Olduvai Gorge, in East Africa, 1 million years ago, or in the cloud of dust and gases that existed before our solar system formed billions of years ago. The principle of uniformity is important to biologists because events that led to life's origin and diversity occurred long before humans lived to observe them. Yet a biologist can feel confident that the same natural laws operating today functioned in the same way at the dawn of time, as life began, and all during the evolution of life on earth.

The Power of Scientific Reasoning

Resting on the twin pillars of causality and uniformity is the power of scientific reasoning. We have seen that Darwin stated two facts from which he drew a grand conclusion: that natural selection is a mechanism of evolution. This kind of thinking is called **inductive reasoning,** or generalizing from specific cases to arrive at broad principles. Inductive reasoning is a particularly creative, intuitive, and exciting part of science. It's like creating a sonnet or sculpture or sonata. The instant when the mind leaps from previously isolated facts to a broad, unifying generalization is as thrilling, some scientists say, as starting down the steepest slope of a roller coaster.

The counterpart to inductive reasoning is **deductive reasoning,** or analyzing specific cases on the basis of preestablished general principles. Let's see how inductive reasoning and deductive reasoning differ in application. A person who knows, for example, that bright red strawberry frogs and red-and-yellow coral snakes are poisonous might conclude through inductive reasoning that all brightly colored organisms are dangerous. Such a tentative generalization is called a **hypothesis.** If that same person then encounters a flashy, black-chinned red salamander, the person might, using deductive reasoning, assume that this brilliant salamander, too, is poisonous and avoid it.

While inductive and deductive reasoning help shape how scientists think, the final and equally crucial element in the scientific process is the method scientists use to try to test their generalizations.

Testing Generalizations

The person who generalized from strawberry frogs and coral snakes to form the hypothesis that all brightly colored organisms are poisonous might one day see a friend eating a bowl of red raspberries and start waving his or her arms at the confused diner. If the friend survived the raspberries, however, that would *disprove* the hypothesis, or show it to be false, and a new hypothesis would be needed—something like: Bright red *animals* (not all organisms) are poisonous. But then, what about cardinals? A quick test could show that these scarlet birds are also nonpoisonous, requiring still further modification of the hypothesis.

A good scientist is always skeptical about hypotheses and is ready to discard or modify them when data from actual tests disprove them. Some hypotheses, however, have so far survived all attempts at disproof. A broad general hypothesis that is tested repeatedly but never disproved comes to be accepted as a **theory,** a general principle about the natural world, like the theory of gravity, the cell theory, or the theory of evolution. (Keep in mind that scientists use the term "theory" very differently than many lay people do. The popular phrase "It's just a theory" implies that something is an untested idea.)

To describe and understand nature accurately, scientists combine the kinds of creative thinking, reasoning, and testing we have been discussing into a series of steps called the **scientific method:**

1. They *ask a question* or identify a problem to be solved based on observations of the natural world.

2. They *propose a hypothesis,* a possible answer to the question or a potential solution to the problem.

3. They *make a prediction,* a statement of what they will observe in a specific situation if the hypothesis is correct.

4. They *test the prediction* by performing an experiment or making further observations.

While these steps may sound regimented, they are really little more than an organized commonsense approach—one you use regularly in your own life. Let's say that one evening you obseve that your desk lamp isn't working. You would pose a question (Step 1): "What made my desk lamp go out?" And you would probably create a hypothesis (Step 2): "Maybe the light bulb burned out." Next you would make a prediction (Step 3): "If the bulb burned out, then when I replace it with a working bulb, the lamp should light." Finally, you would perform an experiment (Step 4): You would remove a bulb from a floor lamp that works, screw it into your desk lamp, and watch what happened.

When you performed the test, you automatically included what scientists call a **control,** a check of the experiment based on keeping all factors the same except for the one in question. Here, the control was the borrowed bulb that worked in the floor lamp. If the borrowed bulb failed to work in the desk lamp, you could conclude, based on your control, that a burned-out bulb was not the problem. You would next discard the faulty-bulb hypothesis and ask new questions: "Is the lamp itself broken? Is something wrong with the wiring to the wall socket?" You could then make new hypotheses, new predictions, and perform new tests until you had ruled out all but one hypothesis.

If you continued to generate tests to try ruling out this last hypothesis, but it continued to make correct predictions time after time, you could begin to believe in its validity, and discard it only after some future test showed the hypothesis to be false. Since we can often disprove hypotheses but can rarely prove one to be true, *scientific knowledge is nearly always tentative and conditional,* relying on the best answer yet available. This is unsatisfying to many, because people, in general, like clear-cut truths (or at least an illusion of them).

No tool is more powerful for understanding the natural world than the scientific method. It does not apply, however, to matters of religion, politics, culture, ethics, or art. These valuable ways of approaching the world and its problems proceed along different lines of inquiry and experience. Nevertheless, many of the world's complex problems have underlying biological bases, and their solutions demand knowledge of biological principles.

➤Concept Challenge

Scientists often say that scientific knowledge is "provisional." What do they mean by that?

HOW BIOLOGICAL SCIENCE CAN HELP SOLVE WORLD PROBLEMS

The Earth Summit in Rio focused on just a few of the world's problems, including climate change, biodiversity, sustainable development, and the world's forests. There are other pressing problems as well, including overpopulation, famine, war, crime, drug addiction, AIDS, cancer, heart disease, pollution, ozone depletion, acid rain, and changes in climate. While these problems tend to have multiple roots, their biological bases may yield to biological solutions, and these solutions, in turn, will help ease the associated pressures on society. For this reason, people in all fields must understand the biological bases of the world's problems.

Many of our most vexing problems stem from our species' enormous and burgeoning population. Five and one-half billion people are currently straining our planet's environmental resources, and by the year 2000, we will number about 6 billion. This immense population is accumulating because the human species, like all others, is finely honed to obtain energy and materials and to reproduce. The resulting human adaptations—the abilities to reason, communicate, and manipulate the

Deforestation in Madagascar: Landscapes Effaced, Healing Plants Lost.

Hills in Madagascar's central plateau lie denuded of their original forests, with precious topsoil washing away each time it rains. The jungles were cleared for firewood and for the creation of new farmland, but after a few years, the land's productivity plummeted, and farmers cleared new jungle. Thousands of species may be lost to this deforestation process.

physical world—have been so successful that our single species is busily exhausting the limited resources that support all life on our small planet. Many observers believe that our future security and quality of life are threatened less by war among nations than by the burden the sheer crush of humanity places on natural resources.

Take, for example, the plight of Madagascar, a large island off the southeast coast of Africa. In the past 35 years, half of Madagascar's forests have been leveled to provide fuel and to uncover farmland for the impoverished and rapidly growing population. Heavy rains, however, cause the cleared hills to erode, bleeding the rich red topsoil into the rivers and destroying the land's ability to grow crops. Farmers plant clove tree seedlings on the cleared slopes and then wait seven years before the first full crop of the pungent clove buds are ready for harvest and export, simply hoping that the slope will not wash away before harvest. Whole villages depend on the developed world's appetite for vanilla ice cream, cola drinks, and other foods that contain extracts from clove buds. Yet the village children go hungry because cloves are not an adequate food source, and not much else is available to eat.

The exploitation of Madagascar's forests and wildlife began about 1500 A.D. when humans first came to the island. As the human population grew, many species became extinct, including the "elephant bird," an astonishing animal that stood 3 m (10 feet) tall, weighed 500 kg (half a ton), and laid 10-kg (22-pound) eggs. The destruction has since accelerated, and with it has come the loss of hundreds of species, including plants that produce potentially life-saving drugs such as the drugs isolated from Madagascar's pink-petaled periwinkle that fight childhood leukemia. Observers fear that many such plants with potential uses in medicine and agriculture will perish along with Madagascar's tropical forests before they are ever studied and applied. And worse, they fear that Madagascar's own people are not even benefiting substantially from the wholesale clearing of forested lands.

Two decades ago, one might have predicted a similar fate for the Central American nation of Costa Rica. Although this small country's national debt is one of the highest in the world per citizen, the leaders are committed to sustainable development based on the application of modern biological principles and practices. Among other things, Costa Ricans are replanting deforested hillsides with fast-growing tropical hardwood trees. They are also growing nutritionally improved food crops, attempting to set aside up to 15 percent of their land as natural preserves for their tropical species, and instituting up-to-date health care and family-planning practices whenever possible. Costa Rica's success is a hopeful sign for the future: clearly these are biological solutions for social problems of biological origin.

In the chapters that follow, you will find many discussions of how biology is helping to solve world problems. We are, in fact, in the midst of a revolution in the biological sciences, with exciting new information surfacing weekly in the fight against cancer, heart disease, AIDS, infertility, and obesity. Researchers are making rapid advances in gene manipulation to create new drugs, crops, and farm animals; in exercise physiology to improve human performance; in the diagnosis of genetic diseases; and in the transplantation of organs, including brain tissue. Across all frontiers of biological science, at all levels of life's organization—from molecules to the biosphere—scientists are learning the most profound secrets of how living things use energy to overcome disorganization and reproduce to overcome death. In studying the living world, you are embarking on an adventure of discovery that will not only excite your imagination and enrich your appreciation of the natural world, but will also provide a basis on which you can contribute intelligently to the difficult choices society must make in the future.

CONNECTIONS

All living things share a mutual interdependence, a common origin, and two fundamental problems: the tendencies toward disorder and death. Each organism must conquer the challenge of disorganization by extracting energy and materials from its environment and using them for growth, repair, and continued activity. While a frog captures ants and recycles the energy stored in the insects' muscles, a periwinkle plant captures energy directly from the sun and absorbs materials from the air and soil. As different as these solutions might be, animals, plants, and all other organisms share a basic set of characteristics that allow them to combat the challenges to survival, and these attest to the common origin and to the unity of all living things.

Because life's characteristics and challenges are common to all species, people, as living organisms, are powerless to escape them. To save ourselves and our world from current ecological problems, biologists and citizens in all fields have begun massive global efforts such as the Earth Summit in Rio, and they must continue to learn about life processes and the interactions of organisms with their environments. The underlying principles of biological science begin with the laws of chemistry and physics and how they govern the atoms and molecules in living things—the subject of our next chapter.

KEY TERMS

adaptation	inductive reasoning
Animalia	motility
Archaebacteria	natural selection
biology	order
causality	Plantae
control	prediction
deductive reasoning	Protista
development	reproduction
Eubacteria	responsiveness
evolution	scientific method
Fungi	theory
gene	uniformity
hypothesis	

HIGHLIGHTS IN REVIEW

1 Living organisms are highly ordered; maintaining order requires energy and material from the environment.

  a The rosy periwinkle and the problems discussed at the Earth Summit illustrate five main themes in biology: the importance of energy in maintaining order; the consequences of reproduction; the evolutionary principles that created life's diversity; the interactions of diverse organisms with each other and the environment; and the utility of the scientific process in learning how nature functions.

  b Biologists have compiled a list of characteristics common to all living things. Order, metabolism, motility, and responsiveness relate to an organism's system for overcoming disorder; reproduction, development, and genes relate to perpetuation; and evolution and adaptation relate to interactions with the environment.

  c Living things exhibit a hierarchy of biological organization that includes the biosphere, ecosystems, communities, populations, individual organisms, organ systems, organs, tissues, cells, organelles, molecules, atoms, and finally, subatomic particles.

    d Living things exhibit metabolism, or the breaking down, re-arrangement, and use of energy compounds, and the synthesis of other compounds.

    e Self-propelled movement is a diagnostic feature of life, even in plants and other organisms that appear to remain stationary.

    f All organisms are responsive; they detect information about their surroundings and react in appropriate ways.

2 Individual organisms eventually die, but life continues via repro-duction and heredity.

    a Development, or change and growth during the life cycle is a key characteristic of life.

    b Living things have genes, or units of heritable information, that pass from one generation to the next and control specific phys-ical, chemical, and behavioral activities within the organism.

3 Over long periods of time, life forms change due to evolution. Natural selection—the ability of individuals with certain traits to reproduce more successfully than those lacking the traits—is a major mechanism of evolution.

    a Adaptations, or particular innovations of structure and function, allow organisms to survive in their particular environments.

    b Life as a whole is characterized by unity, manifested by shared molecular-level characteristics, and diversity, the fantastic vari-ety of living things all related by descent from common ancient progenitors.

    c Biologists categorize each living thing, placing each into a genus and a species, and into increasingly inclusive groups, in-cluding families, orders, classes, phyla or divisions, and six main kingdoms—Eubacteria, Archaebacteria, Protista, Fungi, Plantae, and Animalia.

4 Science is a way of learning how nature functions. Scientists per-form tests that might rule out possible explanations for a particu-lar phenomenon. Explanations that have been repeatedly tested and not disproven are tentatively accepted.

    a Biologists apply the process of science to their study of the nat-ural world. This includes the principles of causality and unifor-mity, as well as inductive and deductive reasoning and the test-ing of hypotheses. The formal scientific method involves asking a question about some puzzling phenomenon, proposing a hy-pothesis, predicting an observable result, then testing the pre-diction through experimentation.

5 The principles of biology can be applied to world problems such as overpopulation, disease, environmental degradation, famine, and drug addiction.
   a Biological research and applications have the potential to help solve many of the world's current problems, a number of which stem from overpopulation and the strain that our sheer numbers place on the environment.
   b We live amidst a revolution in the biological sciences, and citizens in all fields must become informed so that they can contribute to societal choices.

"The Nature of Life: An Introduction" from *The Nature of Life,* 3rd ed., by John H. Postlethwait and Janet L. Hopson, McGraw-Hill, Inc., 1995, pp. 2–24.

COMPREHENSION QUIZ

True or False

Directions: In the blank provided, indicate whether each statement is true or false.

_____ 1. Biology is the science of life.

_____ 2. It is relatively simple to answer the question, "What is life?"

_____ 3. All living things are descended from a common ancestor and arose as a result of genetic modification in species that lived before them in a process of change called evolution.

_____ 4. Many nonliving things have one or more of the characteristics of life.

_____ 5. Nonliving organisms possess a degree of order far greater than anything in the living world.

_____ 6. The hierarchy of life begins with subatomic particles and ends with the organ system.

_____ 7. In the process of replication, one cell divides and yields two identical cells.

_____ 8. Natural selection is believed to be the main mechanism behind evolution in nature.

Multiple Choice

Directions: For each item, select the best answer.

_____ 9. Which of the following is not a characteristic of living things?
   a. responsiveness
   b. adaptations
   c. motility
   d. uniformity

_____10. Adaptations are
    a. the chemical breakdown, conversion, and use of energy-rich compounds
    b. the tendency of living things to sense and react to their surroundings
    c. genetic modifications that allow groups of organisms to cope with their environments in more efficient ways
    d. none of the above

_____11. Organisms are defined as
    a. groups of individuals that live in the same area and actively interbreed with one another
    b. living things in particular regions
    c. an assemblage of interacting organisms living in a particular place
    d. independent individuals that show characteristics of life

_____12. Life characteristics that allow organisms to maintain order and organization within their bodies are
    a. metabolism, motility, and responsiveness
    b. reproduction, development, and heredity
    c. evolution and mutations
    d. none of the above

_____13. Life characteristics directly related to the perpetuation of species are
    a. order, metabolism, motility, and responsiveness
    b. reproduction, development, and heredity
    c. evolution and mutations
    d. none of the above

_____14. Genes
    a. are the hereditary information that directs the development of each individual and that passes from parents to their offspring
    b. control the development of specific physical, chemical, and behavioral traits within the organism
    c. are made up of DNA molecules
    d. are all of the above

_____15. Evolution
    a. accounts for the changes in forms of living organisms over time
    b. suggests that all groups alive today are like the youngest branches of a family tree
    c. helps explain the origin of species
    d. all of the above

_____16. Darwin and Wallace shared all of the following similarities *except*
   a. both were upper-class English gentlemen
   b. both developed a theory of evolution
   c. the term *natural selection* was used by both
   d. at the same time, both published nearly identical theories of evolution

_____17. The series of chemical reactions within cells that makes possible growth, repair, and other processes needed for survival is called
   a. motility
   b. adaptation
   c. metabolism
   d. natural selection

_____18. The scientific method consists of all of the following steps *except*
   a. asking a question or identifying a problem
   b. proposing a hypothesis
   c. making a prediction and testing the prediction through experimentation
   d. publishing the results

_____19. The steps of the scientific method can be used to find answers to puzzling questions in
   a. the world of nature
   b. the world of art
   c. the world of politics and religion
   d. all of the above

_____20. Inductive reasoning
   a. is defined as analyzing specific cases on the basis of preestablished general principles
   b. is not as helpful as deductive reasoning
   c. is used only by scientists
   d. is defined as generalizing from specific cases to arrive at broad principles

_____21. Deductive reasoning
   a. is defined as analyzing specific cases on the basis of preestablished general principles
   b. is not as helpful as inductive reasoning
   c. is used only by scientists
   d. is defined as generalizing from specific cases to arrive at broad principles

_____22. Among the fundamental principles behind the scientific process
are the principles of
a. causality and uniformity
b. causality and natural selection
c. uniformity and natural selection
d. adaptation and prediction

_____23. Biologists define the six kingdoms based on
a. evolutionary relationships
b. cell structures of the species within a kingdom
c. the ways in which species obtain energy
d. all of the above

_____24. Living things share all of the following *except* a
a. common origin
b. mutual interdependence
c. tendency toward order
d. tendency toward disorder and death

_____25. Main themes of biology include
a. the use of energy to maintain order, and reproduction and
heredity to overcome the death of individual organisms
b. evolution and the mechanism of natural selection
c. the use of scientific tests to learn about the natural world
d. all of the above

CHAPTER

8

THINKING CRITICALLY AS YOU READ

1

Determining Subject Matter

2

Locating Directly Stated Main Ideas

3

Formulating Implied Main Ideas

4

Identifying Supporting Details

5

Recognizing Authors' Writing Patterns

6

Applying Comprehension Skills to Longer Passages

7

Remembering College Textbook Material through Organizing

8

Thinking Critically as You Read

477

Reading furnishes our mind only with the materials of knowledge; it is thinking that makes what we read ours.

John Locke (1632–1704)

INTRODUCTION

Perhaps you are familiar with this quotation by John Locke, a famous English philosopher. Because his words ring true, they have appealed to generations of readers.

Reading does furnish the materials necessary for knowledge, but it is *our thinking* about this material that makes it ours and helps us to remember it. This kind of patient thinking and organizing demands concentration, time, and effort. Thinking requires the best of us.

The five writing patterns that textbook authors use were presented in Chapter 5. Knowledge of these patterns has allowed you to expand your awareness of college textbook organization. You now have useful new knowledge.

These same patterns could help you think through various questions you have regarding your intellectual growth in college:

What are my goals for the next year?	Listing pattern
What is the first step I need to take to accomplish my goal? What is the next step, and the next?	Sequence pattern

What is my definition of a "successful" student?	Definition pattern
What kind of a student am I? What kind of student do I wish to become?	Comparison-contrast pattern
What can I do now to get better results from my reading and studying?	Cause-effect pattern

Authors sometimes combine two or more patterns in a passage. This is called a mixed pattern. When you encounter a mixed pattern, ask yourself if one pattern is more important than the other. For example, in a mixed pattern that contains both the definition pattern and the comparison-contrast pattern, the comparison-contrast pattern might be more important. Another example would be a comparison-contrast pattern in which the similarities are listed. The important information is the similarities, and not the fact that they are presented in a list. In this case, the comparison-contrast pattern is the more important pattern. Your knowledge of patterns will help you again and again in your reading and thinking.

You know that as a college reader, you have the responsibility of determining the subject matter, main idea, and supporting details of textbook passages. Once you are sure you have understood these elements, as well as recognized the author's writing pattern, you should monitor your comprehension further. Now, in Chapter 8, you will learn to check the completeness of your understanding to determine whether you need to go *beyond* this basic information to gain additional insights about the passage. Going beyond this basic information to gain additional insights is called ***critical reading.*** *Reading critically* means questioning what you are reading. It involves *thinking critically* about what you are reading. Textbook authors expect you to assume this responsibility as you read, and so do your college professors.

Critical reading involves going beyond the basic information in a passage. It consists of *distinguishing opinions from facts, making inferences,* and *recognizing the author's point of view.*

Critical reading frequently requires taking the time to reread and to reconsider the author's message. This is because thinking critically as you read involves *going beyond* merely locating or formulating the main idea and identifying the supporting details. This chapter focuses on three skills that critical readers possess. These skills are:

1. **Distinguishing opinions from facts.** An author often includes opinions, and critical readers recognize these statements as being opinions. Critical readers ask themselves, "Is the main idea or are any of the supporting details an opinion?"

2. **Making inferences based on the information in passages.** Authors may not always state all of the significant information directly. Instead, they expect readers to draw their own conclusions, or *inferences,* based on information in the passage. In other words, readers sometimes need to go beyond what the author has stated. Critical readers ask themselves, "Based on the information in this passage, what does the author want me to conclude?" and "Is there some action the author wants me to take?"

3. **Recognizing the author's point of view.** Textbook material represents the author's attitudes and point of view. To understand the textbook author's point of view, you must examine how the author presents the information. Critical readers ask themselves, "What point of view is revealed by the author's choice of words?" Critical readers may also note the amount of space an author devotes to a topic.

THE IMPORTANCE OF READING CRITICALLY

It is important to monitor your comprehension and think critically as you read. Many students mistakenly believe that everything that appears in print, especially information that appears in textbooks, is a *fact.* Although many college textbook passages consist mostly of facts, they may also include the author's *opinions* about a subject. In this chapter, you will learn to ask yourself, "Has the author included opinions along with the facts?" If the author has included opinions in the passage, it is your task as a reader to differentiate these opinions from the facts in the passage. In textbooks, most opinions are the author's judgments that are based on specialized knowledge. This is what makes an author's opinions valuable. You must remember, however, that even though opinions are statements which cannot be proved, they can often be supported with facts. A well-supported opinion can be as important and useful as a fact.

A second error students make is to assume that the only information they are responsible for knowing is that which the author states in the textbook. The effective reader, however, realizes that he or she is responsible for understanding both what the author *states* and what the author *suggests* (implies) but does not state. In this chapter, you will learn to make appropriate *inferences* about information the author presents in a passage. You will learn to ask yourself, "Based on the information in the passage, what inference does the author expect me to make?" Making an inference requires the reader to deduce a meaning beyond what the author has stated directly. That is, the reader will have to use the "evidence" and facts that the author presents in order to arrive at the inference the author wants the reader to make. The reader must make the connection between what the author *says* and what the author wants the reader to *conclude* or *do.* An inference is a logical conclusion based on what the author has said, yet goes beyond what has been directly stated.

Even though authors are generally experts on their subjects, various authors may disagree with each other. Do not assume that all textbook authors have the same point of view. Because authors may have different points of view, it is important to recognize what the author's point of view is. *Point of view* refers to an author's interpretation of the subject matter and his or her attitudes and opinions toward the subject matter. A mistake college students often make in reading their textbooks is that they fail to recognize an author's point of view.

These three skills—distinguishing opinions from facts, making inferences, and recognizing the author's point of view—are related, and each involves thinking critically as you read.

EXPLANATIONS AND EXAMPLES

Distinguishing Opinions from Facts

What is the difference between an opinion and a fact? When stating an *opinion,* a textbook author is stating a belief or judgment. Although an opinion cannot be proved true *or* false, it nevertheless can be supported with facts or other knowledgeable opinions. In textbooks, opinions often represent an author's well-considered belief or the beliefs of other experts. *Effective college readers know that although opinions*

> An **opinion** is a belief or judgment that cannot be proved true or false.

cannot be proved, they can be every bit as important as facts. Opinions expressed in textbooks do, after all, typically represent the opinions of experts.

Because opinions are authors' judgments, evaluations, or interpretations, authors often use special words or phrases that alert students that they are reading opinions. The words and phrases below are typical of those that signal the reader that he or she is reading an opinion:

- perhaps
- apparently
- presumably
- one possibility is
- one interpretation is
- in our opinion

- many experts believe
- according to
- it seems likely
- this concept suggests
- in our view
- in most cases

In addition to these words and phrases, any words that show that a value judgment is being made can also indicate an opinion. These include words such as *most, best, greatest, successful, worst, fascinating, interesting,* and *effective,* to name a few. They are examples of judgmental words. Authors may disagree about what might be considered "successful" or "fascinating." An example of an opinion is, "Young adults must go to college in order to be successful." The word *successful* could mean successful financially, personally, socially, or all of these things. Because there is wide disagreement as to what being successful means, it would be impossible to prove a statement like this. Consequently, this statement expresses an opinion.

A *fact* is something that has taken place, or happened, or is assumed to have taken place. Facts can be proved by direct experience or observation. That is, facts are *based* on experience or objective verification. Authors generally use facts to support a main idea or an opinion (which may be a main idea). Facts are also used to support other facts (which may be supporting details). Not all facts are equally important. The most important facts are the ones that directly support the main idea or are essential to the author's argument. Sometimes, though, an author includes facts simply to add color and interest to a passage.

> A **fact** is information that can be proved true by direct experience or objective verification.

This chart may help you understand fact and opinion. Facts and well-supported opinions are useful. For example, scientific theories are well-supported opinions. Unsupported or poorly supported opinions are of little value, and you should be wary of them.

Fact (Can be proved)	Opinion (Cannot be proved *or* disproved)
Correct information	Well-supported opinion
	Unsupported or poorly supported opinion

Often authors combine opinions and facts in the same passage and even in the same sentence. It may be difficult, at times, to distinguish opinions from facts because the author has presented opinions in such a way that they seem like facts. On the other hand, sometimes an author will feel so strongly about an opinion that he will express it in a very obvious way. In either case, it is your job as a reader to think critically as you read and identify the opinions presented in textbook passages.

Now consider two passages that contain both opinions and facts. Read this passage from a management textbook to first determine its subject matter, main idea, and supporting details.

One of the most shocking failures of American history was the bankruptcy of the Penn Central in 1970, only 2 years after a merger was completed between two of the country's largest Eastern railroads, the New York Central and the Pennsylvania Railroad. During the short period of 2 years its stock dropped from a high of $86.50 per share to $5.50 and to $1.00 per share shortly thereafter, and many thousands of investors in bonds as well as stocks lost most of their investment. And this was in a company once regarded as one of the largest and most promising in the United States!

Management
by Harold Koontz et al.

---

bankruptcy (băngk′ rŭp sē) n. Financial ruin; impoverishment.

merger (mûr′ jər) n. The union of two or more commercial interests or corporations.

The subject matter of this passage is *the bankruptcy of the Penn Central transportation company.* The main idea is stated in the first sentence: *One of the most shocking failures of American history was the bankruptcy of the Penn Central in 1970, only 2 years after a merger was completed between two of the country's largest Eastern railroads, the New York Central and the Pennsylvania Railroad.* The supporting details include:

- The price of the stock dropped to $1.00 per share.

- Many thousands of investors in bonds and stocks lost most of their investment.

- This company was once regarded as one of the largest and most promising in the United States.

Thinking critically as you read involves asking yourself additional questions about the main idea and the supporting details. A question that you should ask yourself is, "Is the main idea or are any of the supporting details an opinion?"

The first sentence of this passage, its main idea, can be considered an opinion. The words "most shocking" are judgmental words that signal readers that they are reading an opinion. Notice, however, that this same sentence contains some facts, too (the bankruptcy occurred in 1970; this was two years after the merger; the merger was between two of the country's largest railroads). Facts can be verified by research, experience, or observation. Even though the main idea sentence contains both an opinion and a number of facts, the entire sentence should be considered an opinion.

When you examine the three supporting details in the Penn Central bankruptcy passage, you will find that all of them are facts.

- The price of stock dropped to $1.00 per share.

    This detail is a *fact* because records would show that the stock dropped from $86.50 to $5.50 to $1.00 per share.

ă pat ā pay â care ä father ĕ pet ē be ĭ pit ī tie î pier ŏ pot ō toe
ô paw oi noise ŏŏ took ōō boot ou out th thin *th* this ŭ cut û urge
yōō abuse zh vision ə *a*bout, it*e*m, ed*i*ble, gall*o*p, circ*u*s

- Many thousands of investors in bonds and stocks lost most of their investment.

  This detail is a *fact* because the investors' losses could be verified by research.

- This company was once regarded as one of the largest and most promising in the United States.

  The words "most promising" are judgmental words, which suggests an opinion. However, it could be verified by research that certain people once held this opinion, so it is a *fact*.

Now let's examine a passage from a sociology textbook.

What can be done to prevent domestic violence? Some sociologists argue that a basic attack on both courtship violence and family violence must involve a challenge to the glorification of violence which prevades our society. This could include reducing programs with "macho" themes on television, outlawing use of corporal punishment in schools, and perhaps even eliminating capital punishment. "Hot lines" for counseling of victims, shelters for battered wives and their children, and increased social services were all useful in assisting persons who have experienced abuse (*Time*, 1979).

Sociology
by Richard Schaefer

domestic (də mĕs′ tĭc) adj. Pertaining to the family.

glorification (glôr ə fĭ cā′ shən) n. The giving of glory, honor, or praise; causing something to seem to be glorious.

macho (mä′ chō) adj. Characterized by an exaggerated sense of masculinity.

corporal punishment (kôr′ pər əl) n. Physical punishment (punishment inflicted on the body).

capital punishment (kăp′ ə təl) n. Punishment by death (death penalty).

pervade (pər vād′) v. To spread throughout.

ă pat ā pay â care ä father ĕ pet ē be ĭ pit ī tie î pier ŏ pot ō toe
ô paw oi noise ŏŏ took ōō boot ou out th thin *th* this ŭ cut û urge
yōō abuse zh vision ə *a*bout, it*e*m, ed*i*ble, gall*o*p, circ*u*s

The subject matter of this passage is *the prevention of domestic violence.* One formulation of the main idea of this passage would be, *Although there are some social services to assist persons who have experienced abuse, a major way to prevent domestic violence would be to reduce the glorification of violence in our society.* The supporting details explain that we could reduce our society's glorification of violence by:

- reducing television programs with "macho" themes
- outlawing corporal punishment in schools
- eliminating capital punishment

Again, thinking critically as you read involves asking yourself additional questions about the main idea and the supporting details. A question that you would ask yourself is, "Is the main idea or are any of the supporting details an opinion?"

The main idea of this passage can be considered an opinion. Notice the phrase "Some sociologists argue. . . ." This phrase indicates that this approach to preventing domestic violence has not yet been tried or proved effective. This phrase also suggests that there is not agreement among sociologists about the effectiveness of this approach.

When you examine the three supporting details in this passage, you will find that each one is an opinion as to how we could reduce the glorification of violence in our society.

- reduce television programs with "macho" themes

    This detail is an *opinion* because the author has used the phrase "this could include" in order to suggest this way of deglorifying domestic violence. The word *could* indicates that the author is *suggesting* that this would be a partial solution to the problem.

- outlaw corporal punishment in schools

    This detail is an *opinion* because it also is merely another suggestion for a possible solution to the problem of deglorifying domestic violence.

- eliminate capital punishment

    This detail is also an *opinion* because it is yet another possible suggestion that *could* help solve the problem.

The last sentence in this passage contains facts about social services that were reported (in *Time* magazine) to be useful in assisting abused persons.

Remember, *both* opinions and facts are important, and college professors expect you to know that textbooks contain opinions as well as facts.

Making Inferences

You make inferences continually in your daily life. ***Inferences*** are always based on *something:* They are deductions based on descriptions, facts, opinions, experiences, and observations. For example, assume that a student comes to class late. Her hands are covered with grease and grime, and she seems frustrated and upset. It would be logical to infer that she has had a flat tire or other car trouble and had to fix the problem herself. Your inference would be based on your observations. When you make an inference while reading, you are drawing a logical conclusion that is based on information that you have read. An inference about a passage cannot be correct unless it is logical and is based upon information in the passage.

You have already worked a great deal with making inferences in Chapter 3, "Formulating Implied Main Ideas." You learned to read information in a passage and think about its most important point in order to infer the main idea that the author intended but did not state directly. As you recall, when authors *suggest* an idea, but do not state it directly, they are *implying* it; when a reader comprehends an indirectly stated (implied) idea, he or she is *inferring* the idea. Sometimes formulating the implied main idea is the only inference you need to make about a passage.

Thinking critically sometimes involves making additional inferences about what you have read. Before you can make additional inferences, of course, you must first understand the subject matter, main idea, and supporting details of the passage. To make inferences, you must go beyond the information in a passage and draw logical conclusions. You will need to reason out additional ideas that are based on the passage. Making inferences applies to single paragraphs as well as to longer passages in which you can make the inferences about the entire passage. To summarize, making an inference is a high-level thinking activity in which the reader draws additional conclusions about the passage that are based on material in the passage.

Sometimes, of course, there are no inferences to be made about the material in textbook passages. In this case, you need only to understand the subject matter, main idea, and supporting details.

> An **inference** is a logical conclusion that is based on what you have read, but goes *beyond* what the author has stated.

One way to learn how to make logical inferences is to study examples of correct inferences. This is the approach you will be using in this chapter to gain experience and expertise in making inferences as you read.

You may recall the following passage from a composition textbook from an earlier chapter of this book. The subject matter is *perverse readers;* the main idea is stated in the first sentence: *Readers are perverse creatures who, if given the slightest opportunity, will manage to get lost when they are reading.* The other sentences in the paragraph are supporting details which explain the ways in which readers "get lost." Now read the paragraph to determine the important conclusion the author expects you to draw or infer.

Readers are perverse creatures who, if given the slightest opportunity, will manage to get lost when they are reading. If they encounter a gap between one point and the next, they lose track of the narrative or argument. If they don't get clear directional signals to guide them between sentences and between paragraphs, they will head off in the wrong direction. If the author does not put in the right word to show the relationship between ideas, they will put in the wrong one. And if they cannot sense an underlying pattern in a piece of writing, they are likely to get confused and quit reading.

Contemporary Composition
by Maxine Hairston

The following information is *stated* in the paragraph:

- readers can easily get lost

- gaps between points confuse readers

- unclear directional signals confuse them

- missing relationship words confuse them

- if they can't sense an underlying pattern, they become confused and quit reading

The following conclusion can be *inferred:* Writers should write in such a way that readers will not get lost. Although there are several inferences you could make, this is the most important one, and the one the author wants you to make.

Remember, just as there can be many correct ways to express an implied main idea, there is more than one way to express a conclusion that has been implied by the author. For example, the important inference for the passage above could be expressed this way: If you are writing something, be careful to write in a manner that will not confuse the reader.

Now read this passage from an American history textbook to see what important inferences you can make. You will need to determine the passage's subject matter, main idea, and supporting details to use as the basis for your inferences.

> Television changed the leisure habits of the American people, made them better informed on the news and issues of the day, and even modified the patterns of American politics. In 1947 fewer than 10,000 people owned television sets with which they could view programs a few hours a day from a handful of stations. A decade later over 40,000,000 sets in homes, hotels, and bars were tuned in to 467 stations.
>
> *The Essentials of American History Since 1865*
> by Richard Current et al.

The subject matter of this passage is *the impact of television on the American people.* The main idea is *Television changed the leisure habits of the American people, made them better informed on the news and issues of the day, and even modified the patterns of American politics.* The other sentences are supporting details that explain why television has had such a powerful effect: the staggering increase in the number of television sets and television stations.

Based on the information in the paragraph, you can make the inference that television has affected our society profoundly and will continue to do so. Another reasonable inference that you might make is that major political candidates realize that they must use television effectively if they are to win.

Recognizing the Author's Point of View

As you already know, most college textbook passages are written to inform or instruct. At the same time, though, many of these passages also reveal the author's point of view. You may be wondering, what is a point of view? *Point of view* refers to an author's attitudes toward the subject matter. The author's point of view will influence *what material he chooses to include* and *how he chooses to present it.* Often the author's point of view will be easy to detect, but at other times it will be less obvious.

> **Point of view** is an author's interpretation of the subject matter and his attitude toward it.

An author's point of view, for example, may reveal his approval, sympathy, shock, or even anger toward a subject. It may also indicate the importance he or she places on a subject. Furthermore, the author's point of view may evoke your sympathy, shock you, or challenge your beliefs. Or it may persuade you to accept her point of view or simply convince you of the importance of the topic.

Since an author may indicate his point of view by the *specific words* he uses in discussing the topic, critical readers ask themselves, "Are there words that reveal the author's point of view?" For example, one author might say "This event . . ." and another might say "This scandal . . ." when referring to the same thing. Or an author might begin a sentence with the word "Unfortunately" to signal her point of view to the reader.

Each person's point of view is shaped by her or his background experiences and knowledge. All of us view the world through our own unique set of "lenses." This is why authors have their own particular viewpoint or perspective regarding a subject.

Reading critically allows you to identify the author's perspective. Remember, you are not necessarily reading to determine whether or not the author's point of view matches your own. Instead, you should be reading to become aware of *other* perspectives. Once you are aware of another perspective, you may decide to accept that new perspective, to reject it, to modify your own viewpoint, or simply to be aware that another viewpoint exists. Critical reading is one way of refining your own understanding of a subject and developing your own point of view toward it.

The Importance of Recognizing the Author's Point of View

Why is it important for college students to recognize a textbook author's point of view? As a student, you need to realize that the way an author presents his material reflects his interpretation of facts and theories. Even experts who write textbooks on the same subject may disagree. For example, the authors of different history textbooks will have somewhat different points of view regarding the reunification of East and West Germany in the 1990s.

Few subjects in life are simple enough to allow for only one perspective. Indeed, one might say *no* subject of any importance is simple enough to allow for only one perspective. In other words, no single perspective of a complex subject is ever adequate. The willingness to search for and recognize a variety of perspectives is the foundation of critical thinking and critical reading. As a critical reader you must actively try to see and understand other points of view, even when they are not obvious.

Critical readers and thinkers realize that textbook material contains the viewpoint of a real person. Moreover, this person's interpretation may change as new events occur and as new information becomes available. For example, the way textbook authors present the presidencies of John Kennedy, Lyndon Johnson, Richard Nixon, Jimmy Carter, and Ronald Reagan has changed over the years as more information has become available about their terms of office.

Remember, too, that no single author can present all of what is known about a subject. Every author has to make decisions about what to include and what to leave out. The choices an author makes will reflect her point of view.

In order to develop a more mature and complete understanding of a subject, you must read a variety of viewpoints on the same subject and maintain a questioning attitude. In essence, questioning is the hallmark of a critical reader.

Recognizing the Author's Point of View from Word Choice

As you learned earlier in this chapter, thinking critically as you read involves going beyond basic information to examine the authors' point of view. Now read this paragraph from a U.S. government textbook to determine the authors' point of view. This paragraph is the beginning of a longer section that discusses the second term of Ronald Reagan's presidency. As you will see, the subject matter of this passage is "the difficult second terms of popular American presidents." The main idea of the passage is stated by the first sentence: "Second terms have been hard on many popular presidents, especially those re-elected by wide margins." The supporting details discuss the second terms of several popular presidents.

> Second terms have been hard on many popular presidents, especially those re-elected by wide margins. For George Washington it was factionalism that marred his second term; for Thomas Jefferson, the embargo; for Franklin Roosevelt, the Court-packing plan; for Lyndon Johnson, the Vietnam War; and for Richard Nixon, Watergate. So too Ronald Reagan suffered a precipitous drop in his political fortunes as scandals racked his administration.
>
> *Nation of Nations*
> by James W. Davidson et al.

mar (mär) v. To damage or deface.

precipitous (prĭ sĭp′ ə təs) adj. Extremely steep.

scandal (skăn′ dəl) n. An act or circumstance that brings about disgrace.

rack (răk) v. To torment.

The question you should now ask yourself is, "Are there *words* that suggest the authors' point of view?" In the passage above, the authors end the passage with this sentence:

So too Ronald Reagan *suffered* a *precipitous* drop in his political fortunes as *scandals racked* his administration.

What can the reader infer from the authors' use of the words *suffered, precipitous, scandals,* and *racked?* They are powerful, evocative words that should signal to the critical reader the point of view of the authors. These words the authors chose to describe Ronald Reagan's second term reveal their point of view: the authors clearly feel that Ronald Reagan's second term was just as bad as the other popular presidents who experienced severe problems during their second terms.

ă pat ā pay â care ä father ĕ pet ē be ĭ pit ī tie î pier ŏ pot ō toe
ô paw oi noise o͞o took o͞o boot ou out th thin *th* this ŭ cut û urge
yo͞o abuse zh vision ə *a*bout, it*e*m, ed*i*ble, gall*o*p, circ*u*s

The authors could have written this sentence with these milder, more neutral words:

So too Ronald Reagan *experienced* a drop in his political fortunes as *problems affected* his administration.

An effective reader can see the contrast in the word choice in these two sentences. Incidentally, you can see the importance of developing a college-level vocabulary since it is the authors' choice of words that most clearly reveals their point of view.

Now reread this passage that appeared in the Chapter 2 Review Test. Since you are already familiar with its subject matter and main idea, be alert for *words* that suggest the authors' point of view.

> The European's greatest impact on the Americas was, however, unintended. Diseases carried from the Old World to the New by the alien invaders killed hundreds of thousands, even millions, of Native Americans, who had no immunity to germs that had infested Europe, Asia, and Africa for centuries. The greatest killer was smallpox, which was spread by direct human contact. The epidemic that hit Tenochtitlan in 1520 had begun in Hispaniola two years earlier. Pizzaro easily conquered the Inca partly because their society had been devastated by the epidemic shortly before his arrival. Smallpox was not the only villain; influenza, measles, and other diseases added to the destruction.
>
> *A People and a Nation*
> by Mary Beth Norton et al.

The question you should now ask yourself is, "Are there words that suggest the authors' point of view?"

- Write any words that reveal the authors' point of view:

_____

_____

_____

_____

The authors used these powerful, emotional words in the passage when describing what happened to the Native Americans.

- *alien invaders*

- *hundreds of thousands, even millions*

- greatest *killer,* smallpox

- Pizzaro *easily* conquered the Incas

- who had been *devastated* by the epidemic

- smallpox was not the only *villain*

- other diseases added to the *destruction*

- Based on the authors' choice of these words, what can you infer about their attitude toward what happened to the Native Americans? That is, *What is the authors' point of view?* Write a sentence that describes the authors' point of view.

_____

_____

_____

_____

The authors reveal a sympathetic point of view toward the Native Americans. The authors feel sympathy for the Native Americans because so many of them died from the diseases the invading Europeans infected them with. To describe the Europeans who came to the New World, the authors use the term "alien invaders" rather than such words as *European explorers* or even *European soldiers.* The authors chose words that provoke a stronger emotional reaction from the reader. Similarly, the authors' sympathetic point of view toward the Native Americans is revealed by their use of strong, emotionally charged words such as *devastated, killer,* and *destruction.*

The authors could have written the passage this way:

> The European's greatest impact on the Americas was, however, unintended. Diseases carried from the Old World to the New by the *Europeans* killed *many* Native Americans, who had no immunity to

germs that had infested Europe, Asia, and Africa for centuries. The greatest *problem* was smallpox, which was spread by direct human contact. The epidemic that hit Tenochtitlan in 1520 had begun in Hispaniola two years earlier. Pizarro conquered the Inca partly because their society had been *weakened* by the epidemic shortly before his arrival. Smallpox was not the only *disease;* influenza, measles, and other diseases added to the *problem.*

You can see that if written this way, the passage would not suggest the authors' sympathetic feelings about the devastating impact of diseases on the Native Americans in the New World.

A Word about Point of View and Passage Length

Part of an author's point of view or attitude toward the subject concerns how important the author considers that topic. The *amount of space* may suggest how important the author thinks the topic is. A biology textbook author who devotes several pages to the topic of photosynthesis considers it more important than an author who covers the same topic in less space.

You now know that an author's point of view is reflected by the words the author uses when discussing a subject. In addition, you can often tell how important the author considers a subject by the *amount of space* he or she devotes to the subject. The reason is clear: when an author goes into greater detail and gives a more complete explanation, it requires more space.

Here are two passages about a theory of love. They are taken from two psychology textbooks written by two different authors. Read the first passage to discover how this author presents his description of Sternberg's theory of love.

According to psychologist Robert Sternberg (1986), an even finer differentiation between types of love is in order. He proposes that love is made up of three components: an intimacy component, encompassing feelings of closeness and connectedness; a passion component, made up of the motivational drives related to sex, physical closeness, and romance; and a decision/commitment component, encompassing the cognition that one loves someone (in the short term) and longer-term feelings of commitment to maintain love.

Understanding Psychology
by Robert Feldman

Notice that this author describes Sternberg's theory of the components of love in just one paragraph.

Now read the second passage from a psychology textbook written by a different author. It also presents Sternberg's theory on the components of love. After introducing Sternberg's theory on love in the first paragraph, the author devotes a full paragraph to each component of love and explains each one in detail.

What is Love?

"Is there love at first sight?" "Why doesn't a summer love last?" "Why do some people get married after being in love for just one month?" "Can you be in love and not have sex?" "What's the best kind of love?" are but a sample of questions students ask. Robert Sternberg (1986) answers these questions with his *triangular theory of love,* which has three components: passion, intimacy, and commitment.

If you feel physically attracted to someone, you are experiencing *passion,* which leads to feelings of arousal and romance and the motivation to be physically involved. Passion arises very quickly and has strong influence on our judgments. For example, people rate their satisfaction with a first date almost entirely on the basis of physical attraction. That is, people tend to use the passion component to make initial judgments about their feelings for the person.

If you feel close or connected to someone, you are experiencing the *intimacy* component, which gives rise to your feelings of warmth. One of the primary ways that intimacy develops is through attempts to communicate with another person, usually by discussing one's inner feelings (Sternberg & Grajek, 1984). Other ways of promoting intimacy include sharing one's time, self, and possessions, promoting the other person's well-being, offering emotional and material support, touching, hugging, and engaging in what you would consider appropriate sexual behaviors.

> If you think you are in love and you wish to maintain that love, you are experiencing the *commitment* component, which leads to thoughts and feelings of commitment. Some of the ways of expressing commitment include making promises, agreeing to be sexually faithful to each other, staying in the relationship through hard times, becoming engaged, and getting married.
>
> *Introduction to Psychology*
> by Rod Plotnik

It is obvious that the second author explains Robert Sternberg's theory of love in much greater detail. In contrast with the first author, who describes all three components in one sentence, the second author devotes an entire paragraph to each component of love. You can infer the second author's point of view: He believes that Sternberg's theory is important, and therefore deserves the special emphasis of a more complete explanation.

A critical reader knows that a psychology professor who is using the textbook with the longer explanation of Sternberg's theory and spends time discussing it considers the theory important. He or she might be more likely to ask one or more test questions about this theory since the amount of *space* given to a topic often suggests how important it is. The amount of *time* a professor spends in class discussing a topic can also indicate the importance of the topic—and how likely it is to appear on a test.

In reality, you probably will not find yourself comparing two textbook passages on the same subject. In most courses, you will have only one textbook. The comparison of the two textbook passages above simply illustrates the fact that the amount of space an author devotes to a topic may suggest how important he or she considers it. In other words, the amount of explanation and supporting detail he or she includes suggests its importance. Different authors place different values on certain topics. The material they include in their textbooks and their thoroughness of presentation reflect their differing points of view and the values they place on specific topics.

CHAPTER

8

THINKING CRITICALLY AS YOU READ
Chapter Summary

Critical reading involves going beyond the basic information in a passage. It consists of *distinguishing opinions from facts, making inferences, and recognizing the author's point of view.*

1. DISTINGUISHING OPINIONS FROM FACTS

Opinions are authors' judgments, evaluations, or interpretations. Opinions cannot be proved true or false.

A *fact* has taken place, or happened, or is assumed to have taken place. Most facts can be proved by direct experience or observation or verified by research.

Your task as a reader is to differentiate the opinions from the facts in a passage.
    What to watch for:

- opinions and facts in the same passage or even the same sentence
- words that indicate opinions (such as *in my opinion, it seems likely, apparently*)
- judgmental words (such as *most, best, greatest, worst*)

499

2. MAKING INFERENCES

> Making *inferences* requires you to make the connection be-
> tween what the author says and what the author wants you to un-
> derstand. Inferences are always *based on something;* they are
> logical conclusions based on descriptions, facts, opinions, expe-
> riences, and observations. Using the information the author has
> presented, you must *reason out* more information than what he
> or she has stated directly.

Your task as a reader is to go *beyond* the stated information and deduce
(reason out) additional meaning.

What to watch for:

- important information that may not be directly stated but is merely
  suggested

- insights that give you a clearer, more thorough understanding of what
  you are reading

3. RECOGNIZING THE AUTHOR'S POINT OF VIEW

> *Point of view* refers to an author's interpretation of the subject
> matter and his or her attitude toward it.

Your task as a reader is to determine if the passage reveals or suggests
the author's point of view.

What to watch for:

- *words* that reveal the author's point of view or attitude toward the subject (such as strong, emotional, or evocative words that suggest approval, sympathy, shock, or anger)

- the *amount of space* the author devotes to the topic, and how thorough and detailed the explanation is, since these suggest how important the author considers the topic

Thinking critically as you read will enable you to go beyond the basic information in passages in order to gain additional insights about the information presented in college textbooks.

THINKING CRITICALLY AS YOU READ
Practice Exercises

In the passages below, you will apply the three reading skills you learned in this chapter: distinguishing opinions from facts, making inferences, and recognizing author's point of view. See pages 515–516 for answers and explanations to the exercises in this section.

DISTINGUISHING OPINIONS FROM FACTS

Read each of the passages below and differentiate any opinions from facts. Remember, some passages may consist entirely of facts and some entirely of opinions. If the main idea or any of the supporting details is an opinion, write the word *opinion* beside it in the space provided.

1. This passage comes from a music appreciation textbook.

> Wolfgang Amadeus Mozart (1756–1791), one of the most amazing child prodigies in history, was born in Salzburg, Austria. By the age of six, he could play the harpsichord and violin, improvise fugues, write minuets, and read music perfectly at first sight. At age eight, he wrote a symphony; at eleven, an oratorio; at twelve, an opera.
>
> *Music: An Appreciation*
> by Roger Kamien

prodigy (prŏd′ ə jē) n. A person with exceptional talents.

ă pat ā pay â care ä father ĕ pet ē be ĭ pit ī tie î pier ŏ pot ō toe
ô paw oi noise ŏŏ took ōō boot ou out th thin *th* this ŭ cut û urge
yōō abuse zh vision ə *a*bout, it*e*m, ed*i*ble, gall*o*p, circ*u*s

503

On the blank lines that follow, label the main idea and each of the supporting details as either a fact or an opinion.

_____

_____

_____

_____

Main idea:
Wolfgang Amadeus Mozart (1756–1791) was one of the most amazing child prodigies in history.

Supporting details:
- He was born in Salzburg, Austria.

- By the age of six he could play the harpsichord and violin, improvise fugues, write minuets, and read music perfectly at first sight.

- At age eight, he wrote a symphony; at eleven, an oratorio; at twelve, an opera.

2. This passage comes from a textbook on computer science.

> Modern computer systems vary in physical size from those that fill rooms to those with CPUs that can rest on the nail of your little finger. Generally, the larger the system, the greater its processing speed, storage capacity, cost, and ability to handle larger numbers of more powerful input and output devices. While the smallest processors are typically used by one person at a time, larger systems can simultaneously serve the needs of many users. For example, a large computer at a health insurance company can process hundreds of customer policies while accepting medical claims from scores of online workstations located in hospitals and doctors' offices.
>
> *Computer Concepts and Applications with BASIC*
> by Donald Sanders

CPU n. Central processing unit.

input (in′ pŏŏt) n. Information put into a communications system for transmission or into a data processing system for processing.

ă pat ā pay â care ä father ĕ pet ē be ĭ pit ī tie î pier ŏ pot ō toe
ô paw oi noise ŏŏ took ōō boot ou out th thin *th* this ŭ cut û urge
yōō abuse zh vision ə *about, item, edible, gallop, circus*

output (out′ pŏŏt) n. The information produced by a computer from a specific input.

scores (skôrs) n. pl. Large numbers.

On the blank lines below, label the main idea and each of the supporting details as either a fact or an opinion.

Main idea:
Generally, the larger the computer system's size, the greater its capabilities and cost.

Supporting details:

* Larger computer systems generally have greater speed, storage capacity, cost, and ability to handle more input and output devices.

* Larger systems can simultaneously serve the needs of many users.

3. This passage is taken from a textbook about film as art.

Perhaps the most famous costume in film history is Chaplin's Charlie the tramp outfit. The costume is an indication of both class and character, conveying the complex mixture of vanity and dash that makes Charlie appealing. The moustache, derby hat, and cane all suggest the fastidious dandy. The cane is used to give the impression of self-importance as Charlie swaggers confidently before a hostile world. But the baggy trousers several sizes too large, the oversized shoes, the too-tight coat—all these suggest Charlie's insignificance and poverty. Chaplin's view of mankind is symbolized by that costume: vain, absurd, and, finally, poignantly vulnerable.

Understanding Movies
by Louis Giannetti

complex (kəm plĕks′) adj. Consisting of interconnected parts; involved or intricate; complicated.

ă pat ā pay â care ä father ĕ pet ē be ĭ pit ī tie î pier ŏ pot ō toe
ô paw oi noise ŏŏ took ōō boot ou out th thin *th* this ŭ cut û urge
yōō abuse zh vision ə *a*bout, it*e*m, ed*i*ble, gall*o*p, circ*u*s

dash (dăsh) n. Spirited style; vigor; verve.

fastidious (fă stĭd′ ē əs) adj. Careful in all details; exacting; meticulous.

dandy (dăn′ dē) n. A man who affects extreme elegance in his clothes and manners.

swagger (swăg′ ər) v. To walk or conduct oneself with an insolent air; to strut; to brag or bluster.

poignantly (poin′ yənt lē) adv. Appealingly; touchingly.

vulnerable (vŭl′ nər ə bəl) adj. Unprotected from danger; susceptible to injury.

On the blank lines below, label the main idea and each of the supporting details as either a fact or an opinion.

Main idea:
Chaplin's view of mankind is symbolized by the Charlie the tramp costume: vain, absurd, and, finally, poignantly vulnerable.

Supporting details:
- The Charlie the tramp costume indicates both class and character.

- The moustache, hat, and cane suggest the dandy; the cane suggests self-importance.

- The ill-fitting clothes suggest Charlie's insignificance and poverty.

MAKING INFERENCES

Read each of the passages below in order to make appropriate inferences (go beyond the information that is stated in the passage).

ă pat ā pay â care ä father ĕ pet ē be ĭ pit ī tie î pier ŏ pot ō toe
ô paw oi noise o͝o took o͞o boot ou out th thin *th* this ŭ cut û urge
yo͞o abuse zh vision ə *a*bout, it*e*m, ed*i*ble, gall*o*p, circ*u*s

4. This passage was taken from a psychology textbook.

> The brain stem is responsible for many basic functions. It takes in information from several senses through sensory regions for vision, hearing, taste, balance, and touch in the facial area. It controls involuntary activity of the tongue, the larynx, the eyes, and the facial muscles through specific motor neurons for these areas. It controls levels of sleep and arousal through the reticular formation, nestled within its central core, and it coordinates the motor neurons in the spinal cord that control such activities as walking, breathing, and the beating of our hearts.
>
> *Psychology*
> by Diane Papalia and Sally Olds

sensory (sĕn′ sər ē) adj. Of or pertaining to the senses.

involuntary (ĭn vŏl′ ən tĕr ē) adj. Not performed willingly; not subject to control.

larynx (lăr′ ĭngks) n. The upper part of the respiratory (breathing) tract that controls the vocal cords.

arousal (ə rou′ zəl) n. Being awakened from sleep; the act of stirring up, exciting, or stimulating.

Subject matter: functions of the brain stem

Main idea: The brain stem is responsible for many basic functions.

Supporting details: The brain stem:

- takes in information from several senses

- controls certain involuntary activity

- controls level of sleep and arousal

- coordinates motor neurons and spinal cord

ă pat ā pay â care ä father ĕ pet ē be ĭ pit ī tie î pier ŏ pot ō toe ô paw oi noise o͞o took o͞o boot ou out th thin *th* this ŭ cut û urge y͞o͞o abuse zh vision ə *a*bout, it*e*m, ed*i*ble, gall*o*p, circ*u*s

Based on the information in this passage, what inference do the authors expect you to make about the significance of the brain stem?

Inference: _____

_____

_____

5. This paragraph is from a psychology textbook.

> There are two branches of statistics: descriptive and inferential. Descriptive statistics provide a way to summarize data gathered from research. For example, you could determine the grade-point averages and study schedules of students in your psychology class and use descriptive statistics to summarize your findings. Inferential statistics use data from a sample to generalize and predict results in a larger population. You would need inferential statistics to predict the intelligence and study schedules of future psychology classes composed of students similar to those in your own class. Both descriptive statistics and inferential statistics are needed in psychological research.
>
> *Psychology*
> by Diane Papalia and Sally Olds

Subject matter: descriptive and inferential statistics

Main idea: Both branches of statistics, descriptive and inferential, are needed in psychological research.

Supporting details:

- Descriptive statistics provide a way to summarize data gathered from research.

- Inferential statistics use data from samples to generalize and predict results in a larger population.

Based on the information in the passage, what inference do the authors expect you to make if you are a psychology student?

Inference: _____

_____

6. This passage comes from the same psychology textbook.

The effect of negative experiences in inducing physiological arousal may help to explain the "Romeo and Juliet" effect—the fact that parental interference in a love relationship intensifies the feelings of passionate love between two people. When Driscoll, Davis & Lipetz (1972) asked 140 dating, living-together, or married couples about the extent of their parents' disapproval of their relationships, they found that the more the parents interfered, the more passionately in love the couples were. Couples with interfering parents also, however, had lower levels of the attributes that usually go along with conjugal love—such as trust and uncritical acceptance. Apparently, if lovers don't resolve their problems with disapproving parents, the overall quality of their relationship with each other is likely to suffer.

Psychology
by Diane Papalia and Sally Olds

induce (ĭn dōōs′) v. To lead or move by influence or persuasion; to cause.

physiological (fĭz ē ə lŏj′ ĭ kəl) adj. Characteristic of the normal functioning of a living organism.

arousal (ə rou′ zəl) n. The act of stimulating or exciting.

intensify (ĭn tĕn′ sə fī) v. To make intense or more intense.

passionate (păsh′ ən ĭt) adj. Capable of having intense feelings; excitable.

attribute (ă′ trĭb yōōt) n. A distinctive feature of a person or a thing.

conjugal (kän′ jōō gəl) adj. Of marriage or the marital relationship.

resolve (rĭ zŏlv′) v. To find a solution to.

Subject matter: "Romeo and Juliet" effect

Main idea: The "Romeo and Juliet" effect refers to the fact that parental interference in a love relationship intensifies the feelings of passionate love between two people.

ă pat ā pay â care ä father ĕ pet ē be ĭ pit ī tie î pier ŏ pot ō toe
ô paw oi noise ōō took ōō boot ou out th thin th this ŭ cut û urge
yōō abuse zh vision ə about, item, edible, gallop, circus

Supporting details:

- One study found that the more the parents interfered, the more passionately in love the couples were.

- These couples also had lower levels of trust and uncritical acceptance.

- Unresolved problems with disapproving parents can lessen the quality of the couple's relationship with each other.

If you are a parent whose child is involved in a relationship you disapprove of, what inference should you make:

Inference: _____

_____

_____

If you are involved in a relationship your parents disapprove of, what inference should you make:

Inference: _____

_____

_____

RECOGNIZING AN AUTHOR'S POINT OF VIEW

After you have read the following passages and examined the subject matter, main idea, and supporting details for each, determine the author's point of view. Write it in the space provided.

7. This passage comes from a computer science textbook.

> William James, a turn-of-the-century psychologist, was reported to have said that "the best way to get rid of your fears is to face them." While this may seem to be simplistic advice to us today, it does seem to help when encountering computer phobia. Those people who have a fear of using the computer usually find that after the first few sessions at the keyboard their fear has disappeared. There is virtually

> nothing that a computer user can do to hurt or damage the computer, and so the only real problem is that of making a few mistakes. Fortunately, today's computers are designed to handle our errors and thus as users there is little to fear from initial fumbling as we learn to make use of the computer.
>
> *Understanding Computers*
> by Don Cassel

Subject matter: overcoming computer phobia

Main idea: Computer phobia is easily overcome after the first few sessions at the keyboard because today's computers are designed to handle our errors.

Supporting details:

- According to James, "The best way to get rid of our fears is to face them."

- There is virtually nothing a computer user can do to hurt or damage the computer.

- The only real problem is the fear of making a few mistakes.

Is the author's *point of view* or attitude toward overcoming computer phobia a pessimistic or an optimistic point of view?

---

8. This passage comes from an American history book.

> So Irangate was not Watergate; perhaps it was worse. Harry Truman coined the phrase "The buck stops here," meaning that the president bore final responsibility for the actions of his subordinates. Iran-Contra revealed a presidency in which an unelected segment within the government took upon itself the power to intercept the buck's upward movement and launch a series of illegal diversions of government money to finance an unapproved war. "Dirty hands" worked diligently for the ideals of "clean hearts."
>
> *Nation of Nations*
> by Mary Beth Davidson et al.

Subject matter: Irangate (Iran–Contra)

Main idea: Irangate was perhaps worse than Watergate since it revealed a presidency in which an unelected segment within the government took upon itself the power to divert funds to finance an unapproved war.

Supporting details:

- Truman coined the phrase, "The buck stops here" (i.e., the president bears the responsibility for his subordinates' actions).

- There was a series of illegal diversions of government money.

Is the authors' *point of view* or attitude toward Irangate approving or critical?

9. This passage comes from a sociology textbook.

Creating Geniuses

Many geniuses have been deliberately subjected to a very stimulating environment. A well-known example is Norbert Wiener, a prime mover in the development of computers and cybernetics. He entered college at 11 and received his Ph.D. from Harvard at 18. According to his father, he was "essentially an average boy who had had the advantage of superlative training" (Wiener, 1953). Many musical prodigies of the past, including Mozart and Beethoven, were subjected to rigorous daily training by their parents. Since 1945 a large number of ordinary children have been brought to the famous Japanese music teacher Shinichi Suzuki and he has successfully "trained every one of them—without exception—to be an excellent string musician" (Hoult, 1979). Nature may draw the outline of our traits and potential abilities, but that outline is broad and vague. Nurture appears both to determine the actual boundaries and to fill in the details (Nisbet, 1982).

Sociology: An Introduction
by Alex Thio

subject (sŭb jĕkt′) v. Expose to; cause to experience or undergo.

stimulating (stĭm′ yə lāt ĭng) adj. Eliciting or accelerating physiological or psychological activity; causing a response, excitement, or heightened action.

cybernetics (sī bər nēt′ ĭks) n. Plural in form; used with a singular verb. The theoretical study of control processes in electronic, mechanical, and biological systems, especially the mathematical analysis of the flow of information in such systems.

Ph.D. (Doctor of Philosophy) n. A graduate degree (earned after the undergraduate and master's degrees).

superlative (sōō pûr′ lə tĭv) adj. Of the highest order or quality; surpassing or superior to all others.

prodigy (prŏd′ ə jē) n. A young person with exceptional talents or powers.

rigorous (rĭg′ ər əs) adj. Characterized by or acting with rigor; trying; strict; precisely accurate.

trait (trāt) n. A distinguishing feature, as of the character.

potential (pə tĕn′ shəl) adj. Possible, but not yet realized; capable of being but not yet in existence; latent.

nurture (nûr′ chər) n. The act of promoting development or growth; upbringing; rearing.

Subject matter: the effect of nature (genetics) and nurture (our environment) in developing our abilities. (The heading, "Creating Geniuses," is too general. The passage also mentions ordinary children who became excellent string musicians.)

Main idea: Although nature may draw the outline of our traits and potential abilities, nurture appears both to determine the actual boundaries and to fill in the details.

or

Although we are born with certain abilities, we must receive excellent training in order to reach our potential.

Supporting details:

- Many geniuses have been deliberately subjected to a very stimulating environment.

ă pat ā pay â care ä father ĕ pet ē be ĭ pit ī tie î pier ŏ pot ō toe
ô paw oi noise ŏŏ took ōō boot ou out th thin *th* this ŭ cut û urge
yōō abuse zh vision ə *a*bout, it*e*m, ed*i*ble, gall*o*p, circ*u*s

- Norbert Wiener is an example of someone who had superlative early training.

- Many musical prodigies, such as Mozart and Beethoven, were subjected to rigorous daily training.

- Many ordinary children have become excellent musicians through training in the Suzuki method.

What is the author's *point of view* or attitude regarding early training in order to develop potential?

_____

_____

THINKING CRITICALLY AS YOU READ
Answer Key for Practice Exercises

DISTINGUISHING OPINIONS FROM FACTS

1. It is a fact that Mozart was a child prodigy, but the phrase "one of the *most amazing*" includes judgmental words that indicate that the main idea is an opinion. All of the supporting details are facts that could be verified by research.

2. There are no opinions—only facts—in this passage. The main idea and all of the supporting details are facts which could be verified by research.

3. The sentences in this passage reflect the author's opinions about Charlie Chaplin's "Charlie the tramp" outfit and what it symbolized. The words *perhaps* and *suggest* indicate that the author is making a judgment, and that these ideas represent *his* beliefs about what the tramp outfit symbolizes.

MAKING INFERENCES

4. Reasonable and appropriate inferences include:

    *   Because the brain stem is responsible for many basic functions, it is essential to life.

    *   Damage to the brain stem could disrupt many normal body functions.

5. Reasonable and appropriate inferences include:

    *   If you are a psychology student who will be reading about the results of psychological research studies, you should take a statistics course.

    *   You can have a better understanding of psychology if you understand statistics.

    *   Psychologists need to be knowledgeable about statistics.

6. Reasonable and appropriate inferences include:

- Parents should be aware that their child's intense love relationship may be a response to parental interference rather than being based on the couple's true feelings of trust, love, and uncritical acceptance of each other.

- Parents should refrain from interfering in their children's love relationships.

  and

- You should be aware that the "Romeo and Juliet" effect could be the cause of your attraction to a person whom your parents dislike.

RECOGNIZING THE AUTHOR'S POINT OF VIEW

7. The author has an optimistic point of view about our overcoming computer phobia. To reassure us about how easy it is to overcome computer phobia, the author uses phrases such as:

- *first few* sessions at the keyboard

- fear has *disappeared*

- *virtually nothing* can hurt the computer

- *designed* to handle our errors

8. The authors are critical in their point of view about Irangate.

- They use the words "*dirty* hands" to describe the illegal actions of President Reagan's subordinates.

- They state that Irangate was "perhaps *worse* than Watergate."

9. The author considers early, excellent training crucial to the development of all children's potential abilities. We can assume the author strongly favors this important training for children.

THINKING CRITICALLY AS YOU READ
Review Test

Read each of the following passages carefully. Determine the subject matter, main idea, and supporting details for each passage. In this review test, you will need to check the meaning of unfamiliar words. (Some words have been listed below each passage for you to define.) Using a dictionary, define the words listed below each passage according to the way they are used *in the paragraph.* Remember, you may not need to use the dictionary for a word if the author has defined it for you in the passage. Understanding the terminology in your textbooks is part of your responsibility as a successful student. Finally, apply the critical thinking skill that is emphasized in each section.

DISTINGUISHING OPINIONS FROM FACTS

Read each of the passages below and differentiate any opinions from facts. Remember, some passages may consist entirely of facts or entirely of opinions. If the main idea or any of the supporting details is an opinion, write the word *opinion* beside it in the space provided. If it is a fact, write the word *fact.*

1. This selection is drawn from a government textbook.

> By tradition, the choice of the vice-presidential nominee rests with the presidential nominee. His decision can reflect any number of considerations, including the experience, reputation, political beliefs, ethnic background, and home region of a possible running mate. Mondale in 1984 chose Geraldine Ferraro, the first female vice-presidential nominee of a major party, because his private polls indicated

that a woman would be a stronger addition to the ticket than any of the available men.

The American Democracy
by Thomas Patterson

Define this word:

ethnic: _____

- Write the *subject matter* here:

_____

_____

- Write the *main idea* sentence here:

_____

_____

_____

_____

Is the main idea a fact or an opinion? _____

- List the *supporting details* here; write "fact" or "opinion" in parentheses after each detail.

_____

_____

_____

_____

_____

_____

_____

_____

2.   This selection is taken from a psychology textbook.

> Scientists have offered a variety of explanations for aggressive be-
> havior—inherited tendencies, the results of experience and learning,
> and an interaction between these two major forces. By and large, it
> looks as if we are born with a predisposition toward aggressiveness
> and then we learn when we should express this tendency and when
> we should inhibit it.
>
> *Psychology*
> by Diane Papalia and Sally Olds

Define these words:

aggressive: _____

inherited: _____

tendencies: _____

predisposition: _____

inhibit: _____

- Write the *subject matter* here:

_____

- Write the *main idea* sentence here:

_____

_____

_____

_____

Is the main idea a fact or an opinion? _____

- List the *supporting details* here; write "fact" or "opinion" in parentheses after each detail.

_____

_____

_____

_____

_____

_____

_____

_____

MAKING INFERENCES

Read each of the following passages. After writing the subject matter, main idea, and supporting details, determine if it is necessary to make an inference (to go beyond the information that is stated in the passage).

3.   This selection comes from a business textbook.

> Electronic computers now pervade business data processing as well as other areas in our society. The entire computer revolution has come about during the lifetime of today's middle- and senior-level managers, almost none of whom studied computers as part of their formal education because computer technology either did not exist or was not widely used for business data processing. Business data processing has been extensively taught in colleges and universities only since about 1970.
>
> *Principles of Management Information Systems*
> by George M. Scott

Define these words:

pervade: _____

extensively: _____

- Write the *subject matter* here:

_____

- Write the *main idea* sentence here:

_____

_____

_____

_____

- List the *supporting details* here:

_____

_____

_____

_____

_____

_____

_____

_____

- Write the *inference* the author expects you to make if you are a college student who is considering a career in management.

_____

_____

_____

- Write the *inference* the author expects you to make if you are a manager who finished college before 1970.

_____

_____

_____

4. This passage comes from a marketing textbook.

Essentially, there are only two parts to an advertisement—*what* is said and *how* it is said. One part deals with product attributes to be explained, and the other is made up of the headlines, illustrations, and layouts. A great deal has been done to improve the manner of presentations (the "how"). This has been possible because research has been able to establish criteria to measure its effectiveness. The most commonly used evaluation methods measure the number of people who note, read, and remember the advertisements. But little has been done to aid management in its evaluation of the "what" part of an ad.

Fundamentals of Marketing
by William J. Stanton

Define these words:

attributes: _____

criteria: _____

- Write the *subject matter* here:

  _____

- Write the *main idea* sentence here:

  _____

  _____

  _____

  _____

  _____

- List the *supporting details* here:

  _____

  _____

  _____

  _____

  _____

  _____

  _____

  _____

  _____

- Write the *inference* the author expects you to make about the "what" of an advertisement.

_____

_____

_____

5.   This passage comes from a sociology textbook.

Stratification in Campus Life

Wherever one turns, social inequality confronts the members of the college community, a matter that two students discuss in the following observations: . . . "Time and again I hear it said that universities exist for students and that their primary purpose is to educate and enrich people's lives. I came to college quite idealistic, believing in its visionary commitment. But in the course of my campus experiences I have come to a quite different conclusion. Universities exist chiefly for university officials and the faculty. Student needs have minimal priority. As freshmen we are herded in mass lectures and recitation sections with little concern for our individual experiences, capabilities, or interests. We have little or no voice in what we are taught or who teaches us. These decisions are made in an authoritarian manner by others. It seems to matter little to the powers-that-be whether teaching is good, bad, or indifferent."

Sociology
by James W. Vander Zanden

Define these words:

visionary: _____

authoritarian: _____

- Write the *subject matter* here:

_____

- Write the *main idea* sentence here:

_____

_____

_____

_____

- List the *supporting details* here:

_____

_____

_____

_____

_____

_____

_____

- What is the *point of view* or attitude of this student toward college?

_____

_____

_____

6. This passage is drawn from a computer science textbook.

> ### You Need to Be Good at Math or Be a Programmer to Use a Computer
>
> This mistaken belief has led more than one person to abandon their quest for using a computer in their work. Contrary to popular notion, to use a computer successfully does not require a high level of mathematics. The average businessperson who understands the basic concepts of arithmetic needed to function effectively in business can also use a computer successfully.
>
> *Understanding Computers*
> by Don Cassel

- Write the *subject matter* here:

_____

_____

- Write the *main idea* sentence here:

  _____

  _____

  _____

  _____

- List the *supporting details* here:

  _____

  _____

  _____

  _____

  _____

  _____

  _____

- Describe the author's *point of view* or attitude toward the average person successfully learning to use computers in his or her work.

  _____

  _____

  _____

CHAPTER

8

THINKING CRITICALLY AS YOU READ
Supplemental Exercises

DISTINGUISHING OPINIONS FROM FACTS

1. The following passage comes from a psychology textbook.

> While we know, then, some of the factors that lead to making friends, there has been practically no research on keeping them—on what happens during a relationship, on what makes some friendships enduring and others fleeting, on what makes some people able to make and hold onto several friendships in a lifetime, while others drift along almost friendless. Friendship, then, offers a fertile field for social psychology research studies.
>
> *Psychology*
> by Diane Papalia and Sally Olds

* Write the *subject matter* here:

    _____

* Write the *main idea* sentence here:

    _____

    _____

    _____

    _____

Is the main idea a fact or an opinion? _____

* List the *supporting details* here; write "fact" or "opinion" in parentheses after each detail.

    _____

    _____

_____

_____

_____

_____

_____

_____

2. This passage is taken from an oceanography textbook.

> The lack of domesticated marine species and ignorance of fish diseases have limited the growth of aquaculture in the United States. Also, the legal status of many marine areas is unclear so that it is often impossible to control access in order to prevent loss or damage to a crop. Despite these problems, aquaculture is likely to become an increasingly important source of some foods, such as shrimp or oysters, as it already is in Asia.
>
> *Oceanography*
> by M. Grant Gross

- Write the *subject matter* here:

_____

- Write the *main idea* sentence here:

_____

_____

_____

Is the main idea a fact or an opinion? _____

- List the *supporting details* here; write "fact" or "opinion" in parentheses after each detail.

_____

_____

_____

_____

_____

_____

_____

MAKING INFERENCES

3.   The following passage comes from an art appreciation book.

Iconography

   Loosely, iconography is the "story" within a work of art. Many people find the term confusing, because both subject matter and content could be described in much the same way as iconography. An example may help to clear up the confusion among the three terms. Suppose you see a painting of a boy and a dog. The *subject matter* of that painting is simply "a boy and a dog." Its *content* might be "the love between a boy and his dog." But if you, the observer, see that the dog is a collie, realize that the dog is Lassie, and know the Lassie stories—know that Lassie is an intelligent and heroic dog who often saves people from danger—then you have caught the painting's *iconography.*

   Artists around the world always have assumed a certain iconographical knowledge on the part of their audiences. A viewer's comprehension of the iconography includes familiarity with the people, places, and events that are depicted, as well as any symbolism intended by the artist. Much of the history of art has some literary or historical or religious reference. Quite a lot of Western art is based on the

Subject Matter

_____

Main Idea

_____

_____

Subject Matter

_____

Main Idea

_____

_____

Bible. Most of the time an artist's immediate circle of patrons and viewers will grasp the iconography at once. Problems arise, however, when we confront art from times and places other than our own.

Living with Art
by Rita Gilbert and William McCarter

- Write the *inference* the authors expect you to make about iconography.

_____

_____

_____

4. This passage is taken from a psychology textbook.

One of the most frequent causes of blindness is a restriction of the impulses across the optic nerve. **Glaucoma,** which strikes between 1 and 2 percent of those over age 40, occurs when pressure in the fluid of the eye begins to build up, either because it cannot be properly drained or because it is overproduced. When this first begins to happen, the nerve cells that communicate information about peripheral vision are constricted, leading to a decline in the ability to see anything outside a narrow circle directly ahead. This problem is called **tunnel vision.** Eventually, the pressure can become so great that all the nerve cells are contracted, leading to total blindness. However, if detected early glaucoma is highly treatable, either through medication that reduces the pressure in the eye or through surgery.

Understanding Psychology
by Robert Feldman

- Write the *subject matter* here:

_____

- Write the *main idea* sentence here:

_____

_____

_____

_____

- List the *supporting details* here:

_____

_____

_____

_____

_____

_____

_____

- Write the *inference* the author expects you to make about your vision if you are over age 40.

_____

_____

_____

RECOGNIZING THE AUTHOR'S POINT OF VIEW

5. This passage is drawn from a music appreciation textbook.

> Throughout history, singing has been the most widespread and familiar way of making music. Singers seem always to have had a magnetic appeal, and the exchange between singer and audience contains a bit of magic—something direct and spellbinding. The singer becomes an instrument with a unique ability to fuse words and musical tones.
>
> *Music: An Appreciation*
> by Roger Kamien

- Write the *subject matter* here:

  _____

- Write the *main idea* sentence here:

  _____

  _____

  _____

  _____

- List the *supporting details* here:

  _____

  _____

  _____

  _____

  _____

  _____

  _____

- What is the author's *point of view* or attitude toward singing as a way of making music?

  _____

  _____

  _____

6. This selection is taken from a psychology textbook.

Most people think of rape as a rare crime and one committed by strangers. In fact, it occurs far more frequently than is commonly thought, and rapists are typically acquaintances of their victims (Mahoney, 1983; Koss, in press). For instance, a national survey conducted at thirty-five universities revealed the startling finding that one out of eight women reported having been raped, and of that group, about half said the rapists were first dates, casual dates, or romantic acquaintances—a phenomenon called **date rape** (Sweet, 1985). Statistically, then, a woman is more likely to be raped on a date than by a stranger jumping out of the bushes. But whether on a date or alone, a woman's chances of being raped are shockingly high: According to one researcher, there is a 26 percent chance that a woman will be the victim of a rape during her lifetime (Russell & Howell, 1983).

Understanding Psychology
by Robert Feldman

- Write the *subject matter* here:

_____

- Write the *main idea* sentence here:

_____

_____

_____

_____

- List the *supporting details* here:

_____

_____

_____

_____

_____

_____

_____

- What is the author's *point of view* or attitude toward a woman's chance of being raped?

_____

_____

8

THINKING CRITICALLY AS YOU READ
Textbook Excerpt and Comprehension Quiz

"Ludwig van Beethoven" from *Music: An Appreciation,* 5th ed.,
by Roger Kamien, McGraw-Hill, Inc., 1992, pp. 264–270.

Prepare Yourself to Read

Before you read this selection, read and think about its title. Then, in one or two sentences, write a few of the things that you already know about Beethoven.

_____

_____

_____

_____

_____

Complete your preview of this selection by reading

- the first paragraph
- the headings of each section
- any diagrams, illustrations, and photographs, and
- all of the last paragraph

Ask and answer questions as you read.

Use questions to guide your reading. Turn section headings into questions. If there are no headings, create questions based on what the paragraph or sections seem to be about.

Read actively to find answers to your questions.

LUDWIG VAN BEETHOVEN

For many people, Ludwig van Beethoven (1770-1827) represents the highest level of musical genius. His unique stature is comparable to Shakespeare's in literature and Michelangelo's in painting and sculpture. He opened new realms of musical expression and profoundly influenced composers throughout the nineteenth century.

Beethoven was born on December 16, 1770, in Bonn, Germany. Like Bach and Mozart before him, he came from a family of musicians. His grandfather, also named Ludwig, was music director at the court at Bonn. His father, Johann, was a tenor who held a low position in the court and who saw his talented son as a profitable prodigy like Mozart. It's told that Johann Beethoven and a musician friend would come home from the local tavern late at night, rouse young Ludwig from sleep, and make him practice at the keyboard until morning. At the age of eleven, Beethoven served as assistant to the court organist, and at twelve he had several piano compositions published.

Beethoven went to Vienna when he was sixteen to improvise for Mozart. Mozart reportedly said, "Keep your eyes on him; some day he will give the world something to talk about." Beethoven then returned to Bonn, because his mother was critically ill. She died shortly after. His father, who had become an alcoholic, was soon dismissed from the court choir. Beethoven, at eighteen, became the legal guardian of his two younger brothers. By now, Beethoven had become a court organist and violist and was responsible for composing and performing; suddenly, he was also head of a family.

Shortly before his twenty-second birthday, Beethoven left Bonn to study with Haydn in Vienna, where he spent the rest of his life. In 1792, Haydn was at the height of his fame, too busy composing to devote much time or energy to teaching. As a result, he overlooked errors in Beethoven's counterpoint exercises, and Beethoven felt forced to go secretly to another teacher. (Haydn never learned of this.) Beethoven's drive for thoroughness and mastery—evident throughout his life—is shown by his willingness to subject himself to a strict course in counterpoint and fugue even after he had composed fine works.

Beethoven's first seven years in Vienna brought hard work, growing confidence, a strong sense of identity, and public praise. His letters of introduction from members of the aristocracy in Bonn opened the doors of the social and cultural elite in this music-loving city. People were dazzled by his piano virtuosity and moved by his improvisations. "He knew how to produce such an impression on every listener," reports a contemporary, "that frequently there was not a single dry eye, while many broke out into loud sobs, for there was a certain magic in his expression." Beethoven rebelled against social convention, asserting that an artist deserved as much respect as the nobility. Once, while playing in an aristocrat's drawing room, he was disturbed by the loud conversation of a young count. Beethoven jumped up from the piano, exclaiming, "I will not play for such swine!" For a long time he was a guest of Prince Karl von Lichnowsky, who told his personal servant that if ever he and Beethoven rang at the same time, Beethoven should be served first. Aristocrats showered Beethoven with gifts, and he earned good fees from piano lessons and private concerts. Publishers were quick to buy his compositions, even though some critics complained that they were "bizarre" and "excessively complicated."

Disaster struck during his twenty-ninth year: Beethoven felt the first symptoms of deafness. Doctors could do nothing to halt its progress or to relieve Beethoven's physical and emotional torment. In 1801 he wrote despairingly, "For two years I have avoided almost all social gatherings because it is impossible for me to say to people 'I am deaf.' If I belonged to any other profession it would be easier, but in my profession it is a terrible handicap." On October 6, 1802, Beethoven was in Heiligenstadt, a village outside Vienna where he sought solitude during the summer. That day he expressed his feelings in what is now known as the Heiligenstadt testament, a long, agonized letter addressed to his brothers. Beethoven wrote, "I would have ended my life—it was only my art that held me back. Ah, it seemed to me impossible to leave the world until I had brought forth all that I felt was within me."

Beethoven's victory over despair coincided with an important change in his musical style. Works that he created after his emotional crisis have a new power and heroism. From 1803 to 1804, he composed the gigantic Third Symphony, the *Eroica,* a landmark in music history. At first, he planned to name it *Bonaparte,* after Napoleon, the first consul of the French Republic. Beethoven saw Napoleon as the embodiment of heroism and the champion of the principles underlying the French Revolution. *Liberty, equality, fraternity* were stirring words that expressed Beethoven's democratic ideals. But when he learned that Napoleon had proclaimed himself emperor of the French, Beethoven "flew into a rage and cried out, 'He too is nothing but an ordinary man! Now he will trample under foot all the rights of man and only indulge his ambition. He will exalt himself above all others and become a tyrant!'" Seizing his score, Beethoven tore out the title page bearing Napoleon's name and threw it on the floor. On a new title page, later, Beethoven wrote, "Heroic Symphony composed to celebrate the memory of a great man."

(Granger Collection)

Beethoven opened new realms of musical expression that profoundly influenced composers throughout the nineteenth century.

In 1812, Beethoven met Johann Wolfgang von Goethe, the great German poet he had long worshiped. He played for Goethe, and the two artists walked and talked together. Shortly after this meeting, Goethe described Beethoven to a friend as "an utterly untamed personality." To his wife, the poet wrote, "Never before have I seen an artist with more power of concentration, more energy, more inwardness."

Despite such descriptions by people who knew him, Beethoven remains a mystery. He was self-educated and had read widely in Shakespeare and the ancient classics, but he was weak in elementary arithmetic. He claimed the highest moral principles, but he was often unscrupulous in dealing with publishers. Although orderly and methodical when composing, Beethoven dressed sloppily and lived in incredibly messy apartments. During his thirty-five years in Vienna, he changed dwellings about forty times.

Beethoven fell in and out of love with several women, mostly of noble birth, but was never able to form a lasting relationship. He wrote a passionate letter to a woman referred to as the "immortal beloved"; it was found in a drawer after his death. Only recently has a Beethoven scholar established her identity as the Viennese aristocrat Antonie Brentano. Beethoven took consolation from nature for disappointments in his personal life. Ideas came to him while he walked through the Viennese countryside. His Sixth Symphony, the *Pastoral,* beautifully expresses his recollections of life in the country.

Beethoven was never in the service of the Viennese aristocracy. A growing musical public made it possible for him to earn a fairly good income by selling compositions to publishers. His stature was so great that when he threatened to accept a position outside Austria in 1809, three nobles made a special arrangement to keep him in Vienna. Prince Kinsky, Prince Lobkowitz, and Archduke Rudolf—the emperor's brother and Beethoven's pupil—committed themselves to give Beethoven an annual income. Their only condition was that Beethoven continue to live in the Austrian capital—an unprecedented arrangement in music history.

As Beethoven's hearing weakened, so did his piano playing and conducting. By the time he was forty-four, this once brilliant pianist was forced to stop playing in public. But he insisted on conducting his orchestral works long after he could do it efficiently. The players would become confused by his wild gestures on the podium, and performances were often chaotic. His sense of isolation grew with his deafness. Friends had to communicate with him through an ear trumpet, and during his last eight years he carried notebooks in which people would write questions and comments.

In 1815, his brother Caspar died, leaving a nine-year-old son, Karl, to whom Beethoven and Caspar's widow became coguardians. Young

Karl was the object of a savage tug-of-war. For five years, Beethoven fought legal battles for exclusive custody of his nephew; he finally won. This "victory" was a disaster for everyone. Growing up in the household of a deaf, eccentric bachelor uncle is not easy at best, and for Karl it was complicated by Beethoven's craving for love and companionship. The young man attempted suicide, and Beethoven, whose health was already poor, was shattered.

During the first three years of legal battles over Karl, Beethoven composed less, and the Viennese began to whisper that he was finished. Beethoven heard the rumor and said, "Wait a while; they'll soon learn differently!" And they did. After 1818, Beethoven's domestic problems did not prevent a creative outburst that produced some of his greatest works: the late piano sonatas and string quartets, the *Missa solemnis,* and the Ninth Symphony—out of total deafness, new realms of sound.

BEETHOVEN'S MUSIC

"I must despise the world which does not know that music is a higher revelation than all wisdom and philosophy." For Beethoven, music was not mere entertainment, but a moral force capable of creating a vision of higher ideals. His music directly reflects his powerful, tortured personality. In both art and life, his heroic struggle resulted in victory over despair.

Beethoven's demand for perfection meant long and hard work. Unlike Mozart, he couldn't dash off three great symphonies in six weeks. Sometimes he worked for years on a single symphony, writing other works during the same period of time. He carried music sketchbooks everywhere, jotting down new ideas, revising and refining old ones. These early notes often seem crude and uninspired when compared with the final versions of his works, which were often hammered out through great labor.

Beethoven mostly used classical forms and techniques, but he gave them new power and intensity. The musical heir of Haydn and Mozart, he bridged the classical and romantic eras. Many of his innovations were used by composers who came after him.

In his works, great tension and excitement are built up through syncopations and dissonances. The range of pitch and dynamics is greater than ever before, so that contrasts of mood become more pronounced. Accents and climaxes seem titanic. Tiny rhythmic ideas are often repeated over and over to create momentum. Greater tension called for a larger musical framework, and so Beethoven expanded his forms. For example, the Third Symphony *(Eroica)* is far longer than any symphony by Haydn or Mozart; it takes almost 50 minutes to perform. Beethoven was a musical architect who was unsurpassed in his ability to create large-scale structures in which every note seems inevitable. In describing Beethoven's music, it is perhaps too easy to give the impression that all of it is stormy and powerful. A lot is; but much is gentle, humorous, noble, or lyrical. His range of expression is enormous. Tempo, dynamic, and expressive indications are marked far more extensively in his scores than in those of earlier composers. For example, one direction reads, "Somewhat lively and with deepest feeling." Characteristic of his explicit dynamic markings is ⏝ *p,* a gradual increase in loudness followed by a sudden softness.

More than his predecessors, Beethoven tried to unify the contrasting movements of a symphony, sonata, or string quartet. Musical continuity is heightened in his works in several ways. Sometimes one movement leads directly into the next, instead of ending with a pause, as was traditional. In the Fifth Symphony, for example, the last two movements are linked by a suspenseful bridge section. A musical bond between different movements of the same work is also created when their themes resemble each other. In a few compositions (the Fifth and Ninth Symphonies, for example), a theme from one movement is quoted in a later movement.

Like Haydn and Mozart, Beethoven wrote many movements in sonata form. In his works, however, the development section is greatly expanded and becomes even more dramatic. It often contains a powerful crescendo that leads to a climactic return of the first theme at the start of the recapitulation. The coda is also expanded and serves to develop themes still further. Its length balances what has come before and affirms the victory of the tonic key over the many new keys in the development section.

As the third movement of a symphony or string quartet, Beethoven most often used a scherzo rather than the traditional minuet. Where earlier composers had used a courtly dance, Beethoven composed a rapid movement with rhythmic drive. The character of the scherzo in Beethoven is flexible. In the Fifth Symphony, it's an ominous force, but in the Sixth Symphony *(Pastoral),* it depicts peasants' merrymaking. Beethoven's works often have climactic, triumphant finales, toward which the previous movements seem to build. These mark an important departure from the light, relaxed ending movement favored by Haydn and Mozart.

Beethoven's most popular works are the nine symphonies, which were conceived for larger orchestras than Haydn's or Mozart's. For greater power and brilliance, Beethoven sometimes added the trombone, piccolo, and contrabassoon—instruments that had not previously been used in symphonies. All the orchestral instruments have to play difficult music. For example, the French horn has prominent melodies, and the timpani participate in the musical dialogue, rather than merely mark the beat.

Each of Beethoven's symphonies is unique in character and style. There is a curious alternation of mood between his odd-numbered symphonies (Symphonies No. 3, 5, 7, and 9), which tend to be forceful and assertive, and his even-numbered ones (Symphonies No. 4, 6, and 8), which are calmer and more lyrical. In the finale of the Ninth Symphony *(Choral)*, Beethoven took the unprecedented step of using a chorus and four solo vocalists. They sing the text of Schiller's *Ode to Joy*, a poem about human brotherhood.

A hint of the virtuosity and improvisation that so astounded the Viennese can be gotten from Beethoven's thirty-two piano sonatas, which are far more difficult than the sonatas of Haydn and Mozart. They exploit the stronger, tonally improved piano of Beethoven's time. Beethoven drew many new effects from the piano, ranging from massive chords to the hollow, mystical sounds produced when the right and left hands play far apart on the keyboard. The piano sonatas were experimental grounds for the compositional techniques he later expanded in the symphonies and string quartets.

Beethoven's sixteen string quartets, which span his entire career, are among the greatest music composed. They are unsurpassed in sheer invention, thematic treatment, and heart-rending expressiveness. In three of the last quartets, Beethoven again stepped beyond the conventions of classical form: he used five, six, and seven movements (in Op. 132, Op. 130, and Op. 131 respectively), which he connected in subtle ways. He also wrote five superb piano concertos, each remarkable in its individuality. In the Fourth and Fifth Piano Concertos, the opening movement begins with a brief piano solo rather than the traditional orchestral exposition.

While most of Beethoven's important works are for instruments, his sense of drama was also expressed in vocal music. In his only opera, *Fidelio,* a wife's heroism enables justice to triumph over tyranny. Beethoven also composed two masses. The *Missa solemnis* (*Solemn Mass,* 1819–1823) is one of the most monumental and expressive settings of this sacred text.

Beethoven's total output is usually divided into three periods: early (up to 1802), middle (1803–1814), and late (1815–1827). The music of Haydn and Mozart influences some works of the early period, but other pieces clearly show Beethoven's personal style. The compositions of the middle period are longer and tend to be heroic in tone. And the sublime works of the last period well up from the depths of a man almost totally deaf. During this period Beethoven often used the fugue to express new musical conceptions. The late works contain passages that sound surprisingly harsh and "modern." When a violinist complained that the music was very difficult to play, Beethoven reportedly replied, "Do you believe that I think of a wretched fiddle when the spirit speaks to me?"

"Ludwig van Beethoven" from *Music: An Appreciation,* 5th ed., by Roger Kamien, McGraw-Hill, Inc., 1992, pp. 264–270.

COMPREHENSION QUIZ

True or False

Directions: In the blank provided, indicate whether each statement is true or false.

_____ 1. Beethoven noticed the first symptoms of blindness at age 29.

_____ 2. In both art and life, Beethoven's heroic struggle resulted in victory over despair.

_____ 3. During his lifetime, Beethoven was not regarded as a musical genius.

_____ 4. Beethoven changed the name of his Third Symphony from *Bonaparte* to the *Eroica* because he felt Napoleon no longer possessed democratic ideals when he declared himself emperor.

_____ 5. For Beethoven, music was not mere entertainment, but a moral force capable of creating a vision of higher ideals.

_____ 6. At 16, Beethoven went to Vienna to improvise music for Mozart.

_____ 7. Like Mozart, Beethoven wrote his long works quickly and easily.

Multiple Choice

Directions: For each item, select the best answer.

_____ 8. Beethoven was born on December 16, 1770, in
   a. Vienna, Austria
   b. Paris, France
   c. Venice, Italy
   d. Bonn, Germany

_____ 9. Beethoven earned a fairly good income as a musician due to the
   a. fees collected from his piano concerts
   b. fees collected from his conducting
   c. selling of his compositions to publishers
   d. salary paid to him by three Viennese aristocrats

_____10. Which of the characteristics below does not describe Beethoven's personality?
    a. He was even-tempered.
    b. He was an untamed musical genius.
    c. He was hard-working and driven to achieve perfection.
    d. He lacked the ability to establish lasting personal relationships.

_____11. Beethoven's most popular works are his
    a. operas
    b. piano concertos
    c. sixteen string quartets
    d. nine symphonies

_____12. Which of the following comparisons is not correct?
    a. Beethoven's ending movements often are dramatic and triumphant while those of Haydn and Mozart are light and relaxed.
    b. Beethoven's symphonies were conceived for larger orchestras while Haydn's and Mozart's were not.
    c. Beethoven's piano concertos are far more difficult to play than those of Haydn and Mozart.
    d. Beethoven's symphonies do not feature instruments such as the trombone, piccolo, and contrabassoon while the symphonies of Haydn and Mozart do.

_____13. All of the following information describes Beethoven's early background except that
    a. he had an alcoholic father who exploited him
    b. his family life was serene and secure
    c. he came from a family of court musicians
    d. he was made legal guardian of two younger brothers because of the early death of his mother

_____14. Because of Beethoven's handicap and his triumph over despair, the music he produced in the latter part of his life can be described as
    a. exalted and lofty
    b. sublime
    c. of high spiritual, moral, and intellectual worth
    d. all of the above

_____15. Because the piano had developed into a stronger, more tonally improved instrument, Beethoven's thirty-two piano sonatas were
    a. far less difficult to play than Haydn's and Mozart's
    b. made up of fewer new effects
    c. astounding to the Viennese
    d. all of the above

_____16. The word *scherzo* means
    a. a minuet
    b. music of rapid movement with rhythmic drive
    c. music of a courtly dance
    d. none of the above

_____17. What did Beethoven mean by "spirit" when he asked, "Do you believe that I think of a wretched fiddle when the spirit speaks to me?"
    a. a trusted mentor
    b. God
    c. the spirit of past great composers
    d. Beethoven's creative inner-voice

_____18. Compared with his even-numbered symphonies, Beethoven's odd-numbered symphonies (Symphonies No. 3, 5, 7, and 9) are
    a. calmer and more lyrical
    b. very similar to the even-numbered Symphonies No. 4, 6, and 8
    c. more forceful and assertive
    d. similar only in the use of a chorus

_____19. The musical marking $\prec$ *p,* found in many of Beethoven's scores, means
    a. a sudden softness followed by a gradual increase in loudness
    b. a gradual increase in loudness followed by a sudden softness
    c. soft
    d. loud

_____20. Which of the following describes Beethoven's music?
    a. stormy, powerful
    b. gentle, humorous
    c. noble, lyrical
    d. all of the above

ACKNOWLEDGMENTS

COURTLAND L. BOVEE and JOHN V. THILL.   Excerpt from pp. 59–68 of *Business Communication Today*. Fourth Edition. Copyright © 1995. Reprinted with permission of McGraw-Hill, Inc.

CAPRON, H. L.   Excerpts from *Computers: Tools for an Information Age*. Second Edition. Copyright © 1990 by the Benjamin/Cummings Publishing Company. Reprinted by permission.

DON CASSEL   Excerpts from *Understanding Computers*. Copyright © 1990. Reprinted by permission of Prentice-Hall.

RAYMOND CHANG   Excerpts from *Chemistry*. Copyright © 1988. Reprinted with permission of McGraw-Hill, Inc.

RICHARD CURRENT et al.   Excerpt from *The Essentials of American History Since 1865*. Copyright © 1986. Reprinted with permission of McGraw-Hill, Inc.

JAMES W. DAVIDSON et al.   Excerpts from *Nation of Nations*. Copyright © 1990. Reprinted with permission of McGraw-Hill, Inc.

ROBERT DOTT   Excerpts from *Evolution of the Earth*. Copyright © 1990. Reprinted with permission of McGraw-Hill, Inc.

ROBERT FELDMAN   Excerpt from *Understanding Psychology*. Copyright © 1990. Reprinted with permission of McGraw-Hill, Inc.

LOUIS GIANNETTI   Excerpts from *Understanding Movies*. Copyright © 1987 by Louis Giannetti. Reprinted with permission of Prentice Hall.

RITA GILBERT and WILLIAM MCCARTER   Excerpts from *Living with Art*. Copyright © 1988. Reprinted with permission of McGraw-Hill, Inc.

M. GRANT GROSS   Excerpts from *Oceanography*. Third Edition. Copyright © 1982 by Houghton Mifflin Company. Used with permission.

MAXINE HAIRSTON   Excerpts from *Contemporary Composition*. Copyright © 1986 by Houghton Mifflin Company. Used with permission.

JAMES O. HICKS   Excerpts from *Information Systems in Business: An Introduction*. Copyright © 1986. Reprinted with permission of West Publishing Company.

ROGER KAMIEN   Excerpts from *Music: An Appreciation*. Fourth Edition. Copyright © 1988. Reprinted with permission of McGraw-Hill, Inc.

ROGER KAMIEN   Excerpt from pp. 264–270 of *Music: An Appreciation* Fifth Edition. Copyright © 1992. Reprinted with permission of McGraw-Hill, Inc.

HAROLD KOONTZ et al.   Excerpts from *Management*. Copyright © 1984. Reprinted with permission of McGraw-Hill, Inc.

CONRAD PHILLIP KOTTAK   Excerpt from pp. 132–138 of *Anthropology*. Sixth Edition. Copyright © 1994. Reprinted with permission of McGraw-Hill, Inc.

DONALD LIGHT and SUZANNE KELLER   Excerpts from *Sociology*. Copyright © 1989. Reprinted with permission of McGraw-Hill, Inc.

CAMPBELL MCCONNELL Excerpts from *Economics,* Tenth Edition. Copyright © 1987 by Campbell McConnell. Reprinted with permission of McGraw-Hill, Inc.

CAMPBELL MCCONNELL and STANLEY BRUE Excerpts from *Economics: Principles, Problems, and Policies.* Copyright © 1987. Reprinted with permission of McGraw-Hill, Inc.

SYLVIA MADER Excerpts from *Inquiry into Life.* Fourth Edition. Copyright © 1985 by Sylvia Mader. Reprinted by permission of William C. Brown.

MARY BETH NORTON et al. Excerpts from *A People and a Nation.* Complete Edition. Third Edition. Copyright © 1990 by Houghton Mifflin Company. Used with permission.

DIANE PAPALIA and SALLY OLDS Excerpts from *Psychology.* Copyright © 1988. Reprinted with permission of McGraw-Hill, Inc.

THOMAS E. PATTERSON Excerpts from *The American Democracy.* Copyright © 1990. Reprinted with permission of McGraw-Hill, Inc.

RICHARD PIOUS Excerpts from AMERICAN POLITICS AND GOVERNMENT. Copyright © 1986 by Richard Pious. Reprinted with permission of McGraw-Hill, Inc.

ROD PLOTNIK Excerpts from *Introduction to Psychology.* Copyright © 1989. Reprinted by permission of McGraw-Hill, Inc.

JOHN H. POSTLETHWAIT and JANET L. HOPSON. Excerpt from pp. 2–24 of *The Nature of Life.* Third Edition. Copyright © 1992. Reprinted with permission of McGraw-Hill, Inc.

DONALD SANDERS Excerpts from *Computer Concepts and Application with BASIC.* Copyright © 1987 by Donald Sanders. Reprinted with permission of McGraw-Hill, Inc.

RICHARD SCHAEFER Excerpt from *Sociology.* Copyright © 1986 by Richard Schaefer. Reprinted with permission of McGraw-Hill, Inc.

JOHN R. SCHERMERHORN, JR., et al. Excerpt from *Managing Organizational Behavior.* Copyright © 1985 by John Schermerhorn. Reprinted with permission of John Wiley & Sons, Inc.

BRADLEY SCHILLER Excerpt from *The Economy Today.* Copyright © 1989. Reprinted with permission of McGraw-Hill, Inc.

GEORGE M. SCOTT Excerpts from *Principle of Management Information Systems.* Copyright © 1986 by George M. Scott. Reprinted with permission of McGraw-Hill, Inc.

DENNIS SPORRE Excerpts from *Perceiving the Arts: An Introduction to the Humanities.* Second Edition. Copyright © 1985 by Dennis Sporre. Reprinted by permission of Prentice Hall.

WILLIAM J. STANTON Excerpts from *Fundamentals of Marketing.* Copyright © 1987. Reprinted with permission of McGraw-Hill, Inc.

CECILE STARR and RALPH TAGGART Excerpt from *Biology: The Unity and Diversity of Life.* Fourth Edition, by Cecile Starr and Ralph Taggart. Copyright © 1987 by Wadsworth, Inc. Reprinted by permission of the publisher.

SAMUEL STUMPF Excerpt from *Elements of Philosophy.* Copyright © 1986 by Samuel Stumpf. Reprinted with permission of McGraw-Hill, Inc.

ALEX THIO Excerpts from *Sociology: An Introduction* by Alex Thio. Copyright © 1986 by Harper & Row, Publishers, Inc. Reprinted by permission of HarperCollins Publishers.

JAMES VANDER ZANDEN Excerpts from *Human Development.* Copyright © 1988. Excerpts from *Sociology.* Copyright © 1986. Reprinted with permission of McGraw-Hill, Inc.

M. A. WITT et al. Excerpts from *The Humanities.* Copyright © 1985 with M. A. Witt. Reprinted by permission of D. C. Heath and Company.

INDEX

Abacus, 212
Absolutism, 170–171
Acupuncture, 57
Adaptation, 459–460
Adult learners, 323–325
Advertisement, two parts of, 521–522
Age segregation and nursing homes, 25–26
Aggressive behavior, explanation for, 519
Alzheimer's disease, 235, 293–294
Ameslan, 338
Annotating a textbook*, 354–358
Aquaculture, 528
Aristotle, 259
Artists, the social role of, 327–329
Asexual reproduction, in plants, 130–131
Asian immigrants, influx of, 89, 186
Atomic theory, development of, 259–260
Atoms, definition of, 217

Bach, Johann Sebastian, 218
Background knowledge, importance of, 6–7
Baker, Howard, 191
Balance sheet, 145–146
Baroque era, 218
Beethoven, Ludwig van, 133, 512, 537–544
Body language, 266–267
Body systems, 120, 181
Bourgeois, 171
Brain stem functions, 19–20, 151, 507
Business data processing, managers' lack of
    knowledge of, 37, 520

Calendaring, electronic, 61
Call systems, 337
Campus life, stratification in, 523
Cause-effect pattern, 203, 223–228
Cell activity, 39
Chaplin, Charlie, tramp costume of, 70–71, 505
Chronological order, 210
Classification of living things, 452
Cold War, sources of, 250–251
Communicating interculturally, 262–272
Communications, channels of, 429–432
Comparable worth, 17

Comparison-contrast pattern, 202,
    218–223
Comprehension monitoring, 5, 33–34
Computer(s):
    crime, 59–60
    criminals, 321–322
    electronic nature of, 18, 72, 154–155,
        201
    level of math required for using, 524
    phobia, overcoming, 510–511
    replacing humans with, 105
    rise of (history of), 31–32
    systems, size of, 504
    video conferencing and, 61
    virus, 64
Confederate draft, inequities of,
    304–305
Conflict, managers' handling of, 166
Creativity:
    artists' versus others', 147–148
    enhancing, 27, 147–148
    intelligence and, 99
    nature of, 65
Crime:
    computer, 59–60
    definition of, 54
    organized, 41
    victimless, 48, 76
Critical reading:
    definition of, 479–480
    importance of, 480–481
    summary of, 499–501
Cultural context, 265–266
Cultural differences, 262
Cultural transmission, 339
Culture:
    high-context, 265–266
    low-context, 265–266

da Vinci, Leonardo, interpretation of fossils
    by, 86
Dalton, John, 259–260
Darwin, Charles, 42, 49, 456–458
Data processing, advances in, 31–32, 139,
    180

---

* Entries appearing in boldface pertain to reading improvement.

Date rape, 532–533
Death, preparing psychologically for, 103
Declaration of Independence, 168
Deductive reasoning, 463
Definition pattern, 202, 215–218
Democritus, 259
Descartes, René, 53
Diseases from Old World to New World, 101, 493
Displacement, linguistic, 340
Domestic violence, prevention of, 485
Dreams, content of, 111
Drinking age, minimum, 23
Dying, preparatory stages of, 253

Earth summit, 440–442
Ecology, 449
Economics:
    definition of, 40
    shift to an information age, 254
Economizing problem, 143–144
Ego, 238, 308–309
Eisenhower, Dwight, 142
Electronic calendaring, 61
Endorphins, 56
Energy costs, effect on poor and rich families, 75
Eniac, 31–32, 139, 180
Enterprise, 206
Entrepreneurial ability, 206–207
Environmental design, 189
Erikson, Eric, stages of man, 410–414
Ethics:
    and being aware of others, 50
    and being responsible for our behavior, 16
Ethnocentric reactions, 271–272
Ethnocentrism, 271–272
Evolution, concept of, 42, 459

Facsimile, transmission (fax), 62
Facts, definition of, 482–483
Fashions, reasons for, 128, 178
Feral children, 239–240
Ferraro, Geraldine, 22, 91, 517
Flowering plant, root and shoot system, 102
Foot-in-the-door technique, 146–147
Forgetting:
    as a normal occurrence, 73, 177
    theories of, 164
Fossils, da Vinci's interpretation of, 86
French Revolution, causes of, 385–386, 395-402
Fresco, 38
Freud, Sigmund, 238, 308–309
Freudian psychoanalytical theory in marketing, 308–309

Friends, factors in keeping them, 527
Friendship, dimensions of, 245
Full-production, 100

Gate control theory of pain, 55–58
George III, King, 168
Glaucoma, 530
Government, definition of, 47, 202
Groups, characteristics of, 208–209

Hawthorne effect, 140, 184–185
Hierarchy of needs, 213–214, 249
Hollerith, Herman, 241
Holmes, Oliver Wendell, 196
"Honeymoon" period of presidents, 141–142
Humanities, definition of, 216
Hypothesis, 463

Iconography, 529
Id, 238, 308–309
Idea density, 5
Inductive reasoning, 463
Inference, definition of, 487
Inflation, 13, 84
Information-processing technology and productivity, 254
Information systems, the three activities of, 163
Inoculation, smallpox, 112, 203
Intellectual despair, 6
Intelligence:
    creativity and, 99
    estimating in children, 98
Intercultural communication, 262–272
International trade, 59
Iran-contra, 511
Irangate, 511

Jacquard, Joseph Marie, 241
James, William, 510–511
Jefferson, Thomas, 104, 166, 190, 328, 492
Johnson, Andrew, impeachment hearing of, 114
Johnson, Lyndon, 104, 115, 190, 492

Kennedy, John F., 142
Kingdom of living things, 453–455
Kübler-Ross, Elizabeth, theory of, 253

Language barriers, 268–269
Laser:
    applications of, 257–258
    definition of, 255

Leibniz, Gottfried von, 212
L'Enfant, Pierre, 189
Life, characteristics of, 442–444
Listing pattern, 201, 204–210
Locke, John, 83, 478
Louis XIV, King, 170–171
Louis XVI, King, 386
Louvre, 170
Love, Sternberg's theory of, 495–497
Lower class, 288–289

Main idea:
    implied, 108–109
    importance of, 69, 109–110
    overall, 286, 298–299
    stated, 68
    summary of implied, 125–126
    summary of stated, 79–80
Malls, role of, 53
Malthus, Thomas:
    failure of theory of, 226
    theory of population control, 142
Mapping textbook passages, 361–362
Mare liberum, doctrine of, 306–307
Marketing:
    decisions of Univac and IBM, 132
    psychoanalytical theory and, 308–309
    research, 211
Marketing information system, 246–247
Marriage, 355, 357–358
Marx, Karl, 83
Maslow, Abraham, 213, 249
Material wants, 317–319
Maternity policies, discriminatory, 40–41, 129
Mather, Cotton, 112, 203
Mauchley, John, and Eckert, J. Presper, 31–32, 139, 180
Memorizing textbook material, 351–353
Memory:
    basic steps of, 29–30, 201
    disorders of, 293–294
    loss, two kinds of, 222
Metabolism, 445–446
Metaphor, purposes of, 205
Microcomputer systems, importance of, 421–422
Middle Ages:
    definition of, 85
    music in the, 192–193
Middle class, 287
Mixed pattern, 229
Mondale, Walter, 22, 91, 517
Motives, 87–88
Mozart, Wolfgang Amadeus:
    as a child prodigy, 145, 503
    as an example of genius, 133, 512
    music of, 90

Natural selection, 456, 460–461
Nature and nurture, role in development, 133, 512
Needs hierarchy, 213
Nixon, Richard, 104, 115, 190, 492

Oceans, free use of, 306–307
O'Connor, Sandra Day, 123
Oligopoly, 104
Opinion, definition of, 481–482
Organ systems, 444–445
Organism:
    characteristics of living, 442–444
    definition of, 444
Organized crimes, 41–42
Origin of Species, 42, 458, 460
Osmosis, 15, 73
Outlining textbook passages, 358–360
Overall main idea, 285–286
Overall subject matter, 285–286
Owen, Robert, 81, 179–180

Pain, gate control theory of, 55–58
Pascal, Blaise, 212
Penn Central, bankruptcy of, 483
Perverse readers, 488
Philosophy, reason for studying, 483
Piaget, Jean, theory of cognitive stages, 367–369, 375–383
Pizarro, Francisco, 101, 493
Plants, reproduction in:
    asexual (vegetative), 130
    sexual, 51
Plato, 205, 259
Point of view (author's), 490
Polyandry, 248, 355
Polygyny, 248, 355
Positive checks, 642
Potential, developing, 133, 512
Presidents:
    public's confidence in, 141–142
    as scapegoats, 115–116
    second-term problems of, 104–105, 190–191, 492
Preventive checks, 142
Primates, 335–344
Productivity, linguistic, 339–340
Punch cards, history and use of, 241

Rape, 532–533
Readers (perverse), 97, 488
Reading:
    characteristics of college-level, 5–6
    process, 4–5

Reading a textbook assignment, 281–285, 292–298

Reagan, Ronald, 104, 142, 190, 492

Reasoning:
inductive, 463
deductive, 463

Record keepers, early, 212

Renaissance, 86–87

Reproduction in plants:
asexual, 447
sexual, 447–448

Retailing management, challenges of, 156

Retardation, organic, 227

Robotics, 229

"Romeo and Juliet" effect, 509

Roosevelt, Franklin, 104, 190, 492

Scapegoats, presidential, 115–116

Scientific method, 464–465

Sequence pattern, 201, 210–215

Settlers of the Plains, 315–316

Sexual reproduction in plants, 51

Singing, 531

Sleep:
deprivation, effects of, 38, 118
number of hours of, 54
patterns, changes in, 24–25

Sleepers, personality traits and intelligence of, 122, 202–203

Smallpox, inoculations, 112, 203

Social Darwinism, 49

Social stratification, patterns of, 291–292

Social systems, open and closed, 291–292

Social values, 262–263

Sociology, perspective of, 82

Socrates, disagreement with Sophists, 117

Sophists, 117

Spencer, Herbert, 49

Statistics, two branches of, 183, 508

Status, 14, 77

Sternberg, Robert, 495–497

Stratification in campus life, 523

Stress, Type A and Type B behavior and, 236–237

Study cards, 362–364

Study techniques, importance of, 350–351

Style, 403–404

Subject matter:
importance of, 12
overall, 286, 298–299
summary of, 35

Sudden Infant Death Syndrome (SIDS), 301–302

Summary, preparing a, 295–296, 300

Sumner, William Graham, 49

"Sun King," 171

Superego, 238, 308–309

Supporting details:
importance of, 151–152
summary of, 161–162

Suzuki, Shinichi, 133

Syphilis, from the New World, 121

Systems of the body, 120, 181

Talmud, 280

Television:
in America, 53
impact on American people, 489

Tempera, 20–21, 159

Test, preparing for, 351–353

Thirst, 106

Thoreau, Henry David, 350

Time order, 210

Tools, primates' use of, 336–337

Topic, 12

Topic sentence, 68

Trade, international, 59

Truman, Harry S., 250, 511

Type A and Type B behavior, 236–237

Underlining a textbook, 354–358

United States, increasing diversity and complexity in, 224

Upper class, 220–221

Vegetative propagation, 130–131

Versailles, 170

Vice-presidential nominee, choice of, 91, 517

Victimless crimes, 48, 76

Victor, "wild boy of Aveyron," 239–240

Violence, domestic, prevention of, 485

Virus, computer, 64

Vocabulary, technical, 5

Voice mail, 60

Wallace, Alfred Russel, 456–458

Washington, George, 104, 167, 492

Watergate, 104, 115, 190, 492

Wiener, Norbert, 133, 512

Women:
lack of, in government, 123
role in the workplace, 24

Writing patterns, authors':
definition of, 198–199
importance of, 199–200
summary of, 231–233

Wyeth, Andrew, 20, 159